D VI COLLEGE

¡F

Centre for Innovation in Mathematics Teaching
University of Exeter

FURTHER MECHANICS

Writers   David Burghes
                Elwyn Williams

Editor   Nigel Price

Assistant
Editor   Andy Martin

Heinemann Educational

Heinemann Educational

a division of Heinemann Educational Books Ltd.

Halley Court, Jordan Hill, Oxford OX2 8EJ

OXFORD LONDON EDINBURGH
MADRID ATHENS BOLOGNA PARIS
MELBOURNE SYDNEY AUCKLAND SINGAPORE
TOKYO IBADAN NAIROBI HARARE
GABORONE PORTSMOUTH NH (USA)

C.No: 519
A.No: 011318

ISBN 0 435 51609 4

First Published 1995

© CIMT, 1995

Typseset by ISCA Press, CIMT, University of Exeter

Printed in Great Britain by The Bath Press, Avon

FURTHER MECHANICS

This is one of the texts which has been written to support the AEB Mathematics syllabus for A and AS level awards first available in Summer 1996.

The development of these texts has been coordinated at the

Centre for Innovation in Mathematics Teaching

at Exeter University in association with Heinemann and AEB.

The overall development of these texts has been directed by David Burghes and coordinated by Nigel Price.

Enquiries regarding this project and further details of the work of the Centre should be addressed to

Margaret Roddick
CIMT
School of Education
University of Exeter
Heavitree Road
EXETER EX1 2LU

CONTENTS

PREFACE

Mechanics is now a well established discipline which has vital relevance to science and technology. The fact that

- manned space flights take place

- high speed trains have been developed

- precision bombing is a reality

are all testament to the practical application of mechanical theories.

The subject itself can be divided into Statics (bodies at rest) and Dynamics (bodies in motion); the majority of the text is about describing motion and what causes motion. Behind the applications is the concept of a mathematical model, which represents mathematically the situation under study. This is usually, but not always, based on the assumptions of

Newton's Laws of Motion

These will be extended in this *Further Mechanics* text from the earlier examples in the *Mechanics* text. Above all it is our intention to show that mechanics is an interesting, practical and important topic, which embraces both the real world and our mathematical world.

This text has been produced for students and includes examples, activities and exercises. It should be noted that the activities are not optional but are an important part of the learning philosophy in which you are expected to take a very active part. The text integrates

- **Exposition**   in which the concept is explained;

- **Examples**   which show how the techniques are used;

- **Activities**   which either introduce new concepts or reinforce techniques;

- **Discussion Points**   which are essentially 'stop and think' points, where discussion with other students and teachers will be helpful;

  Discussion points are written in a special typeface as illustrated here.

- **Exercises**   at the end of most sections in order to provide further practice;

- **Miscellaneous Exercises**   at the end of each chapter, providing opportunities for reinforcement of the main points of the chapter.

Note that answers to the exercises are given at the back of the book. You are expected to have a calculator available throughout your study of this text and occasionally to have access to a computer.

Some of the sections, exercises and questions are marked with an asterisk *. This means that they are **not** central to the development of the topics in this text and can be omitted without causing problems.

This text is one of a series of texts written specially for the new AEB Mathematics syllabus for A and AS level coursework. The framework is shown opposite. Essentially each module corresponds to an AS level syllabus and two suitable modules provide the syllabus for an A level award. Optional coursework is available for students taking any of the three applied modules
Mechanics, Statistics and Discrete Mathematics.

Full details of the scheme are available from
  AEB, Stag Hill House, Guildford GU2 5XJ

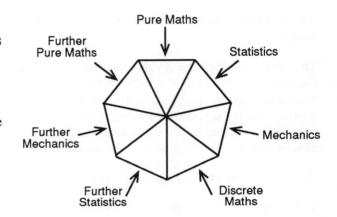

We hope that you enjoy working through the book. We would be very grateful for comments, criticisms and notification of any errors. These should be sent to

> Margaret Roddick
> CIMT
> School of Education
> University of Exeter
> EXETER EX1 2LU

ACKNOWLEDGEMENTS

This text has been written for the new AEB Mathematics syllabus and assessment, which will be examined for the first time in Summer 1996. I am grateful for the continued support from AEB through its mathematics officer, Jackie Bawden, and to the staff at Heinemann, particularly Philip Ellaway.

I am grateful for contributions from Elwyn Williams, Nigel Price and Andy Martin, and from staff at CIMT, Liz Holland, Margaret Roddick and Ann Tylisczuk for producing camera-ready copy and still smiling despite the pressure I put them under.

David Burghes
(Series Editor)
March 1995

1 VECTOR METHODS

Objectives

After studying this chapter you should

- understand and be able to use the vector product;
- be able to find and use vector equations of a straight line and plane.

1.0   Introduction

Some physical quantities, such as temperature or time, are completely specified by a number given in appropriate units e.g. 20° C, 14.30 hours. Quantities of this sort, which have only magnitude, are referred to as **scalars**; whereas quantities for which it is necessary to give a direction as well as a magnitude are called **vectors**. Examples of vectors include

> wind velocity
>
> force
>
> displacement.

In this text we will print vectors in **bold** type; for example

> **a**, **b**, etc.

Unfortunately, when **writing** vectors you cannot distinguish them from scalars in this way. The standard way of hand writing vectors is to underline them; for example

> a̲, b̲, etc.

It is very important for you to conform to this notation. Always remember to underline your vectors, otherwise great confusion will arise!

Activity 1

Make a list of scalar and vector quantities, distinguishing between them.

In the *Mechanics* module you have already met the concept of a vector and covered a number of important aspects of vector algebra. These are revised below to make sure that you have fully understood these concepts.

A vector can be represented by a section of a straight line, whose length is equal to the magnitude of the vector, and whose direction represents the direction of the vector.

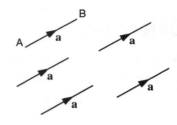

All the lines shown opposite have the same magnitude and direction, and so all represent the same vector **a**. Sometimes the notation

$$\overrightarrow{AB}$$

is used to represent the vector **a**.

Modulus

The **modulus** of a vector **a** is its magnitude. It is written as $|\mathbf{a}|$, and is equal to the length of the line representing the vector.

Equal vectors

The vectors **a** and **b** are equal if, and only if,

$|\mathbf{a}| = |\mathbf{b}|$ and

a and **b** are in the same direction.

Example
How are the vectors shown opposite, $\mathbf{a} = \overrightarrow{AB}$ and $\mathbf{b} = \overrightarrow{PQ}$, related?

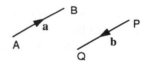

Solution
Since $|\mathbf{a}| = |\mathbf{b}|$, and they are in opposite directions, you can write

$$\mathbf{b} = -\mathbf{a}.$$

Multiplication of a vector by a scalar

If λ is a positive real number, then $\lambda\mathbf{a}$ is a vector in the same direction as **a** and is of magnitude $\lambda|\mathbf{a}|$. If $\lambda = 0$, then $\lambda\mathbf{a}$ is the zero vector **0**, and if $\lambda < 0$ then $\lambda\mathbf{a}$ is the vector in the opposite direction to **a** and of magnitude $|\lambda||\mathbf{a}|$.

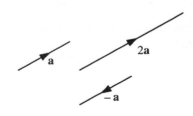

Does the definition make sense when $\lambda = -1$?

Activity 2

Draw any vector **b** on a sheet of paper, and then also draw

(a) $-\mathbf{b}$

(b) $2\mathbf{b}, 3\mathbf{b}, 4\mathbf{b}$

(c) $\frac{1}{2}\mathbf{b}$

(d) $-2\mathbf{b}, -\frac{1}{2}\mathbf{b}$

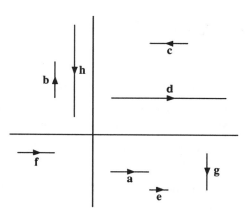

Activity 3

The diagram opposite shows a number of vectors. Express vectors **c**, **d**, **e**, **f**, **g** and **h** in terms of **a** or **b**.

If the sides AB and BC of a triangle ABC represent the vectors **p** and **q**, then the third side, AC, is defined as the vector sum of **p** and **q**; that is

$$\overrightarrow{AB} = \mathbf{p}, \ \overrightarrow{BC} = \mathbf{q} \ \Rightarrow \ \overrightarrow{AC} = \mathbf{p} + \mathbf{q}$$

This definition of vector addition is referred to as the **triangle law of addition**. You can then subtract vectors, for $\mathbf{a} - \mathbf{b}$ simply means $\mathbf{a} + (-\mathbf{b})$. For example

$$\overrightarrow{AB} = \overrightarrow{AC} - \overrightarrow{BC}$$

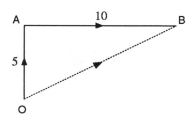

As an example, consider two displacement vectors. If you walk in the direction North for 5 miles, then East for 10 miles, you can represent these two displacements as vectors, $\overrightarrow{OA}$ and $\overrightarrow{AB}$, as shown opposite. The vector addition of $\overrightarrow{OA}$ and $\overrightarrow{AB}$ is $\overrightarrow{OB}$, and this indeed is the final displacement from O.

Example

In the triangle ABC, $\overrightarrow{AB}$ represents **a**, $\overrightarrow{BC}$ represents **b**. If D is the midpoint of AB, express $\overrightarrow{AC}$, $\overrightarrow{CA}$ and $\overrightarrow{DC}$ in terms of **a** and **b**.

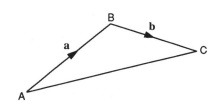

Solution

$$\overrightarrow{AC} = \overrightarrow{AB} + \overrightarrow{BC} = \mathbf{a} + \mathbf{b}$$

$$\overrightarrow{CA} = -\overrightarrow{AC} = -\mathbf{a} - \mathbf{b}$$

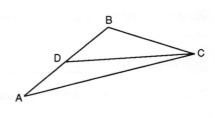

$$\vec{DC} = \vec{DA} + \vec{AC}$$

$$= -\vec{AD} + \vec{AC}$$

$$= -\tfrac{1}{2}\mathbf{a} + (\mathbf{a} + \mathbf{b}) \text{ (since D is the midpoint of AB)}$$

$$= \tfrac{1}{2}\mathbf{a} + \mathbf{b}$$

Exercise 1A

1. Four points, O, A, B and C are such that
    $$\vec{OA} = 10\mathbf{a}, \quad \vec{OB} = 5\mathbf{b}, \quad \vec{OC} = 4\mathbf{a} + 3\mathbf{b}.$$
    Find $\vec{AB}$ and $\vec{BC}$ in terms of **a** and **b** and hence show that A, B and C are collinear.

2. ABCD is a quadrilateral. Find a single vector which is equivalent to

    (a) $\vec{AB} + \vec{BC}$ (b) $\vec{BC} + \vec{CD}$ (c) $\vec{AB} + \vec{BC} + \vec{CD}$

    Hence deduce that

    $$\vec{AB} + \vec{BC} + \vec{CD} + \vec{DA} = \mathbf{0}.$$

3. If **a**, **b** and **c** are represented by $\vec{AB}$, $\vec{AD}$ and $\vec{AF}$ in the cube shown, find in terms of **a**, **b** and **c**, the vectors represented by the other edges.

    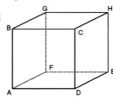

4. OABC is a tetrahedron with
    $$\vec{OA} = \mathbf{a}, \quad \vec{OB} = \mathbf{b}, \quad \vec{OC} = \mathbf{c}.$$

    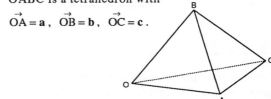

    Find $\vec{AC}$, $\vec{AB}$ and $\vec{CB}$ in terms of **a**, **b** and **c** and hence show that

    $$\vec{AB} + \vec{BC} + \vec{CA} = \mathbf{0}.$$

5. In a regular hexagon ABCDEF, $\vec{AB} = \mathbf{a}$ and $\vec{BC} = \mathbf{b}$. Find expressions for $\vec{DE}$, $\vec{DC}$, $\vec{AD}$ and $\vec{BD}$ in terms of **a** and **b**.

6. Given that $\vec{OA} + \vec{OC} = \vec{OB} + \vec{OD}$, show that the quadrilateral ABCD is a parallelogram.

1.1   Components of a vector

In general, a vector has no specific location in space. However, if $\mathbf{a} = \vec{OA}$, where O is a fixed origin, then **a** is referred to as the position vector of A relative to O.

Now if **a** is any non-zero vector, with magnitude $|\mathbf{a}|$, then the vector

$$\hat{\mathbf{a}} = \frac{\mathbf{a}}{|\mathbf{a}|}$$

is a unit vector, parallel to **a**.

Introducing cartesian axes O*xyz* in the usual way, unit vectors in the direction O*x*, O*y* and O*z* are represented by

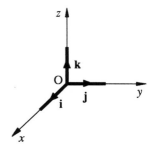

$$\mathbf{i}, \mathbf{j} \text{ and } \mathbf{k}$$

as shown in the diagram opposite.

Suppose P is any point with coordinates (x, y, z) relative to O as illustrated.

What is the magnitude and direction of the vector x $=x\mathbf{i}$?

Clearly $\quad \overrightarrow{OA} = x\mathbf{i} \ (=\mathbf{x})$

and $\quad \overrightarrow{OA} + \overrightarrow{AB} = x\mathbf{i} + \overrightarrow{OC}$

$$= x\mathbf{i} + y\mathbf{j}$$

and $\quad \overrightarrow{OA} + \overrightarrow{AB} + \overrightarrow{BP} = x\mathbf{i} + y\mathbf{j} + \overrightarrow{OD}$

$$= x\mathbf{i} + y\mathbf{j} + z\mathbf{k}$$

What is the vector $\overrightarrow{OA} + \overrightarrow{AB} + \overrightarrow{BP}$?

Thus

$$\boxed{\mathbf{r} = \overrightarrow{OP} = x\mathbf{i} + y\mathbf{i} + z\mathbf{k}}$$

This vector is often written as a 3×1 column matrix

$$\mathbf{r} = \begin{bmatrix} x \\ y \\ z \end{bmatrix}$$

and the notation $\mathbf{r} = (x, y, z)$ is also sometimes used.

Activity 4

For vectors with two dimensions, using unit vectors **i** and **j** as shown opposite, express **a**, **b**, **c**, **d**, **e** and **f** in terms of **i** and **j**.

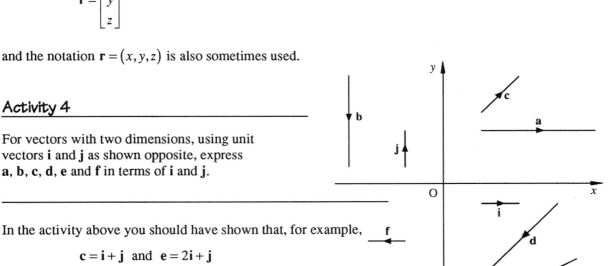

In the activity above you should have shown that, for example,

$$\mathbf{c} = \mathbf{i} + \mathbf{j} \quad \text{and} \quad \mathbf{e} = 2\mathbf{i} + \mathbf{j}$$

Then the vector $\mathbf{c} + \mathbf{e}$ is simply $3\mathbf{i} + 2\mathbf{j}$: adding vectors in this form is just a matter of adding components.

For vectors in 2 dimensions, in general

$$\mathbf{r} = \overrightarrow{OP} = x\mathbf{i} + y\mathbf{j}$$

and its magnitude is given by the length OP,

where $\qquad OP = \sqrt{x^2 + y^2}$

$$\Rightarrow \qquad |\mathbf{r}| = \sqrt{x^2 + y^2}$$

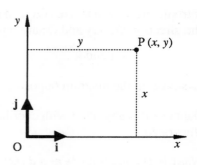

Example

If $\ \mathbf{a} = \mathbf{i} + 3\mathbf{j}, \ \ \mathbf{b} = 2\mathbf{i} - 5\mathbf{j}, \ \ \mathbf{c} = -2\mathbf{i} + 4\mathbf{j}, \ $ find

(a)   the component form of the vectors

      (i) $\mathbf{a} + \mathbf{b}$ (ii) $\mathbf{b} + \mathbf{c}$ (iii) $\mathbf{a} - \mathbf{b}$ (iv) $\mathbf{a} + \mathbf{b} - \mathbf{c}$ (v) $3\mathbf{a} + 2\mathbf{b}$;

(b)   the magnitude of the vectors in (a);

(c)   unit vectors in the direction of $\mathbf{a} + \mathbf{b}$ and $\mathbf{b} + \mathbf{c}$.

Solution

(a)   (i) $\mathbf{a} + \mathbf{b} = (\mathbf{i} + 3\mathbf{j}) + (2\mathbf{i} - 5\mathbf{j}) = 3\mathbf{i} - 2\mathbf{j}$

     (ii) $\mathbf{b} + \mathbf{c} = (2\mathbf{i} - 5\mathbf{j}) + (-2\mathbf{i} + 4\mathbf{j}) = 0\mathbf{i} - \mathbf{j} = -\mathbf{j}$

     (iii) $\mathbf{a} - \mathbf{b} = (\mathbf{i} + 3\mathbf{j}) - (2\mathbf{i} - 5\mathbf{j}) = -\mathbf{i} + 8\mathbf{j}$

     (iv) $\mathbf{a} + \mathbf{b} - \mathbf{c} = (\mathbf{a} + \mathbf{b}) - \mathbf{c} = 3\mathbf{i} - 2\mathbf{j} - (-2\mathbf{i} + 4\mathbf{j}) = 5\mathbf{i} - 6\mathbf{j}$

     (v) $3\mathbf{a} + 2\mathbf{b} = 3(\mathbf{i} + 3\mathbf{j}) + 2(2\mathbf{i} - 5\mathbf{j}) = 3\mathbf{i} + 9\mathbf{j} + 4\mathbf{i} - 10\mathbf{j} = 7\mathbf{i} - \mathbf{j}$

(b)   (i) $|\mathbf{a} + \mathbf{b}| = \sqrt{3^2 + (-2)^2} = \sqrt{9 + 4} = \sqrt{13}$

     (ii) $|\mathbf{b} + \mathbf{c}| = 1$

     (iii) $|\mathbf{a} - \mathbf{b}| = \sqrt{(-1)^2 + 8^2} = \sqrt{65}$

     (iv) $|\mathbf{a} + \mathbf{b} - \mathbf{c}| = \sqrt{5^2 + (-6)^2} = \sqrt{61}$

     (v) $|3\mathbf{a} + 2\mathbf{b}| = \sqrt{7^2 + (-1)^2} = \sqrt{50}$

(c)   If $\ \mathbf{n} = \mathbf{a} + \mathbf{b}, \ \ \hat{\mathbf{n}} = \dfrac{1}{\sqrt{13}}(3\mathbf{i} - 2\mathbf{j}) = \dfrac{3}{\sqrt{13}}\mathbf{i} - \dfrac{2}{\sqrt{13}}\mathbf{j}$

     If $\ \mathbf{n} = \mathbf{b} + \mathbf{c}, \ \ \hat{\mathbf{n}} = \dfrac{1}{1}(-\mathbf{j}) = -\mathbf{j}$

For vectors in 3 dimensions, the position vector of the point P with coordinates (x, y, z) is given by

$$\mathbf{r} = x\mathbf{i} + y\mathbf{j} + z\mathbf{k}$$

and its magnitude is given by

$$|\mathbf{r}| = \sqrt{x^2 + y^2 + z^2}$$

Why is this result true?

You can perform algebraic operations in the usual way; for example, if

$$\mathbf{a} = 3\mathbf{i} + 2\mathbf{j} + \mathbf{k}$$
$$\mathbf{b} = \mathbf{i} - 2\mathbf{j} + \mathbf{k}$$

then

$$\mathbf{a} + \mathbf{b} = (3\mathbf{i} + 2\mathbf{j} + \mathbf{k}) + (\mathbf{i} - 2\mathbf{j} + \mathbf{k})$$

$$= 4\mathbf{i} + 2\mathbf{k}$$

$$\mathbf{a} - \mathbf{b} = (3\mathbf{i} + 2\mathbf{j} + \mathbf{k}) - (\mathbf{i} - 2\mathbf{j} + \mathbf{k})$$

$$= 2\mathbf{i} + 4\mathbf{j}$$

$$|\mathbf{a}| = \sqrt{3^2 + 2^2 + 1^2} = \sqrt{14}$$

$$|\mathbf{b}| = \sqrt{1^2 + \left(-2^2\right) + 1^2} = \sqrt{6}$$

Note that two vectors, $\mathbf{a}$ and $\mathbf{b}$ are **parallel** if $\mathbf{a} = \lambda\mathbf{b}$ for some non-zero λ; furthermore, if $\lambda > 0$ they are in the same direction.

Also note that two vectors

$$\mathbf{a} = a_1\mathbf{i} + a_2\mathbf{j} + a_3\mathbf{k} \quad \text{and} \quad \mathbf{b} = b_1\mathbf{i} + b_2\mathbf{j} + b_3\mathbf{k}$$

are equal if, and only if, their components are equal,

i.e. $\qquad a_1 = b_1, \ a_2 = b_2, \ a_3 = b_3$

Activity 5

If $\mathbf{a} = 2\mathbf{i} + \mathbf{j} - \mathbf{k}, \ \mathbf{b} = \mathbf{i} - 2\mathbf{j} + 3\mathbf{k}$, which of the vectors below are parallel to $\mathbf{a}$ or $\mathbf{b}$?

(a) $-2\mathbf{i} - \mathbf{j} + \mathbf{k}$ (b) $5\mathbf{i} - 10\mathbf{j} + 15\mathbf{k}$ (c) $4\mathbf{i} + 2\mathbf{j} - 2\mathbf{k}$

(d) $6\mathbf{i} + 3\mathbf{j} - 3\mathbf{k}$ (e) $-2\mathbf{i} + 4\mathbf{j} - 6\mathbf{k}$ (f) $-4\mathbf{i} - 2\mathbf{j} + 2\mathbf{k}$

Exercise 1B

1. Write in the form $x\mathbf{i} + y\mathbf{j} + z\mathbf{k}$, the vectors represented by $\overrightarrow{OP}$ if P is the point

   (a) $(1, 1, 1)$ (b) $(2, 1, -1)$ (c) $(1, -1, 0)$

2. $\overrightarrow{OP}$ represents the vector $\mathbf{r}$. Write down the coordinates of P if

   (a) $\mathbf{r} = 3\mathbf{i} - 4\mathbf{j} + \mathbf{k}$ (b) $\mathbf{r} = \mathbf{i} + 2\mathbf{j} - \mathbf{k}$ (c) $\mathbf{r} = -4\mathbf{k}$

3. Find the magnitude of the vectors

   (a) $\mathbf{a} = 6\mathbf{i} + 2\mathbf{j} + 3\mathbf{k}$ (b) $\mathbf{b} = 2\mathbf{i} - \mathbf{j} - 2\mathbf{k}$

   (c) $\mathbf{c} = \mathbf{a} + \mathbf{b}$ (d) $\mathbf{d} = \mathbf{a} - \mathbf{b}$

   Also find unit vectors in the direction of $\mathbf{a}$ and $\mathbf{b}$.

4. If $\mathbf{a} = 2\mathbf{i} + 5\mathbf{j} - \mathbf{k}$, $\mathbf{b} = \mathbf{i} + \mathbf{j} + 2\mathbf{k}$, $\mathbf{c} = -2\mathbf{i} + 3\mathbf{j} - \mathbf{k}$ find

   (a) $\mathbf{a} + \mathbf{b}$ (b) $(\mathbf{a} + \mathbf{b}) + \mathbf{c}$ (c) $\mathbf{a} + (\mathbf{b} + \mathbf{c})$

   (d) $\mathbf{a} - 5\mathbf{b} + 11\mathbf{c}$

5. Show that the points $A(4, -2, -16)$, $B(0, -10, -4)$ and $C(-6, -22, 14)$ are collinear.

1.2 Products of vectors

The 'algebra' of vectors has been developed in the previous sections. You can add and subtract vectors and multiply a vector by a scalar $(\lambda\mathbf{a})$, but as yet you cannot 'multiply' vectors.

There are, in fact, two ways of multiplying vectors: one, the **scalar product** is a scalar quantity; the other, the **vector product**, is a vector.

Scalar product

For any two vectors $\mathbf{a}$ and $\mathbf{b}$, the **scalar product**, denoted by $\mathbf{a}.\mathbf{b}$ is defined by

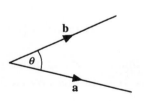

$$\boxed{\mathbf{a}.\mathbf{b} = |\mathbf{a}||\mathbf{b}|\cos\theta}$$

Here $|\mathbf{a}|$ is the modulus of $\mathbf{a}$, $|\mathbf{b}|$ is the modulus of $\mathbf{b}$, and θ is the angle between the direction of the two vectors. (Some texts refer to the scalar product as the 'dot' product, and you say '$\mathbf{a}$ dot $\mathbf{b}$' for $\mathbf{a}.\mathbf{b}$)

Example

If $\mathbf{a} = 2\mathbf{i}$, $\mathbf{b} = 5\mathbf{j}$ and $\mathbf{c} = \mathbf{i} + \mathbf{j}$, find

(a) $\mathbf{a}.\mathbf{b}$ (b) $\mathbf{a}.\mathbf{c}$ (c) $\mathbf{b}.\mathbf{c}$

Solution

(a) $\mathbf{a}.\mathbf{b} = |\mathbf{a}||\mathbf{b}|\cos 90°$

$\qquad = 2 \times 5 \times 0 = 0$

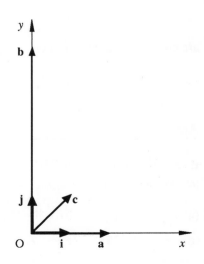

(b) $\mathbf{a}.\mathbf{c} = |\mathbf{a}||\mathbf{c}|\cos 45°$

$$= 2 \times \sqrt{2} \times \frac{1}{\sqrt{2}} \quad \left(\text{since } |\mathbf{c}| = \sqrt{2}\right)$$

$$= 2$$

(c) $\mathbf{b}.\mathbf{c} = |\mathbf{b}||\mathbf{c}|\cos 45°$

$$= 5 \times \sqrt{2} \times \frac{1}{\sqrt{2}}$$

$$= 5$$

From the definition of the scalar product:

(i)   If $\mathbf{a}$ and $\mathbf{b}$ are perpendicular (as in (a) above), then $\theta = 90°$ and $\cos\theta = 0$, which gives $\mathbf{a}.\mathbf{b} = 0$.

(ii) If, for non-zero vectors $\mathbf{a}$ and $\mathbf{b}$, $\mathbf{a}.\mathbf{b} = 0$, then
$$|\mathbf{a}||\mathbf{b}|\cos\theta = 0 \implies \cos\theta = 0,$$
since $|\mathbf{a}| \neq 0$, $|\mathbf{b}| \neq 0$;
then $\theta = 90°$ and $\mathbf{a}$ and $\mathbf{b}$ are perpendicular.

To summarise, for non-zero vectors $\mathbf{a}$ and $\mathbf{b}$

$$\boxed{\mathbf{a}.\mathbf{b} = 0 \Leftrightarrow \mathbf{a}, \mathbf{b} \text{ perpendicular}}$$

Also it is clear that

$$\boxed{\mathbf{a}.\mathbf{a} = |\mathbf{a}|^2}$$

Activity 6

Evaluate the scalar products

(a) $\mathbf{i}.\mathbf{i}$, $\mathbf{i}.\mathbf{j}$, $\mathbf{i}.\mathbf{k}$

(b) $\mathbf{j}.\mathbf{i}$, $\mathbf{j}.\mathbf{j}$, $\mathbf{j}.\mathbf{k}$

(c) $\mathbf{k}.\mathbf{i}$, $\mathbf{k}.\mathbf{j}$, $\mathbf{k}.\mathbf{k}$

(d) $(\mathbf{i}+\mathbf{j}).\mathbf{j}$, $(2\mathbf{i}+\mathbf{k}).\mathbf{k}$

Check, in (d), that for example,

$$(2\mathbf{i}+\mathbf{k}).\mathbf{k} = 2\mathbf{i}.\mathbf{k} + \mathbf{k}.\mathbf{k}$$

Assuming that the scalar product always behaves in this natural way, deduce a formula for $\mathbf{a}.\mathbf{b}$ when $\mathbf{a}$ and $\mathbf{b}$ are expressed in component form

$$\mathbf{a} = a_1\mathbf{i} + a_2\mathbf{j} + a_3\mathbf{k}, \quad \mathbf{b} = b_1\mathbf{i} + b_2\mathbf{j} + b_3\mathbf{k}$$

You should have found in Activity 6 that

$$\mathbf{i}.\mathbf{i} = \mathbf{j}.\mathbf{j} = \mathbf{k}.\mathbf{k} = 1 \quad (\mathbf{i}, \mathbf{j}, \mathbf{k} \text{ are unit vectors})$$

$$\mathbf{i}.\mathbf{j} = \mathbf{j}.\mathbf{k} = \mathbf{k}.\mathbf{i} = 0 \quad (\mathbf{i}, \mathbf{j}, \mathbf{k} \text{ are mutually perpendicular})$$

So if **a** and **b** are expressed in component form

$$\mathbf{a}.\mathbf{b} = (a_1\mathbf{i} + a_2\mathbf{j} + a_3\mathbf{k}).(b_1\mathbf{i} + b_2\mathbf{j} + b_3\mathbf{k})$$

$$= a_1(b_1\mathbf{i}.\mathbf{i} + b_2\mathbf{i}.\mathbf{j} + b_3\mathbf{i}.\mathbf{k})$$

$$+ a_2(b_1\mathbf{j}.\mathbf{i} + b_2\mathbf{j}.\mathbf{j} + b_3\mathbf{j}.\mathbf{k})$$

$$+ a_3(b_1\mathbf{k}.\mathbf{i} + b_2\mathbf{k}.\mathbf{j} + b_3\mathbf{k}.\mathbf{k})$$

$$= a_1 b_1 + a_2 b_2 + a_3 b_3 \qquad \text{(using the results above)}$$

So

$$\boxed{\mathbf{a}.\mathbf{b} = a_1 b_1 + a_2 b_2 + a_3 b_3}$$

Example

If $\mathbf{a} = 2\mathbf{i} + \mathbf{j} + 3\mathbf{k}$, $\mathbf{b} = -3\mathbf{i} + \mathbf{j} - 2\mathbf{k}$, find **a.b** and the cosine of the angle between **a** and **b**.

Solution

$$\mathbf{a}.\mathbf{b} = (2\mathbf{i} + \mathbf{j} + 3\mathbf{k}).(-3\mathbf{i} + \mathbf{j} - 2\mathbf{k})$$

$$= 2 \times (-3) + 1 \times 1 + 3 \times (-2) = -6 + 1 - 6 = -11$$

So

$$\mathbf{a}.\mathbf{b} = |\mathbf{a}||\mathbf{b}|\cos\theta = -11$$

$$\Rightarrow \quad \sqrt{14}\sqrt{14}\cos\theta = -11$$

$$\Rightarrow \quad \cos\theta = -\frac{11}{14}$$

Example

Show that the vectors $\mathbf{a} = \mathbf{i} + 2\mathbf{j} - \mathbf{k}$ and $\mathbf{b} = 2\mathbf{i} - 2\mathbf{j} - 2\mathbf{k}$, are perpendicular.

Solution

$$\mathbf{a}.\mathbf{b} = (\mathbf{i} + 2\mathbf{j} - \mathbf{k}).(2\mathbf{i} - 2\mathbf{j} - 2\mathbf{k})$$

$$= 1 \times 2 + 2 \times (-2) + (-1) \times (-2)$$

$$= 2 - 4 + 2$$

$$= 0$$

Hence vectors **a** and **b** are perpendicular.

Activity 7

For the vectors $x = 3i + 2j$, $y = i + mj$, determine the values of m for which

(a) x is perpendicular to y

(b) x is parallel to y

(c)   the angle between x and y is $30°$.

Example

If $a = 3i - j + 2k$ and $b = mi - 2j - 3k$, find the value of m for which a and b are perpendicular.

Solution

$$a.b = (3i - j + 2k).(mi - 2j - 3k)$$

$$= 3m + (-1)(-2) + 2(-3)$$

$$= 3m + 2 - 6$$

$$= 3m - 4$$

If a and b are perpendicular $a.b = 0$, so $3m - 4 = 0$

$$\Rightarrow \quad m = \frac{4}{3}$$

So a and b are perpendicular when $m = \frac{4}{3}$.

Vector product

For any two vectors, a and b, the vector product, denoted by $a \times b$ (or $a \wedge b$) is defined by

$$\boxed{a \times b = |a||b| \sin \theta \, \hat{n}}$$

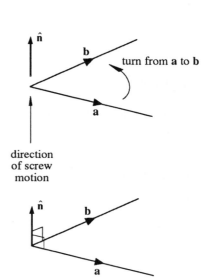

Here $|a|$ is the magnitude of a, $|b|$ is the magnitude of b, and $\hat{n}$ is a unit vector, perpendicular to both a and b and in the direction of linear motion when a screw turns from a to b as illustrated. In the figure if a and b are in a horizontal plane, then $\hat{n}$ is vertical.

This implies that a, b and $\hat{n}$ form a right-handed system similar to the i, j, k system.

What is the magnitude of the vectors $\mathbf{a} \times \mathbf{b}$ **and** $\mathbf{b} \times \mathbf{a}$?

What is the direction of the vector $\mathbf{b} \times \mathbf{a}$?

To follow the direction of a screw's motion turning from $\mathbf{b}$ to $\mathbf{a}$ gives the direction $-\hat{\mathbf{n}}$, that is

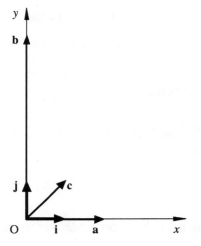

turn from $\mathbf{b}$ to $\mathbf{a}$

$$\mathbf{b} \times \mathbf{a} = |\mathbf{a}||\mathbf{b}|\sin\theta(-\hat{\mathbf{n}})$$

$$= -\mathbf{a} \times \mathbf{b}$$

So $\qquad \mathbf{b} \times \mathbf{a} + \mathbf{a} \times \mathbf{b} = \mathbf{0}$

and the vector product is not, in general, commutative; i.e. $\mathbf{a} \times \mathbf{b} \neq \mathbf{b} \times \mathbf{a}$.

Example

If $\mathbf{a} = 2\mathbf{i}$, $\mathbf{b} = 5\mathbf{j}$ and $\mathbf{c} = \mathbf{i} + \mathbf{j}$, find

(a) $\mathbf{a} \times \mathbf{b}$ (b) $\mathbf{b} \times \mathbf{c}$ (c) $\mathbf{a} \times \mathbf{c}$ (d) $\mathbf{a} \times \mathbf{a}$

Solution

(a) $\mathbf{a} \times \mathbf{b} = 2 \times 5 \times \sin 90° \mathbf{k} = 10\mathbf{k}$ ($\mathbf{k}$ is perpendicular to $\mathbf{a}$ and $\mathbf{b}$)

(b) $\mathbf{b} \times \mathbf{c} = 5 \times \sqrt{2} \times \sin 45°(-\mathbf{k}) = -5\mathbf{k}$

(c) $\mathbf{a} \times \mathbf{c} = 2 \times \sqrt{2} \times \sin 45°(\mathbf{k}) = 2\mathbf{k}$

(d) $|\mathbf{a} \times \mathbf{a}| = 2 \times 2 \times \sin 0° = 0 \qquad \Rightarrow \quad \mathbf{a} \times \mathbf{a} = \mathbf{0}$

In a similar way, you can see that

$$\mathbf{i} \times \mathbf{j} = |\mathbf{i}||\mathbf{j}|\sin 90° \mathbf{k} = \mathbf{k}$$

(since $\mathbf{k}$ is perpendicular to $\mathbf{i}$ and $\mathbf{j}$, and $\mathbf{i}, \mathbf{j}, \mathbf{k}$ form a right-handed system).

Activity 8

Determine all the vector products

(a) $\mathbf{i} \times \mathbf{i}$, $\mathbf{i} \times \mathbf{j}$, $\mathbf{i} \times \mathbf{k}$

(b) $\mathbf{j} \times \mathbf{i}$, $\mathbf{j} \times \mathbf{j}$, $\mathbf{j} \times \mathbf{k}$

(c) $\mathbf{k} \times \mathbf{i}$, $\mathbf{k} \times \mathbf{j}$, $\mathbf{k} \times \mathbf{k}$

You should have found that

$$\mathbf{i} \times \mathbf{j} = \mathbf{k}, \quad \mathbf{j} \times \mathbf{k} = \mathbf{i}, \quad \mathbf{k} \times \mathbf{i} = \mathbf{j}$$

whereas

$$\mathbf{j} \times \mathbf{i} = -\mathbf{k}, \quad \mathbf{k} \times \mathbf{j} = -\mathbf{i}, \quad \mathbf{i} \times \mathbf{k} = -\mathbf{j}$$

and

$$\mathbf{i} \times \mathbf{i} = \mathbf{j} \times \mathbf{j} = \mathbf{k} \times \mathbf{k} = \mathbf{0}$$

Again assuming that addition and subtraction behave in a natural way, you can use these results to find a formula for $\mathbf{a} \times \mathbf{b}$ in terms of their components. If

$$\mathbf{a} = a_1 \mathbf{i} + a_2 \mathbf{j} + a_3 \mathbf{k}, \quad \mathbf{b} = b_1 \mathbf{i} + b_2 \mathbf{j} + b_3 \mathbf{k}$$

then it can be shown that

$$\mathbf{a} \times \mathbf{b} = \left(a_2 b_3 - a_3 b_2 \right) \mathbf{i} + \left(a_3 b_1 - a_1 b_3 \right) \mathbf{j} + \left(a_1 b_2 - a_2 b_1 \right) \mathbf{k}$$

Activity 9

Prove the formula above for $\mathbf{a} \times \mathbf{b}$.

Writing out an array

$$\begin{bmatrix} \mathbf{i} & \mathbf{j} & \mathbf{k} \\ a_1 & a_2 & a_3 \\ b_1 & b_2 & b_3 \end{bmatrix}$$

work out an easy way of remembering the formula for $\mathbf{a} \times \mathbf{b}$.

Example

If $\mathbf{a} = \mathbf{i} + \mathbf{j} + \mathbf{k}$, $\mathbf{b} = 2\mathbf{i} + 3\mathbf{j} - \mathbf{k}$, find $\mathbf{a} \times \mathbf{b}$.

Solution

$$\mathbf{a} \times \mathbf{b} = \left(\mathbf{i} + \mathbf{j} + \mathbf{k} \right) \times \left(2\mathbf{i} + 3\mathbf{j} - \mathbf{k} \right)$$

$$= \mathbf{i} \times \left(2\mathbf{i} + 3\mathbf{j} - \mathbf{k} \right) + \mathbf{j} \times \left(2\mathbf{i} + 3\mathbf{j} - \mathbf{k} \right) + \mathbf{k} \times \left(2\mathbf{i} + 3\mathbf{j} - \mathbf{k} \right)$$

$$= (2)\mathbf{0} + 3\mathbf{k} - (-\mathbf{j}) + (-2\mathbf{k}) + (3)\mathbf{0} - \mathbf{i} + 2\mathbf{j} - 3\mathbf{i} - \mathbf{0}$$

$$= -4\mathbf{i} + 3\mathbf{j} + \mathbf{k}$$

Alternatively you can quickly evaluate the vector product using the formula from Activity 9; this gives

$$\mathbf{a} \times \mathbf{b} = (-1 - 3)\mathbf{i} + \big(2 - (-1)\big)\mathbf{j} + (3 - 2)\mathbf{k}$$
$$= -4\mathbf{i} + 3\mathbf{j} + \mathbf{k}$$

Note that if two vectors $\mathbf{a}$ and $\mathbf{b}$ are parallel (or anti-parallel) then $\theta = 0$ or π, and

$$\mathbf{a} \times \mathbf{b} = 0\hat{\mathbf{n}} = \mathbf{0}$$

Conversely, for non-zero vectors $\mathbf{a}$ and $\mathbf{b}$,

$$\mathbf{a} \times \mathbf{b} = \mathbf{0} \Rightarrow \sin \theta = 0 \Rightarrow \theta = 0, \ \pi$$

Hence

$$\boxed{\mathbf{a} \times \mathbf{b} = \mathbf{0} \Leftrightarrow \mathbf{a} = \mathbf{0} \ \text{or} \ \mathbf{b} = \mathbf{0} \ \text{or} \ \mathbf{a}, \mathbf{b} \ \text{parallel}}$$

Example

If $\mathbf{a} = \mathbf{i} - 3\mathbf{j} + 2\mathbf{k}$ and $\mathbf{b} = -2\mathbf{i} + 6\mathbf{j} - 4\mathbf{k}$, find $\mathbf{a} \times \mathbf{b}$. What can you say about $\mathbf{a}$ and $\mathbf{b}$?

Solution

$$\mathbf{a} \times \mathbf{b} = (\mathbf{i} - 3\mathbf{j} + 2\mathbf{k}) \times (-2\mathbf{i} + 6\mathbf{j} - 4\mathbf{k})$$
$$= (-2)\mathbf{0} + 6\mathbf{k} + 4\mathbf{j} - 6\mathbf{k} + (-18)\mathbf{0} + 12\mathbf{i} - 4\mathbf{j} - 12\mathbf{i} + (-8)\mathbf{0}$$
$$= \mathbf{0}$$

Hence $\mathbf{a}$ and $\mathbf{b}$ are parallel. In fact you can readily see that $\mathbf{b} = -2\mathbf{a}$.

You can use the vector product to find the area of a triangle.

For the triangle AOB shown opposite, let

$$\mathbf{a} = \overrightarrow{OA}, \ \ \mathbf{b} = \overrightarrow{OB}$$

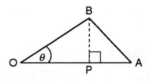

So
$$|\mathbf{a} \times \mathbf{b}| = |\mathbf{a}||\mathbf{b}| \sin \theta$$

$$= OA \times (OB \sin \theta)$$

$$= OA \times BP \qquad (= \text{base} \times \text{height})$$

and

$$\boxed{\text{area of } \triangle OAB \ = \ \frac{1}{2}|\mathbf{a} \times \mathbf{b}|}$$

Example

If A is the point $(5, 0)$ and B is the point $(3, 0)$, find the area of the triangle OAB.

Solution

$$\mathbf{a} = 5\mathbf{i}, \quad \mathbf{b} = 3\mathbf{i} + 6\mathbf{j}$$

$$\text{Area of triangle} = \frac{1}{2} |\mathbf{a} \times \mathbf{b}|$$

$$= \frac{1}{2} |5\mathbf{i} \times (3\mathbf{i} + 6\mathbf{j})|$$

$$= \frac{1}{2} |150 + 30\mathbf{k}|$$

$$= \frac{1}{2} |30\mathbf{k}| = \frac{1}{2} \times 30 = 15$$

Example

The triangle ABC is defined by the points

$$A\,(0, 1, 2), \quad B\,(1, 5, 5) \quad \text{and} \quad C\,(2, 3, 1).$$

Find the area of ABC.

Solution

$$\vec{AB} = (1, 4, 3) \quad \text{and} \quad \vec{AC} = (2, 2, -1)$$

So you can think of $\vec{AB}$ as $\mathbf{i} + 4\mathbf{j} + 3\mathbf{k}$ and $\vec{AC}$ as $2\mathbf{i} + 2\mathbf{j} - \mathbf{k}$ and calculate $\vec{AB} \times \vec{AC}$ as

$$\big(4(-1) - 3 \times 2\big)\mathbf{i} + \big(3 \times 2 - 1(-1)\big)\mathbf{j} + (1 \times 2 - 4 \times 2)\mathbf{k}$$

or

$$-10\mathbf{i} + 7\mathbf{j} - 6\mathbf{k}$$

Hence

$$\text{area of triangle} = \frac{1}{2} |(-10, 7, -6)|$$

$$= \frac{1}{2} \sqrt{100 + 49 + 36}$$

$$= \frac{1}{2} \sqrt{185}$$

Exercise 1C

1. If $\mathbf{a} = 2\mathbf{i} + \mathbf{j} - 2\mathbf{k}$ and $\mathbf{b} = -3\mathbf{i} + 4\mathbf{k}$, find

    (a) $\mathbf{a}.\mathbf{b}$

    (b) the acute angle between these vectors (to the nearest degree)

    (c) a vector which is perpendicular to both $\mathbf{a}$ and $\mathbf{b}$.

2. For $\mathbf{a}$ and $\mathbf{b}$ in Question 1, find $\mathbf{a} \times \mathbf{b}$. Use this to find the angle between these vectors (to the nearest degree).

3. Let $\mathbf{a} = \mathbf{i} - 2\mathbf{j} + \mathbf{k}$, $\mathbf{b} = 2\mathbf{i} + \mathbf{j} - \mathbf{k}$. Given that $\mathbf{c} = \lambda\mathbf{a} + \mu\mathbf{b}$ and that $\mathbf{c}$ is perpendicular to $\mathbf{a}$, find the ratio of λ to μ.

4. Find the value of λ for which the vectors $2\mathbf{i} - 3\mathbf{j} + \mathbf{k}$ and $3\mathbf{i} + 6\mathbf{j} + \lambda\mathbf{k}$ are perpendicular.

5. Given the vectors $\mathbf{u} = 3\mathbf{i} + 2\mathbf{j}$ and $\mathbf{v} = 2\mathbf{i} + \lambda\mathbf{j}$, determine the value of λ so that

    (a) $\mathbf{u}$ and $\mathbf{v}$ are at right angles

    (b) $\mathbf{u}$ and $\mathbf{v}$ are parallel

    (c) the acute angle between $\mathbf{u}$ and $\mathbf{v}$ is $45°$.

6. The angle between the vectors $\mathbf{i} + \mathbf{j}$ and $\mathbf{i} + \mathbf{j} + \lambda\mathbf{k}$ is $45°$. Find the possible values of λ.

7. Given that $\mathbf{a} = 2\mathbf{i} + \mathbf{k}$ and $\mathbf{b} = \mathbf{i} - 2\mathbf{j} + 3\mathbf{k}$ calculate

    (a) the scalar product $\mathbf{a}.\mathbf{b}$

    (b) the vector product $\mathbf{a} \times \mathbf{b}$

8. The vectors $\mathbf{u}$ and $\mathbf{v}$ are given by $\mathbf{u} = 2\mathbf{i} - \mathbf{j} + 2\mathbf{k}$, $\mathbf{v} = p\mathbf{i} + q\mathbf{k}$.

    Given that $\mathbf{u} \times \mathbf{v} = \mathbf{i} + s\mathbf{k}$, find p, q and s. Find also the cosine of the angle between $\mathbf{u}$ and $\mathbf{v}$.

9. The points A, B and C have coordinates $(2, 1, -1)$, $(1, -7, 3)$ and $(-2, 5, 1)$ respectively.

    Find the area of the triangle ABC.

1.3 Vector equation of a straight line

A straight line, L, is uniquely defined by giving two distinct points on the line.

Are there other ways to define uniquely a straight line?

If the coordinates of A and B are given, then the vectors $\mathbf{a} = \overrightarrow{OA}$ and $\mathbf{b} = \overrightarrow{OB}$ are known. Let P be any point on the line AB with position vector

$$\mathbf{r} = x\mathbf{i} + y\mathbf{j} + z\mathbf{k}.$$

Then $$\mathbf{r} = \overrightarrow{OP} = \overrightarrow{OA} + \overrightarrow{AP}$$

$$\Rightarrow \quad \mathbf{r} = \mathbf{a} + \overrightarrow{AP}$$

But $\overrightarrow{AP}$ is a linear multiple of $\overrightarrow{AB}$ and $\overrightarrow{AB} = \mathbf{b} - \mathbf{a}$

so $$\mathbf{r} = \mathbf{a} + \lambda(\mathbf{b} - \mathbf{a})$$

for some parameter λ. This is the form of the vector equation of a straight line. The parameter can take any real value, giving different points on the line.

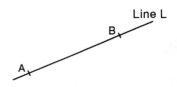

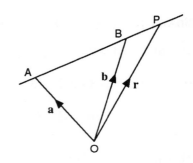

What value of λ gives the point A?

What value of λ gives the point B?

Example

Find the vector equation of the straight line passing through the points A $(1, 0, 1)$ and B $(0, 1, 3)$.

Solution

Here $\mathbf{a} = \mathbf{i} + \mathbf{k}$ and $\mathbf{b} = \mathbf{j} + 3\mathbf{k}$

so $\mathbf{r} = (\mathbf{i}+\mathbf{k}) + \lambda\left((\mathbf{j}+3\mathbf{k}) - (\mathbf{i}+\mathbf{k})\right)$

$\mathbf{r} = (\mathbf{i}+\mathbf{k}) + \lambda\left(-\mathbf{i} + \mathbf{j} + 2\mathbf{k}\right)$ (or $\mathbf{r} = (1,\ 0,\ 1) + \lambda(-1,\ 1,\ 2)$)

This vector equation of a line can readily be turned into a cartesian equation by noting that the coordinates of the point on the line are

$$(x,\ y,\ z) = (1-\lambda,\ \lambda,\ 1+2\lambda)$$

This gives

$$\left.\begin{array}{l} x = 1-\lambda \\ y = \lambda \\ z = 1+2\lambda \end{array}\right\} \text{ or } \frac{x-1}{(-1)} = \frac{y-0}{1} = \frac{z-1}{2} \quad (= \lambda)$$

This is the form of the cartesian equation of a straight line.

In general, the vector equation can be written as

$$\mathbf{r} = \mathbf{a} + \lambda\,\mathbf{t}$$

where $\mathbf{t}$ is a vector in the direction of the line.

If $\mathbf{a} = a_1\mathbf{i} + a_2\mathbf{j} + a_3\mathbf{k}$ and $\mathbf{t} = t_1\mathbf{i} + t_2\mathbf{j} + t_3\mathbf{k}$

then

$$\left.\begin{array}{l} x = a_1 + \lambda t_1 \\ y = a_2 + \lambda t_2 \\ z = a_3 + \lambda t_3 \end{array}\right\} \text{ or } \frac{x-a_1}{t_1} = \frac{y-a_2}{t_2} = \frac{z-a_3}{t_3}$$

Example

The cartesian equation of a straight line is given by

$$\frac{x-1}{2} = \frac{y+1}{4} = \frac{z-2}{(-2)}$$

Rewrite it in vector form.

Solution

Writing $\dfrac{x-1}{2} = \dfrac{y+1}{4} = \dfrac{z-2}{(-2)} = \lambda$ for some parameter λ, then

$$\left. \begin{array}{l} x = 1 + 2\lambda \\ y = -1 + 4\lambda \\ z = 2 - 2\lambda \end{array} \right\} \text{ or } \mathbf{r} = (\mathbf{i} - \mathbf{j} + 2\mathbf{k}) + \lambda(2\mathbf{i} + 4\mathbf{j} - 2\mathbf{k})$$

Note that this equation is not unique (although the line is unique).

For example, you can write

$$\mathbf{r} = (\mathbf{i} - \mathbf{j} + 2\mathbf{k}) + 2\lambda(\mathbf{i} + 2\mathbf{j} - \mathbf{k})$$

and with $\mu = 2\lambda$,

$$\mathbf{r} = (\mathbf{i} - \mathbf{j} + 2\mathbf{k}) + \mu(\mathbf{i} + 2\mathbf{j} - \mathbf{k})$$

Similarly, check for yourself that

$$\mathbf{r} = (-3\mathbf{j} + 3\mathbf{k}) + \sigma(\mathbf{i} + 2\mathbf{j} - \mathbf{k}) \qquad (\text{put } \mu = \sigma - 1)$$

and $\qquad \mathbf{r} = (3\mathbf{i} + 3\mathbf{j}) + \rho(-\mathbf{i} - 2\mathbf{j} + \mathbf{k})$

describe the same line. In all cases the first part of the vector is the position vector of a point on the line and the second part is a vector parallel to the line.

Example

Find a vector equation of the line which passes through the point

A $(1, -1, 0)$ and is parallel to the line $\overrightarrow{BC}$ where B and C are the points with coordinates $(-3, 2, 1)$ and $(2, 1, 0)$. Show that the point D $(-14, 2, 3)$ lies on the line.

Solution

The line required is parallel to the line $\overrightarrow{BC}$, which has equation

$$(2 - (-3))\mathbf{i} + (1 - 2)\mathbf{j} + (0 - 1)\mathbf{k} = 5\mathbf{i} - \mathbf{j} - \mathbf{k}.$$

Its equation is given by

$$\mathbf{r} = \mathbf{i} - \mathbf{j} + \lambda(5\mathbf{i} - \mathbf{j} - \mathbf{k}).$$

To show that the point D lies on the line, you must check whether

$$\mathbf{r} = \mathbf{i} - \mathbf{j} + \lambda(5\mathbf{i} - \mathbf{j} - \mathbf{k})$$

can ever equal $-14\mathbf{i} + 2\mathbf{j} + 3\mathbf{k}$ for some value of λ.

Equating coefficients of **i**, **j** and **k**, you need

$$[\mathbf{i}]\ 1 + 5\lambda = -14 \quad [\mathbf{j}]\ -1 - \lambda = 2 \quad [\mathbf{k}]\ -\lambda = 3$$

and all three of these **are** satisfied when $\lambda = -3$. Hence D does lie on the line.

Exercise 1D

1. Find the vector and cartesian equations of the straight line joining the points A and B, whose coordinates are $(-2, 1, 4)$ and $(1, 7, 6)$ respectively.

2. If $\vec{OA} = \mathbf{i} - 2\mathbf{j} + \mathbf{k}$, $\vec{OB} = -\mathbf{i} - 3\mathbf{k}$,

    $\vec{OC} = 3\mathbf{i} + \mathbf{j} - 2\mathbf{k}$, $\vec{OD} = 8\mathbf{i} + \mathbf{j} + 4\mathbf{k}$

    find the vector equation of a straight line

    (a) through A and B;

    (b) through D parallel to BC;

    (c) through C parallel to AB.

3. The three lines L, M and N, are given by the equations

    L: $\mathbf{r} = 7\mathbf{i} - 3\mathbf{j} + 3\mathbf{k} + \lambda(3\mathbf{i} - 2\mathbf{j} + \mathbf{k})$

    M: $\mathbf{r} = 7\mathbf{i} - 2\mathbf{j} + 4\mathbf{k} + \mu(-2\mathbf{i} + \mathbf{j} - \mathbf{k})$

    N: $\mathbf{r} = \mathbf{i} + \nu(\mathbf{j} - \mathbf{k})$

    (a) Show that L and M intersect and find their point of intersection.

    (b) Show that L and N do not intersect.

    (c) Do M and N intersect?

1.4   Vector equation of a plane

There are a number of ways of specifying a plane – you can deduce its equation in each case. Here you will consider two specific ways:

(1)   a point in the plane and a perpendicular vector to the plane are given;

(2)   three non-collinear points in the plane are given.

Point and perpendicular vector

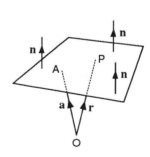

Let the given point in the plane be A with $\vec{OA} = \mathbf{a}$. Also let **n** be a vector perpendicular to the plane, i.e. a **normal** to the plane.

If P is any point in the plane, with position vector **r**, then

$$\vec{AP} = \mathbf{r} - \mathbf{a}$$

is perpendicular to **n**; so

$$(\mathbf{r} - \mathbf{a}).\mathbf{n} = 0.$$

Thus the vector equation of a plane is of the form

$$\boxed{\mathbf{r}.\mathbf{n} = \mathbf{a}.\mathbf{n}}$$

Example

Find the vector equation of a plane which passes through the point
$(0, 1, 1)$ and has normal vector $\mathbf{n} = \mathbf{i} + \mathbf{j} + \mathbf{k}$. Also find its
cartesian equation and show that the points $(1, 0, 1)$ and $(1, 1, 0)$
lie on the plane. Sketch the plane.

Solution

The equation is given by

$$\mathbf{r}.(\mathbf{i} + \mathbf{j} + \mathbf{k}) = (0\mathbf{i} + 1\mathbf{j} + 1\mathbf{k}).(\mathbf{i} + \mathbf{j} + \mathbf{k})$$

$$\Rightarrow \quad \mathbf{r}.(\mathbf{i} + \mathbf{j} + \mathbf{k}) = 0 + 1 + 1 = 2$$

$$\Rightarrow \quad \mathbf{r}.(\mathbf{i} + \mathbf{j} + \mathbf{k}) = 2.$$

The cartesian equation is found by writing $\mathbf{r}$ as

$$\mathbf{r} = x\mathbf{i} + y\mathbf{j} + z\mathbf{k}$$

giving $(x\mathbf{i} + y\mathbf{j} + z\mathbf{k}).(\mathbf{i} + \mathbf{j} + \mathbf{k}) = 2$

$$\Rightarrow \quad x + y + z = 2.$$

For the point $(1, 0, 1)$, $x = 1$, $y = 0$ and $z = 1$, which satisfies the
equation. Similarly $(1, 1, 0)$ satisfies the equation, so these two
points are on the plane.

A sketch of the plane is shown opposite.

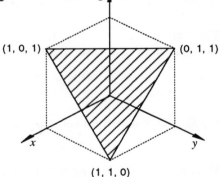

Note that for any particular choice of the normal $\mathbf{n}$, the equation

$$\mathbf{r}.\mathbf{n} = \mathbf{a}.\mathbf{n}$$

gives a unique equation for the plane despite the fact that $\mathbf{a}$ is the
position vector of any point on the plane. For example, another
point on the plane has coordinates $(3, 1, -2)$. In this case, the
equation is

$$\mathbf{r}.(\mathbf{i} + \mathbf{j} + \mathbf{k}) = (3\mathbf{i} + \mathbf{j} - 2\mathbf{k}).(\mathbf{i} + \mathbf{j} + \mathbf{k}) = 2$$

as before. Different choices for the normal $\mathbf{n}$ (which must be a
scalar multiple of $\mathbf{i} + \mathbf{j} + \mathbf{k}$) will give essentially the same equation.

Three non-collinear points

Three non-collinear points are sufficient to define uniquely a plane.

What shape will be defined by four non-collinear points?

Suppose the points A, B and C all lie on the plane and

$$\overrightarrow{OA} = \mathbf{a}, \quad \overrightarrow{OB} = \mathbf{b}, \quad \overrightarrow{OC} = \mathbf{c}.$$

Now the vector $\vec{AB} = \mathbf{b} - \mathbf{a}$ lies in the plane. Similarly

$\vec{AC} = \mathbf{c} - \mathbf{a}$ lies in the plane. Now if P is any point on the plane with position vector $\mathbf{r}$, then

$$\vec{OP} = \vec{OA} + \vec{AP}$$

$$\mathbf{r} = \mathbf{a} + \vec{AP}$$

By construction you can see that

$$\vec{AP} = \vec{AD} + \vec{DP}$$

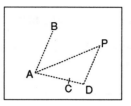

where D is on AC, produced such that DP is parallel to AB.

So, if

$$AD = n\,AC \quad \text{and} \quad DP = m\,AB$$

for some parameters m and n, then

$$\vec{AP} = m\,\vec{AB} + n\,\vec{AC}$$

$$= m(\mathbf{b} - \mathbf{a}) + n(\mathbf{c} - \mathbf{a})$$

Finally, you can write the equation as

$$
\boxed{
\begin{array}{c}
\mathbf{r} = \mathbf{a} + m(\mathbf{b} - \mathbf{a}) + n(\mathbf{c} - \mathbf{a}) \\
\text{or} \\
\mathbf{r} = (1 - m - n)\mathbf{a} + m\mathbf{b} + n\mathbf{c}
\end{array}
}
$$

where m and n are parameters.

Example

Find the vector equation of the plane that passes through the points $(0, 1, 1)$, $(1, 1, 0)$ and $(1, 0, 1)$. Deduce its cartesian form.

Solution

With $\mathbf{a} = \mathbf{j} + \mathbf{k}$, $\mathbf{b} = \mathbf{i} + \mathbf{j}$, $\mathbf{c} = \mathbf{i} + \mathbf{k}$,

$$\mathbf{r} = \mathbf{j} + \mathbf{k} + m(\mathbf{i} - \mathbf{k}) + n(\mathbf{i} - \mathbf{j})$$

$$\mathbf{r} = (m + n)\mathbf{i} + (1 - n)\mathbf{j} + (1 - m)\mathbf{k}.$$

To find the cartesian equation of the plane, note that

$$\mathbf{r} = x\mathbf{i} + y\mathbf{j} + z\mathbf{k}$$

so $\qquad x = m + n$, $y = 1 - n$, $z = 1 - m$.

Eliminating m and n,

$$x = (1-z) + (1-y)$$

$$\Rightarrow \quad x+y+z = 2$$

as deduced in the previous example.

Activity 10

Deduce the general equation of a plane passing through the point A, where $\overrightarrow{OA} = \mathbf{a}$, and such that the vectors $\mathbf{s}$ and $\mathbf{t}$ are parallel to the plane.

Example

The lines L_1 and L_2 have equations

$$\mathbf{r} = (3\mathbf{i}+\mathbf{j}-\mathbf{k}) + \alpha(\mathbf{i}+2\mathbf{j}+3\mathbf{k})$$

and

$$\mathbf{r} = (2\mathbf{i}+5\mathbf{j}) + \beta(\mathbf{i}-\mathbf{j}+\mathbf{k})$$

respectively.

(a) Prove that L_1 and L_2 intersect and find the point of intersection.

(b) Determine the equation of the plane π containing L_1 and L_2.

(AEB)

Solution

(a) If L_1 and L_2 intersect, then

$$(3\mathbf{i}+\mathbf{j}-\mathbf{k}) + \alpha(\mathbf{i}+2\mathbf{j}+3\mathbf{k}) = (2\mathbf{i}+5\mathbf{j}) + \beta(\mathbf{i}-\mathbf{j}+\mathbf{k}).$$

Equating coefficients,

$$\left.\begin{array}{l}[\mathbf{i}] \; 3+\alpha=2+\beta \\ [\mathbf{j}] \; 1+2\alpha=5-\beta\end{array}\right\} \left.\begin{array}{l}\alpha-\beta=-1 \\ 2\alpha+\beta=4\end{array}\right\} \; 3\alpha=3 \; \Rightarrow \; \alpha=1, \; \beta=2$$

$$[\mathbf{k}] \; -1+3\alpha=\beta$$

Now $\alpha=1$, $\beta=2$ satisfies the third equation, and so the lines intersect at the point $(4, 3, 2)$.

(b) The plane contains the point with position vector

$$4\mathbf{i}+3\mathbf{j}+2\mathbf{k}$$

and the directions of $(\mathbf{i}+2\mathbf{j}+3\mathbf{k})$ and $(\mathbf{i}-\mathbf{j}+\mathbf{k})$.

Hence

$$\mathbf{r} = 4\mathbf{i} + 3\mathbf{j} + 2\mathbf{k} + m(\mathbf{i} + 2\mathbf{j} + 3\mathbf{k}) + n(\mathbf{i} - \mathbf{j} + \mathbf{k})$$

for parameters m and n.

Note that you can find the cartesian form by writing
$\mathbf{r} = x\mathbf{i} + y\mathbf{i} + z\mathbf{k}$, giving

$$\left.\begin{array}{l} x = 4 + m + n \\ y = 3 + 2m - n \\ z = 2 + 3m + n \end{array}\right\} \quad \left.\begin{array}{l} x + y = 7 + 3m \\ \\ y + z = 5 + 5m \end{array}\right\} \Rightarrow \quad 5x + 2y - 3z = 20$$

Activity 11

Show that the equation of a plane containing the points A, B and C,
where $\overrightarrow{OA} = \mathbf{a}$, $\overrightarrow{OB} = \mathbf{b}$, $\overrightarrow{OC} = \mathbf{c}$, can be written in the form

$$\mathbf{r} = \lambda \mathbf{a} + \mu \mathbf{b} + \nu \mathbf{c}$$

where $\lambda + \mu + \nu = 1$.

Exercise 1E

1. Find the equation of the plane that contains the
    points
    A $(2, -1, 0)$, B $(-1, 3, 4)$ and C $(3, 0, 2)$.

2. Find the equation of the plane that contains the
    point A $(2, -1, 0)$ and for which the vector
    $$\mathbf{r} = 4\mathbf{i} + 10\mathbf{j} - 7\mathbf{k}$$
    is perpendicular to the plane.

3. Compare your answers to Questions 1 and 2.
    What do you deduce?

4. Find the equation of the plane passing through
    $(0, 0, 0)$ and with normal vector $\mathbf{i} + 2\mathbf{j} - 3\mathbf{k}$.

5. Show that the line with equation
    $$\mathbf{r} = \mathbf{k} + \lambda(2\mathbf{i} + 6\mathbf{j} + 8\mathbf{k})$$
    is perpendicular to the plane with equation
    $$x + 3y + 4z = 8$$

6. Show that the point A $(2, 3, 1)$ lies on the plane
    $$\mathbf{r} \cdot (2\mathbf{i} - \mathbf{k}) = 3$$
    Also show that the line with vector equation
    $$\mathbf{r} = 3\mathbf{i} + \mathbf{j} + 3\mathbf{k} + \lambda(\mathbf{i} - 2\mathbf{j} + 2\mathbf{k})$$
    is contained in the plane.

7. Find the point of intersection of the line
    $$\mathbf{r} = \mathbf{k} + \lambda(2\mathbf{i} + \mathbf{j} + \mathbf{k})$$
    with the plane $\mathbf{r} \cdot \mathbf{i} = 4$.

8. The planes
    $$\mathbf{r} \cdot (2\mathbf{i} - 3\mathbf{j} - \mathbf{k}) = 19 \quad \text{and} \quad \mathbf{r} \cdot (-\mathbf{i} + 2\mathbf{j} + 2\mathbf{k}) = -9$$
    intersect in a line L. Find the cartesian equation
    of the plane which contains L and is parallel to
    the vector $\mathbf{i}$.

1.5 Miscellaneous Exercises

1. Find the sum of the vectors $2\mathbf{i}+\mathbf{j}-\mathbf{k}$, $\mathbf{i}+3\mathbf{j}+\mathbf{k}$, $3\mathbf{i}+2\mathbf{j}$.

2. Find the magnitude of the vector $\mathbf{a}=3\mathbf{i}-2\mathbf{j}+6\mathbf{k}$.

3. If $(a+2)\mathbf{i}+(b-1)\mathbf{j}$ and $(b-1)\mathbf{i}-a\mathbf{j}$ are equal vectors, find the values of a and b.

4. If $\lambda\mathbf{i}-4\mathbf{j}$ is parallel to $2\mathbf{i}-6\mathbf{j}$, find the value of λ.

5. Find the unit vector in the direction of $2\mathbf{i}-\mathbf{j}+2\mathbf{k}$.

6. Find the vector with magnitude 3 that is parallel to $6\mathbf{i}-3\mathbf{j}+2\mathbf{k}$.

7. If $\overrightarrow{OA}=4\mathbf{i}+14\mathbf{j}-5\mathbf{k}$, $\overrightarrow{OB}=\mathbf{i}+2\mathbf{j}+7\mathbf{k}$, and $\overrightarrow{OC}=2\mathbf{i}+6\mathbf{j}+3\mathbf{k}$, show that the vectors $\overrightarrow{BC}$ and $\overrightarrow{CA}$ are parallel. Hence deduce that the points A, B and C are collinear.

8. Show that $3\mathbf{i}+7\mathbf{j}+2\mathbf{k}$ is perpendicular to $5\mathbf{i}-\mathbf{j}-4\mathbf{k}$.

9. Given that $\overrightarrow{OA}=\mathbf{i}+\mathbf{j}$, $\overrightarrow{OB}=5\mathbf{i}+7\mathbf{j}$, find the position vectors of the other two vertices of the square of which A and B are one pair of opposite vertices.

10. Given that $\mathbf{p}=t^2\mathbf{i}+(2t+1)\mathbf{j}+\mathbf{k}$ and $\mathbf{q}=(t-1)\mathbf{i}+3t\mathbf{j}-(t^2+3t)\mathbf{k}$ where t is a scalar variable, determine

    (a) the values of t for which $\mathbf{p}$ and $\mathbf{q}$ are perpendicular.

    (b) the angle between the vectors $\mathbf{p}$ and $\mathbf{q}$ when $t=1$, giving your answer to the nearest $0.1°$.
    (AEB)

11. The point P has position vector
$$(1+\mu)\mathbf{i}+(3-2\mu)\mathbf{j}+(4+2\mu)\mathbf{k}$$
where μ is a variable parameter. The point Q has position vector $4\mathbf{i}+2\mathbf{j}+3\mathbf{k}$.

    (a) The points P_0 and P_1 are the positions of P when $\mu=0$ and $\mu=1$ respectively. Calculate the size of angle P_0QP_1, giving your answer to the nearest degree.

    (b) Show that $PQ^2=(3\mu-1)^2+10$ and hence, or otherwise, find the position vector of P when it is closest to Q. (AEB)

12. The lines l_1 and l_2 have vector equations
$$l_1: \mathbf{r}=2\mathbf{i}+3\mathbf{j}+5\mathbf{k}+\lambda(\mathbf{i}+\mathbf{j}+2\mathbf{k})$$
$$l_2: \mathbf{r}=4\mathbf{j}+6\mathbf{k}+\mu(-\mathbf{i}+2\mathbf{j}+3\mathbf{k})$$

    (a) Show that l_1 and l_2 intersect and find the position vector of the point of intersection.

    (b) Find the acute angle between l_1 and l_2, giving your answer correct to the nearest degree. (AEB)

13. With respect to a fixed origin O, the points L and M have position vectors $6\mathbf{i}+3\mathbf{j}+2\mathbf{k}$ and $2\mathbf{i}+2\mathbf{j}+\mathbf{k}$ respectively.

    (a) Form the scalar product $\overrightarrow{OL}.\overrightarrow{OM}$ and hence find the cosine of angle LOM.

    (b) The point N is on the line LM, produced such that angle MON is $90°$. Find an equation for the line LM in the form $\mathbf{r}=\mathbf{a}+\mathbf{b}t$ and hence calculate the position vector of N.
    (AEB)

2 VECTOR APPLICATIONS

Objectives

After studying this chapter you should

- be able to find the moment of a force;
- understand the concept of equivalent systems of forces;
- be able to reduce a system of forces;
- understand the concept of relative velocity.

2.0 Introduction

The first chapter revised the concept and use of vectors. It should be noted that the use of vectors in mechanics problems is just a convenient way of coping with equations in more than one direction by having one vector equation. Sometimes it might not seem particularly helpful to use vectors but the real gain comes later in mathematical studies in higher education where vectors are not just a convenient method but a vital tool, for example, in the analysis of fluid flow.

2.1 Applications

Work done by a force

You have already met this concept in the *Mechanics* module. Work is done when a force moves a particle through a distance. If **F** is the **constant** force being applied, and the particle is moved from A to B where $\overrightarrow{AB} = \mathbf{d}$, then

$$\text{work done} = \mathbf{F}.\mathbf{d}$$

Since force is measured in Newtons and distance in metres, the unit of work can be expressed as the Newton metre (N m), but more usually it is referred to as the Joule (J), so that 1 J is the work done in moving a force of 1 N through 1 m.

Example

A block slides down an inclined plane from A to B. Ignoring friction, the forces acting on the block are its weight, *W* and a normal reaction *R*. Calculate the work done by the forces in terms of *h*.

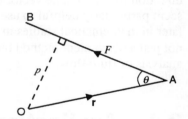

Solution

$$\mathbf{W} = -W\mathbf{j}, \quad \mathbf{d} = -h\mathbf{j} + a\mathbf{i}$$

$$\mathbf{W}.\mathbf{d} = -W\mathbf{j}.(-h\mathbf{j} + a\mathbf{i}) = Wh$$

and

$$\mathbf{R}.\mathbf{d} = 0$$

since **R** and **d** are perpendicular.

So the work done is simply *Wh*.

Moment of a force

In the *Mechanics* text, you met the concept of the moment of a force. The definition is repeated here.

> The **moment** of a force acting at point A about point O is equal to the force times the perpendicular distance from O to the line along which the force acts.

So, in the notation shown in the figure opposite,

$$\text{moment } = F \times p$$

$$= F \times (\text{OA} \sin \theta)$$

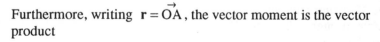

This definition assumes the force *F* is a scalar, but in reality it is a vector **F**, of magnitude *F* and in the direction AB.

Furthermore, writing $\mathbf{r} = \overrightarrow{\text{OA}}$, the vector moment is the vector product

$$\boxed{\mathbf{M} = \mathbf{r} \times \mathbf{F}}$$

which has magnitude

$$|\mathbf{M}| = |\mathbf{r}||\mathbf{F}||\sin\theta|$$

$$= pF$$

$$= \text{scalar moment of } F \text{ about O}$$

Example

Forces act along the sides of a square OABC of side 1 m as shown opposite. Find the resultant moment about O.

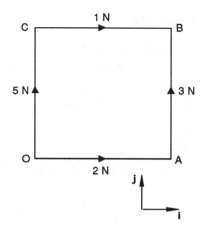

Solution

Introducing unit vectors in the plane as shown,

$$\mathbf{F}_1 = 2\mathbf{i}, \qquad \mathbf{r}_1 = 0 \quad \text{(since the point O is on the line}$$
$$\text{of action of } \mathbf{F}_1 \text{)}$$

$$\mathbf{F}_2 = 3\mathbf{j}, \qquad \mathbf{r}_2 = \mathbf{i} \quad \text{(point A)}$$

$$\mathbf{F}_3 = \mathbf{i}, \qquad \mathbf{r}_3 = \mathbf{j} \quad \text{(point C)}$$

$$\mathbf{F}_4 = 5\mathbf{j}, \qquad \mathbf{r}_4 = 0 \quad \text{(point O)}$$

Hence the resultant moment is given by

$$\mathbf{r}_1 \times \mathbf{F}_1 + \mathbf{r}_2 \times \mathbf{F}_2 + \mathbf{r}_3 \times \mathbf{F}_3 + \mathbf{r}_4 \times \mathbf{F}_4$$

$$= 0 + \mathbf{i} \times 3\mathbf{j} + \mathbf{j} \times \mathbf{i} + 0$$

$$= 3\mathbf{k} - \mathbf{k}$$

$$= 2\mathbf{k}$$

Note that the use of vectors in this example almost complicates the analysis rather than simplifies it. From your earlier definition of moment, you can note that the moment is zero for the forces along OA and OC, since their perpendicular distances from O are zero.

The moment of the force 3 N along AB is

$$3 \times 1 = 3 \quad \text{(in an anticlockwise direction)}$$

and similarly for force 1 N along CB,

$$1 \times (-1) = -1 \quad \text{(in a clockwise direction)}$$

giving a resultant moment of 2 Nm in an anticlockwise direction.

Is the resultant moment about the point B the same as the resultant moment about O?

Activity 1

For the system of coplanar forces shown opposite, find the resultant moment about

(a)   point A;

(b)   point B;

(c)   point O.

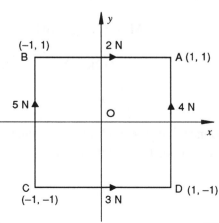

Example

Two forces $\mathbf{F}_1$ and $\mathbf{F}_2$ of magnitudes $3\sqrt{5}$ N and $\sqrt{5}$ N act through the point with position vector $2\mathbf{i} + \mathbf{j}$ in directions $\mathbf{i} + 2\mathbf{j}$ and $\mathbf{i} - 2\mathbf{j}$ respectively. Calculate $\mathbf{F}_1$ and $\mathbf{F}_2$ and hence state $\mathbf{R}$ the resultant of these forces. What is the moment of $\mathbf{R}$ about the origin?

Solution

A unit vector in the direction of $\mathbf{F}_1$ is given by

$$\frac{\mathbf{i} + 2\mathbf{j}}{|\mathbf{i} + 2\mathbf{j}|} = \frac{\mathbf{i} + 2\mathbf{j}}{\sqrt{1^2 + 2^2}} = \frac{\mathbf{i} + 2\mathbf{j}}{\sqrt{5}}$$

Hence $\mathbf{F}_1$ is of the form

$$\mathbf{F}_1 = 3\sqrt{5}\,\frac{(\mathbf{i} + 2\mathbf{j})}{\sqrt{5}}$$

$$= 3(\mathbf{i} + 2\mathbf{j})$$

and, similarly,

$$\mathbf{F}_2 = \sqrt{5}\,\frac{(\mathbf{i} - 2\mathbf{j})}{\sqrt{1 + 2^2}}$$

$$= \mathbf{i} - 2\mathbf{j}$$

Hence $\qquad \mathbf{R} = \mathbf{F}_1 + \mathbf{F}_2 = 3(\mathbf{i} + 2\mathbf{j}) + (\mathbf{i} - 2\mathbf{j})$

$$= 4\mathbf{i} + 4\mathbf{j} = 4(\mathbf{i} + \mathbf{j})$$

So the resultant force, $\mathbf{R}$, is in the direction of $\mathbf{i} + \mathbf{j}$ (i.e. parallel to $y = x$) and of magnitude $4\sqrt{2}$.

Why is the magnitude of the vector R given by $4\sqrt{2}$?

Now, taking moments about the origin gives

$$\mathbf{M} = (2\mathbf{i} + \mathbf{j}) \times 3(\mathbf{i} + 2\mathbf{j}) + (2\mathbf{i} + \mathbf{j}) \times (\mathbf{i} - 2\mathbf{j})$$

$$= 12\mathbf{k} - 3\mathbf{k} - 4\mathbf{k} - \mathbf{k}$$

$$= 4\mathbf{k}$$

Hence $|\mathbf{M}| = 4$, and this must equate to the magnitude of the moment of $\mathbf{R}$ about the origin.

Couple

A couple is formed by two equal parallel forces (acting in opposing directions) which are coplanar.

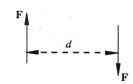

Activity 2

A couple acting on a rod is illustrated opposite.

Ignoring all other forces (e.g. gravity) acting on the rod, find the total moment of the couple about

(a) A   (b) O   (c) B   (d) any other points.

What do you deduce?

This activity should lead you to hypothesise that the total moment of a couple about a particular point is in fact independent of the point under consideration; that is, the total moment of a couple is constant about any point.

Exercise 2A

1. The forces $\mathbf{F}_1 = 3\mathbf{i}$, $\mathbf{F}_2 = 4\mathbf{j}$, $\mathbf{F}_3 = 2\mathbf{i}$ act through the points $\mathbf{i} + 2\mathbf{j}$, $3\mathbf{i} + 4\mathbf{j}$ and $\mathbf{i} + 7\mathbf{j}$ respectively. Find the resultant force and find its moment about the origin O.

2. A uniform rod AB, of length 150 mm and mass 50 g, has a load of X grams attached at a point C of the rod such that AC = 30 mm. The rod rests horizontally on a smooth support placed at a point D where AD = 60 mm. Calculate the numerical value of X.

   A second smooth support is now placed at B and the load of X grams is removed. A new load of 60 g is attached to the rod at a point E such that EB = 35 mm. If the rod still rests in a horizontal position, calculate the thrust on each support.

3. A thin, non-uniform beam AB, of length 6 m and mass 50 kg, is in equilibrium resting horizontally on two smooth supports which are respectively 2 m and 3.5 m from A. The thrusts on the two supports are equal. Find the position of the centre of gravity of the beam.

   The original supports are removed and a load of 10 kg is attached to the beam at B. The loaded beam rests horizontally on two new smooth supports at A and C, where C is a point on the beam 1 m from B. Calculate the thrusts on each of the new supports.

4.

   The figure shows a light horizontal beam AB, of length 9 m, supported at its ends by a force **S** acting vertically and a force **R** acting at an angle of a to the line of the beam. A force of 30 N is applied to the beam, at an angle of 30°, 3 m from B. If the beam is in equilibrium, calculate:

   (a) S   (b) α (c) **B**.

   Calculate the magnitude and direction of the necessary moment that would have to be applied at A to reduce the reaction at B to zero.

5. A non-uniform rod AB of length $6a$ rests in a horizontal position on two pegs at a distance a from each end. (Draw your diagram with B to the right of A.) The rod will just tilt if a weight W is attached to A or a weight $2W$ is attached to B. Find the weight of the rod and the distance of its centre of gravity from A.

   When the rod is resting on the pegs (with neither of the weights attached) a clockwise couple of moment Wa is applied to the rod in the vertical plane containing the rod. Find the magnitudes of the reactions of the pegs on the rod.

2.2 Reduction of a system of forces

Two or more systems of **coplanar** forces which produce exactly the same linear and turning effects on a rigid body are called **equivalent** systems of forces. It is, for example, often easier to reduce a system of many forces acting on a rigid body to a single force which essentially has the same effect.

To test whether two coplanar force systems are equivalent you need to show that

(i)   the vector sums of the two force systems are equal or, equivalently, the sums of the resolved forces in two perpendicular directions are identical in both systems; and

(ii) the resulting moment about a point in the plane containing the forces is identical in both systems.

Both these conditions need to be satisfied if two force systems are to be equivalent.

How many equations are produced by satisfying conditions (i) and (ii) above?

Example

Show that the two force systems illustrated below are equivalent.

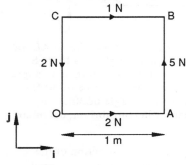
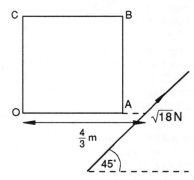

Solutions

Using a vector approach (although there is no need to for this example) you can write, for the first system,

$$F_1 = 2i, \qquad r_1 = 0$$

$$F_2 = 5j, \qquad r_2 = i$$

$$F_3 = i, \qquad r_3 = j$$

$$F_4 = -2j, \qquad r_4 = 0$$

Here r_i are points on the line of action of the force F_i.

For the second system,

$$R = \frac{\sqrt{18}\,(i+j)}{\sqrt{2}} = 3i + 3j, \quad r = \frac{4}{3}i$$

Thus
$$F_1 + F_2 + F_3 + F_4 = 2i + 5j + i - 2j$$
$$= 3i + 3j$$
$$= R$$

satisfying condition (i).

Similarly

$$r_1 \times F_1 + r_2 \times F_2 + r_3 \times F_3 + r_4 \times F_4$$
$$= (0 \times 2i) + (i \times 5j) + (j \times i) + (0 \times (-2j))$$
$$= 5k - k$$
$$= 4k$$

and
$$r \times R = \frac{4}{3}i \times (3i + 3j) = 4k$$

Condition (ii) is satisfied and the two systems of forces are equivalent.

> The **resultant** of a system of coplanar forces which is not in equilibrium, is either a **single force** or a **couple**.

A system of coplanar forces will reduce to a **single force** provided that the resultant force, **R**, is non-zero; that is, provided that at least one of the resolved forces in two perpendicular directions is non-zero. To locate the position of the line of action of the resultant force, you must take moments about any point in the plane.

Example

OABC is a square of side 2 m, with forces acting along the sides as shown opposite.

Calculate

(a) the resultant force;

(b) the moment of the force about O;

(c) the distance from O of the point where the line of action of the resultant force cuts OA.

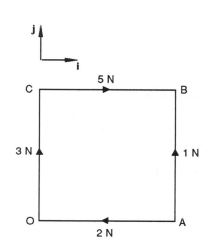

Solution

(a)   With the usual notation

$$\mathbf{F}_1 = -2\mathbf{i}, \quad \mathbf{r}_1 = \mathbf{0} \quad (\mathbf{r}_1 \text{ is a point on the line of action of } \mathbf{F}_1)$$

$$\mathbf{F}_2 = \mathbf{j}, \quad \mathbf{r}_2 = \mathbf{i}$$

$$\mathbf{F}_3 = 5\mathbf{i}, \quad \mathbf{r}_3 = \mathbf{j}$$

$$\mathbf{F}_4 = 3\mathbf{j}, \quad \mathbf{r}_4 = \mathbf{0}$$

So $\mathbf{R} = \mathbf{F}_1 + \mathbf{F}_2 + \mathbf{F}_3 + \mathbf{F}_4$

$$= -2\mathbf{i} + \mathbf{j} + 5\mathbf{i} + 3\mathbf{j}$$

$$= 3\mathbf{i} + 4\mathbf{j}$$

(b) $\mathbf{M} = \mathbf{r}_1 \times \mathbf{F}_1 + \mathbf{r}_2 \times \mathbf{F}_2 + \mathbf{r}_3 \times \mathbf{F}_3 + \mathbf{r}_4 \times \mathbf{F}_4$

$$= \mathbf{0} \times (-2\mathbf{i}) + \mathbf{i} \times \mathbf{j} + \mathbf{j} \times 5\mathbf{i} + \mathbf{0} \times 3\mathbf{j}$$

$$= \mathbf{k} - 5\mathbf{k}$$

$$= -4\mathbf{k}$$

(c)   If d is the perpendicular distance of the line of action of $\mathbf{R}$ from the point O, then

$$l = \frac{d}{\sin\theta}, \text{ where } \sin\theta = \frac{4}{5} \quad (\text{since } \tan\theta = \frac{4}{3})$$

and from (b) above

$$-4 = |\mathbf{R}|d = 5d$$

Hence

$$l = \frac{5d}{4} = \frac{5}{4}\left(-\frac{4}{5}\right) = -1$$

the negative sign indicating that it is on the negative x-axis as shown opposite.

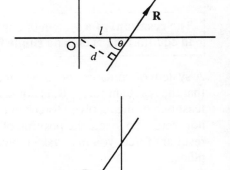

Example

Forces $2P$, $3P$ and $4P$ act along the sides $\overrightarrow{\text{OA}}$, $\overrightarrow{\text{AB}}$ and $\overrightarrow{\text{BO}}$ of an equilateral triangle OAB of side of length a. Find

(a)   the resultant force;

(b)   the distance from O of the point where it cuts OB.

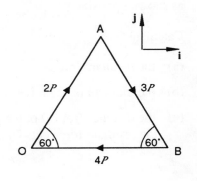

Solution

(a) In vector terms

$$\mathbf{F}_1 = 2P\cos 60°\,\mathbf{i} + 2P\sin 60°\,\mathbf{j} = P\mathbf{i} + \sqrt{3}\,P\mathbf{j}$$

$$\mathbf{F}_2 = 3P\cos 60°\,\mathbf{i} - 3P\sin 60°\,\mathbf{j} = \frac{3}{2}P\mathbf{i} - \frac{3\sqrt{3}}{2}\,P\mathbf{j}$$

$$\mathbf{F}_3 = -4P\mathbf{i}$$

So the resultant force is given by

$$\mathbf{R} = \mathbf{F}_1 + \mathbf{F}_2 + \mathbf{F}_3$$

$$= P\mathbf{i} + \sqrt{3}\,P\mathbf{j} + \frac{3}{2}P\mathbf{i} - \frac{3\sqrt{3}}{2}P\mathbf{j} - 4P\mathbf{i}$$

$$= -\frac{3}{2}P\mathbf{i} - \frac{\sqrt{3}}{2}P\mathbf{j}$$

Its magnitude is given by

$$|\mathbf{R}| = P\sqrt{\frac{9}{4} + \frac{3}{4}} = \sqrt{3}\,P$$

and its direction is given by

$$\tan\theta = \left(\frac{\frac{\sqrt{3}}{2}}{\frac{3}{2}}\right) = \frac{1}{\sqrt{3}}$$

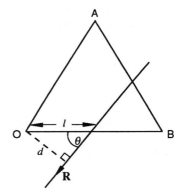

where θ is as shown in the diagram opposite.

Thus $\theta = 30°$.

(b) If d is the perpendicular distance of the line of action of **R** from the origin, then

$$d\,|\mathbf{R}| = P\sqrt{3}\,d$$

must equal the clockwise magnitude of the moment of the three forces about O. This moment is given by

$$\mathbf{M} = \mathbf{0}\times\mathbf{F}_1 + (a\cos 60°\,\mathbf{i} + a\sin 60°\,\mathbf{j})\times\mathbf{F}_2 + \mathbf{0}\times\mathbf{F}_3$$

$$= \left(\frac{a}{2}\mathbf{i} + \frac{a\sqrt{3}}{2}\mathbf{j}\right)\times\left(\frac{3}{2}P\mathbf{i} - \frac{3\sqrt{3}}{2}P\mathbf{j}\right)$$

$$= -\frac{3\sqrt{3}}{4}aP\mathbf{k} - \frac{3\sqrt{3}}{4}aP\mathbf{k}$$

i.e. $\mathbf{M} = -\dfrac{3\sqrt{3}}{2}aP\mathbf{k}$

(The negative sign shows that this is a clockwise rotation.)

Thus $P\sqrt{3}\,d = +\dfrac{3\sqrt{3}}{2}aP$, giving $d = \dfrac{3}{2}a$,

and

$l = \dfrac{p}{\sin 30°} = 3a$

as illustrated opposite.

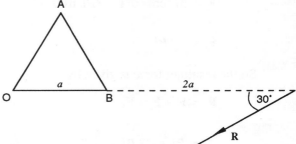

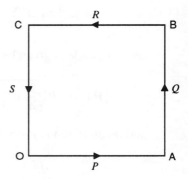

Activity 3

Consider a general case of forces acting along the sides of a square as shown opposite.

(a)   What is the resultant force?

(b)   Can the system have a zero resultant force, but not be in equilibrium?

(c)   What are the conditions for equilibrium?

(*Hint:* You could consider looking at special cases where the values of P, Q, R and S are given.)

A system of coplanar forces reduces to a **couple** if both the following conditions are satisfied:

(i)   the resultant force is zero;

(ii)   the resultant moment about any point in the plane is non-zero.

An alternative condition is that the resultant moment about any three non-collinear points is non-zero.

Example

Show that the system of forces shown opposite is equivalent to a couple. Find its moment. (The square is of side 1 m.)

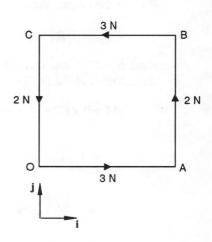

Solution

Clearly $\mathbf{R} = 3\mathbf{i} + 2\mathbf{j} - 3\mathbf{i} - 2\mathbf{j} = \mathbf{0}$

so the resultant force is zero.

Taking moments about O,

$$\mathbf{M} = (0 \times 3\mathbf{i}) + (\mathbf{i} \times 2\mathbf{j}) + (\mathbf{j} \times (-3\mathbf{i})) + (0 \times (-2\mathbf{j}))$$

$$= 2\mathbf{k} + 3\mathbf{k} = 5\mathbf{k}$$

Hence the system of forces is equivalent to a couple of moment 5 N m.

Example

ABC is an isosceles triangle with $AB = AC = 10$ cm, and $BC = 12$ cm. M is the midpoint of BC. Forces act as shown in the diagram. Show that this system of forces is equivalent to a couple.

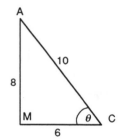

Solution

The forces can be written, in vector form, as

$$\mathbf{F}_1 = 12\mathbf{i}$$

$$\mathbf{F}_2 = 8\mathbf{j}$$

$$\mathbf{F}_3 = -5\cos\theta\,\mathbf{i} + 5\sin\theta\,\mathbf{j}$$

$$\mathbf{F}_4 = -15\cos\theta\,\mathbf{i} - 15\sin\theta\,\mathbf{j}$$

where $\cos\theta = \dfrac{3}{5}, \quad \sin\theta = \dfrac{4}{5}$

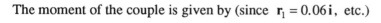

Hence $\quad \mathbf{F}_1 = 12\mathbf{i}, \ \ \mathbf{F}_2 = 8\mathbf{j}, \ \ \mathbf{F}_3 = -3\mathbf{i} + 4\mathbf{j}, \ \ \mathbf{F}_4 = -9\mathbf{i} - 12\mathbf{j}$

and $\quad \mathbf{R} = \mathbf{F}_1 + \mathbf{F}_2 + \mathbf{F}_3 + \mathbf{F}_4$

$$= 12\mathbf{i} + 8\mathbf{j} + (-3\mathbf{i} + 4\mathbf{j}) + (-9\mathbf{i} - 12\mathbf{j})$$

$$= \mathbf{0}$$

so that the resultant force is zero.

The moment of the couple is given by (since $\mathbf{r}_1 = 0.06\mathbf{i}$, etc.)

$$\mathbf{M} = 0 \times \mathbf{F}_1 + \left(\frac{6}{100}\mathbf{i}\right) \times 8\mathbf{j} + \left(\frac{12}{100}\mathbf{i}\right) \times (-3\mathbf{i} + 4\mathbf{j}) + 0 \times \mathbf{F}_4$$

$$= 0.48\mathbf{k} + 0.48\mathbf{k}$$

$$= 0.96\mathbf{k}$$

and its magnitude is 0.96 N m.

Any system of coplanar forces acting on a rigid body may be replaced by an equivalent system consisting of a **single force**, acting at a **particular point** in the plane of the forces, together with a **couple**.

Example

Forces act along the sides of an equilateral triangle, of side of length a, as shown opposite. A force of 2 N acts along BC. Find the force at O and the couple which together are equivalent to this system.

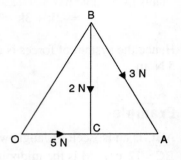

Solution

Let **R** be the single force, at angle θ to OA, and **G** be the anticlockwise moment of the couple.

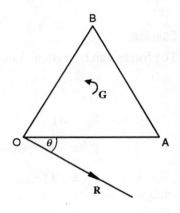

Then, in vector notation,

$$\mathbf{F}_1 = 5\mathbf{i}, \qquad \mathbf{r}_1 = \mathbf{0}$$

$$\mathbf{F}_2 = -2\mathbf{j}, \quad \mathbf{r}_2 = \frac{a}{2}\mathbf{i}$$

$$\mathbf{F}_3 = (3\cos 60°)\mathbf{i} - (3\sin 60°)\mathbf{j}, \quad \mathbf{r}_3 = a\mathbf{i}$$

Hence $\mathbf{R} = \mathbf{F}_1 + \mathbf{F}_2 + \mathbf{F}_3$

$$= 5\mathbf{i} - 2\mathbf{j} + \frac{3}{2}\mathbf{i} - \frac{3\sqrt{3}}{2}\mathbf{j}$$

$$= \frac{13}{2}\mathbf{i} - \frac{\left(4 + 3\sqrt{3}\right)}{2}\mathbf{j}$$

giving $|\mathbf{R}| = \left(\dfrac{169}{4} + \dfrac{\left(4 + 3\sqrt{3}\right)^2}{4}\right)^{\frac{1}{2}} \approx 7.96 \text{ N}$

and $\tan\theta = \left(\dfrac{4 + 3\sqrt{3}}{13}\right) \Rightarrow \theta \approx 35.3°$

Moments about O give

$$\mathbf{M} = \mathbf{0} \times \mathbf{F}_1 + \frac{a}{2}\mathbf{i} \times (-2\mathbf{j}) + a\mathbf{i} \times \left(\frac{3}{2}\mathbf{i} - \frac{3\sqrt{3}}{2}\mathbf{j}\right)$$

$$= -a\mathbf{k} - a\frac{3\sqrt{3}}{2}\mathbf{k}$$

$$= -a\frac{\left(2+3\sqrt{3}\right)}{2}\mathbf{k}$$

Thus the couple has a clockwise moment of magnitude

$$a\frac{\left(2+3\sqrt{3}\right)}{2}\ \text{N m}$$

Activity 4

For the system of coplanar forces shown opposite, find an equivalent set of forces of the form

(a)   force at A and couple;

(b)   force at C and couple.

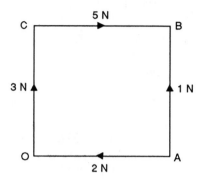

You have now covered the full analysis for **coplanar** forces. The following example illustrates these concepts.

Example

A rectangular lamina has consecutive vertices A, B, C and D whose position vectors with respect to a given origin O are $2\mathbf{i}+5\mathbf{j},\ 5\mathbf{i}+9\mathbf{j},\ -3\mathbf{i}+15\mathbf{j}$ and $-6\mathbf{i}+11\mathbf{j}$ respectively, where $\mathbf{i}$ and $\mathbf{j}$ are perpendicular unit vectors. Forces represented in magnitude, direction and line of action by

$$p\,\overrightarrow{AB},\ q\,\overrightarrow{BC},\ r\,\overrightarrow{CD}\ \text{and}\ \overrightarrow{DA}$$

act on the lamina.

(a)   Express the above forces in the form $a\mathbf{i}+b\mathbf{j}$ and hence express their resultant in this form.

(b)   Show that the magnitude of the moment of these forces about A is $\left|50q+50r\right|$.

    (i)   Given that the lamina is in equilibrium, find p, q and r.

    (ii)   Given that the lamina is **not** in equilibrium and that the resultant force passes through the midpoint of BC, show that $p+r+2=0$.

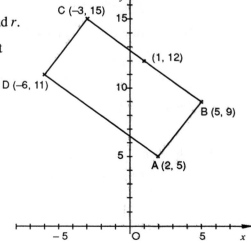

Solution

(a) $\mathbf{F}_1 = p\,\overrightarrow{AB} = p(3\mathbf{i}+4\mathbf{j})$

      $\mathbf{F}_2 = q\,\overrightarrow{BC} = q(-8\mathbf{i}+6\mathbf{j})$

      $\mathbf{F}_3 = r\,\overrightarrow{CD} = r(-3\mathbf{i}-4\mathbf{j})$

      $\mathbf{F}_4 = \overrightarrow{DA} = 8\mathbf{i}-6\mathbf{j}$

37

$$\mathbf{R} = \mathbf{F}_1 + \mathbf{F}_2 + \mathbf{F}_3 + \mathbf{F}_4$$

$$= p(3\mathbf{i} + 4\mathbf{j}) + q(-8\mathbf{i} + 6\mathbf{j}) + r(-3\mathbf{i} - 4\mathbf{j}) + 8\mathbf{i} - 6\mathbf{j}$$

$$= (3p - 8q - 3r + 8)\mathbf{i} + (4p + 6q - 4r - 6)\mathbf{j}$$

(b)   To find the moment about the point A, you require the position vector relative to A of a point on the line of each force; for example

$$\mathbf{r}_1 = \mathbf{0} \ , \ \mathbf{r}_2 = \overrightarrow{AB} = 3\mathbf{i} + 4\mathbf{j} \ , \ \mathbf{r}_3 = \overrightarrow{AD} = -8\mathbf{i} + 6\mathbf{j} \ , \ \mathbf{r}_4 = \mathbf{0}$$

giving

$$\mathbf{M}_A = \mathbf{0} \times \mathbf{F}_1 + (3\mathbf{i} + 4\mathbf{j}) \times q(-8\mathbf{i} + 6\mathbf{j}) + (-8\mathbf{i} + 6\mathbf{j}) \times r(-3\mathbf{i} - 4\mathbf{j}) + \mathbf{0} \times \mathbf{F}_4$$

$$= q(18\mathbf{k} + 32\mathbf{k}) + r(32\mathbf{k} + 18\mathbf{k})$$

$$= (50q + 50r)\mathbf{k}$$

Hence

$$\left| \mathbf{M}_A \right| = \left| 50q + 50r \right|$$

(i)   If the lamina is in equilibrium

$$\mathbf{R} = \mathbf{F}_1 + \mathbf{F}_2 + \mathbf{F}_3 + \mathbf{F}_4 = \mathbf{0}$$

and $\mathbf{M}_A = \mathbf{0}$

This gives

$$p(3\mathbf{i} + 4\mathbf{j}) + q(-8\mathbf{i} + 6\mathbf{j}) + r(-3\mathbf{i} - 4\mathbf{j}) + 8\mathbf{i} - 6\mathbf{j} = \mathbf{0}$$

[i] : $3p - 8q - 3r + 8 = 0$

[j] : $4p + 6q - 4r - 6 = 0$

and

$$50q + 50r = 0 \ \Rightarrow \ q + r = 0$$

Substituting $q = -r$ in the first two equations gives

$$\left. \begin{array}{r} 3p + 5r = -8 \\ 4p - 10r = 6 \end{array} \right\} \ 5p = -5$$

Thus $p = -1$, $r = -1$ and $q = 1$.

(ii)   The resultant force, $\mathbf{R}_1$, passes through the point with coordinates (1, 12) and position vector, relative to A, $-\mathbf{i} + 7\mathbf{j}$.

Hence the moment of $\mathbf{R}_1$ about A is given by

$$\mathbf{M}_A = (-\mathbf{i}+7\mathbf{j})\times\{(3p-8q-3r+8)\mathbf{i}+(4p+6q-4r-6)\mathbf{j}\}$$
$$= (-4p-6q+4r+6)\mathbf{k}-7(3p-8q-3r+8)\mathbf{k}$$
$$= (-25p+50q+25r-50)\mathbf{k}$$

From above, this must equal $(50q+50r)\mathbf{k}$; hence

$$-25p-25r-50=0$$
$$\Rightarrow \qquad p+r+2=0$$

Finally in this section, it should be noted that systems of non-coplanar forces can be reduced in a similar way. This is illustrated in the example below.

Example

Three forces $\mathbf{F}_1$, $\mathbf{F}_2$ and $\mathbf{F}_3$ act on a rigid body at points with position vectors $\mathbf{r}_1$, $\mathbf{r}_2$ and $\mathbf{r}_3$ respectively, relative to an origin O, where

$$\mathbf{F}_1 = (\mathbf{i}-\mathbf{j}+2\mathbf{k}), \qquad \mathbf{r}_1 = (3\mathbf{i}-\mathbf{j}+\mathbf{k})$$

$$\mathbf{F}_2 = (\mathbf{i}+3\mathbf{j}-\mathbf{k}), \qquad \mathbf{r}_2 = (\mathbf{j}+2\mathbf{k})$$

$$\mathbf{F}_3 = (\alpha\mathbf{i}+\beta\mathbf{j}+2\mathbf{k}), \qquad \mathbf{r}_3 = (\mathbf{k})$$

and α and β are constants.

Find

(a) the shortest distance from the point with position vector $\mathbf{r}_2$ to the line of action of the force $\mathbf{F}_1$;

(b) the single force $\mathbf{F}$ acting at O and the couple $\mathbf{G}$ to which the system of forces $\mathbf{F}_1$, $\mathbf{F}_2$ and $\mathbf{F}_3$ reduces.

Determine α and β such that $\mathbf{G}$ is parallel to $\mathbf{F}$.

Solution

(a) The equation of the line of action of $\mathbf{F}_1$ is given by

$$\mathbf{r} = 3\mathbf{i}-\mathbf{j}+\mathbf{k}+\lambda(\mathbf{i}-\mathbf{j}+2\mathbf{k})$$

(since the line is parallel to $\mathbf{F}_1$)

$$= (3+\lambda)\mathbf{i}-(1+\lambda)\mathbf{j}+(1+2\lambda)\mathbf{k}$$

So, if P is the point on the line which has the shortest distance from A (0, 1, 2) then P will have coordinates of the form

$$(3+\lambda, \ -1-\lambda, \ 1+2\lambda)$$

and, if $d = AP$,

$$d^2 = (3+\lambda-0)^2 + (-1-\lambda-1)^2 + (1+2\lambda-2)^2$$

$$= (3+\lambda)^2 + (-2-\lambda)^2 + (-1+2\lambda)^2$$

$$= 6\lambda^2 + 6\lambda + 14$$

The function d^2 (and hence d) has a minimum value when its differential is zero; that is

$$12\lambda + 6 = 0 \quad \Rightarrow \quad \lambda = -\frac{1}{2}$$

and

$$d^2 = 6\left(-\frac{1}{2}\right)^2 + 6\left(-\frac{1}{2}\right) + 14$$

$$= \frac{3}{2} - 3 + 14$$

$$= \frac{25}{2}$$

Hence $d = \frac{5\sqrt{2}}{2}$

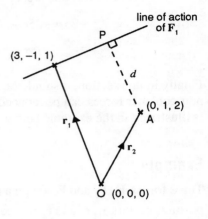

(b)   The single force $\mathbf{F}$ is given by

$$\mathbf{F} = \mathbf{F}_1 + \mathbf{F}_2 + \mathbf{F}_3$$

$$= (\mathbf{i} - \mathbf{j} + 2\mathbf{k}) + (\mathbf{i} + 3\mathbf{j} - \mathbf{k}) + (\alpha\mathbf{i} + \beta\mathbf{j} + 2\mathbf{k})$$

$$= (2+\alpha)\mathbf{i} + (2+\beta)\mathbf{j} + 3\mathbf{k}$$

The moment of the forces about O is given by

$$\sum_{i=1}^{3} \mathbf{r}_i \times \mathbf{F}_i = \begin{vmatrix} \mathbf{i} & \mathbf{j} & \mathbf{k} \\ 3 & -1 & 1 \\ 1 & -1 & 2 \end{vmatrix} + \begin{vmatrix} \mathbf{i} & \mathbf{j} & \mathbf{k} \\ 0 & 1 & 2 \\ 1 & 3 & -1 \end{vmatrix} + \begin{vmatrix} \mathbf{i} & \mathbf{j} & \mathbf{k} \\ 0 & 0 & 1 \\ \alpha & \beta & 2 \end{vmatrix}$$

$$= (-\mathbf{i} - 5\mathbf{j} - 2\mathbf{k}) + (-7\mathbf{i} + 2\mathbf{j} - \mathbf{k}) + (-\beta\mathbf{i} + \alpha\mathbf{j})$$

$$= (-8-\beta)\mathbf{i} + (-3+\alpha)\mathbf{j} - 3\mathbf{k}$$

To balance this, a couple $\mathbf{G}$ is required, where

$$\mathbf{G} = (8+\beta)\mathbf{i} + (3-\alpha)\mathbf{j} + 3\mathbf{k}$$

so $|\mathbf{G}| = \left[(8+\beta)^2 + (3-\alpha)^2 + 9\right]^{\frac{1}{2}}$

The vectors $\mathbf{G}$ and $\mathbf{F}$ are parallel, since the $\mathbf{k}$ components are equal, provided

$$\left.\begin{array}{r} 8+\beta = 2+\alpha \\ 3-\alpha = 2+\beta \end{array}\right\} \quad \alpha = \frac{7}{2}, \ \beta = -\frac{5}{2}$$

Exercise 2B

1. Forces of 2, X, Y, $3X - Y$ Newtons, act along the sides AB, CB, CD, AD of a square, the length of whose side is b. Prove that they are not in equilibrium and that there is just one pair of values of X, Y for which the system is a couple. Find the moment of this couple.

2. Forces of 2, 4, $X - Y$, $X + Y$ Newtons act along the sides AB, BC, CD, DA of a square of side 2 m. If they form a couple, find X, Y and the moment of the couple.

3. ABCD is a square of side 2 m, and forces act as follows: 8 N along AB, 2 N along BC, 5 N along CD and 2 N along AD. Prove that this system is equivalent to a force through A together with a couple. Find the magnitude and direction of the force and the moment of the couple.

4. A rectangle is defined by the four points A(0, 0), B(5, 0), C(5, 3) and D(0, 3), distances being measured in metres. Forces of magnitude 6 N, 8 N, 4 N and 2 N act along AB, BC, CD and DA respectively in directions indicated by the letters.

   Calculate

   (a) the magnitude of the resultant of this system of forces;

   (b) the angle between the line of action of the resultant and the x-axis.

   The line of action of this resultant cuts the x-axis at $(a, 0)$.

   (c) Find a value for a by consideration of moments about A. Hence determine the equation of the line of action of this resultant.

5. The square ABCD has each side of length 6 m. Forces of magnitude 1, 2, 8, 5, $5\sqrt{2}$ and $2\sqrt{2}$ N respectively act along AB, BC, CD, DA, AC and DB respectively, in the directions indicated by the order of the letters. Prove that these forces are equivalent to a couple. Calculate the magnitude and direction of this couple.

   (AEB)

6. OABC is a square of side 1 m. Forces of magnitude 2, 3, 4 and $5\sqrt{2}$ Newtons act along AO, AB, CB and AC respectively in directions indicated by the order of the letters, and a couple of moment 7 N acts in the plane of the square in the sense OCBA. Find the magnitude and direction of the resultant of the system and the equation of its line of action referred to OA and OC as axes. What is the magnitude and direction of the least force introduced at A if the resultant of the original system and this new force is to pass through O?

7. At time t seconds two forces $\mathbf{F}_1$ and $\mathbf{F}_2$ are given by

   $$\mathbf{F}_1 = (\mathbf{i}\cos t + \mathbf{j}\cos t + 2\mathbf{k}\sin t)\,\text{N}$$

   $$\mathbf{F}_2 = (\mathbf{i}\sin t + \mathbf{j}\sin t - \mathbf{k}\sin t)\,\text{N}$$

   The force $\mathbf{F}_1$ acts through the fixed origin O and the force $\mathbf{F}_2$ acts through the point with position vector $(\mathbf{i} + \mathbf{j} + \mathbf{k})$ m relative to O. Find the sum of the moments of the forces about the point with position vector $(a\mathbf{i} + b\mathbf{j} + c\mathbf{k})$ m, where a, b, c are constants, showing that the component of this sum in the direction of $\mathbf{i}$ is

   $$((b + c - 1)\cos t + (c - 2b - 1)\sin t)\,\text{N m}.$$

   Hence, or otherwise, find the position vector of the point A (independent of time) such that the system of the two forces $\mathbf{F}_1$ and $\mathbf{F}_2$ reduces, for all values of t, to a single force at A.

   (AEB)

8. Forces $\mathbf{F}_1$ and $\mathbf{F}_2$ where

   $$\mathbf{F}_1 = (4\mathbf{i} + 5\mathbf{j} + 2\mathbf{k})\,\text{N}, \quad \mathbf{F}_2 = (3\mathbf{i} + \mathbf{j} + 4\mathbf{k})\,\text{N}$$

   act through the points with position vectors, referred to an origin O, $(a\mathbf{i} + 7\mathbf{j} + 3\mathbf{k})$ m and $(4\mathbf{i} + 3\mathbf{j} + a\mathbf{k})$ m respectively, where a is a constant. Given that the lines of action of the forces intersect at a point, find

   (a) the value of a,

   (b) a vector equation of the line of action of the resultant of the forces $\mathbf{F}_1$ and $\mathbf{F}_2$,

   (c) the sum of the moments of $\mathbf{F}_1$ and $\mathbf{F}_2$ about O.

   (AEB)

9. Two forces $\mathbf{F}_1 = (\mathbf{i} + \mathbf{j} + 2\mathbf{k})\,\text{N}$ and $\mathbf{F}_2 = (2\mathbf{i} - \mathbf{j} + \mathbf{k})\,\text{N}$ act at the points whose position vectors relative to an origin O are $\mathbf{r}_1 = (\mathbf{i} + 2\mathbf{k})$ m and $\mathbf{r}_2 = (2\mathbf{j} - \mathbf{k})$ m respectively.

   (a) Determine the shortest distance between the lines of action of these forces.

   (b) Find the force $\mathbf{R}$ at the origin and the couple $\mathbf{G}$ to which the system reduces.

   (c) Determine the moment $\mathbf{G}'$ of the forces $\mathbf{F}_1$ and $\mathbf{F}_2$ about the point with position vector $x\mathbf{i} + y\mathbf{j} + z\mathbf{k}$. Hence, or otherwise show that $\mathbf{R}.\mathbf{G}'$ is independent of x, y and z.

   (AEB)

2.3 Relative velocity

In the *Mechanics* text, you met the idea of relative position. Here this is taken a stage further by using the concept of **relative velocity**.

Consider two boats A and B, moving with constant velocity as shown opposite. At time t_1 the boats are in positions A_1 and B_1 and at time t_2 the boats are in positions A_2 and B_2.

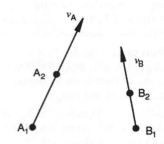

The position of B_1 relative to A_1 is given by

$$\overrightarrow{A_1B_1} = \mathbf{r}_{B_1} - \mathbf{r}_{A_1}$$

Similarly the position of B_2 relative to A_2 is given by

$$\boxed{\overrightarrow{A_2B_2} = \mathbf{r}_{B_2} - \mathbf{r}_{A_2}}$$

If the changes occur in a time interval of $t_2 - t_1$, then the change in relative position, i.e. the relative velocity, is given by

$$\frac{\left(\mathbf{r}_{B_2} - \mathbf{r}_{A_2}\right) - \left(\mathbf{r}_{B_1} - \mathbf{r}_{A_1}\right)}{t_2 - t_1}$$

$$= \frac{\left(\mathbf{r}_{B_2} - \mathbf{r}_{B_1}\right)}{t_2 - t_1} - \frac{\left(\mathbf{r}_{A_2} - \mathbf{r}_{A_1}\right)}{t_2 - t_1}$$

But $\dfrac{\mathbf{r}_{B_2} - \mathbf{r}_{B_1}}{t_2 - t_1} = \mathbf{v}_B$ and $\dfrac{\mathbf{r}_{A_2} - \mathbf{r}_{A_1}}{t_2 - t_1} = \mathbf{v}_A$

So the velocity of B relative to A is given by

$$\boxed{\text{relative velocity} = \mathbf{v}_B - \mathbf{v}_A}$$

This is the definition of relative velocity and this definition holds whether or not the individual velocities are constant.

Example

A car and a cyclist are travelling with constant velocities v_1 m s^{-1} and v_2 m s^{-1} respectively, where $\mathbf{v}_1 = 9\mathbf{i} + 3\sqrt{3}\mathbf{j}$, $\mathbf{v}_2 = 2\mathbf{i} + 2\sqrt{3}\mathbf{j}$ and $\mathbf{i}$ and $\mathbf{j}$ are unit vectors pointing due east and north respectively. At time $t = 0$ the cyclist is 52 m due east of the car. Find the position vector of the cyclist relative to the car at time t seconds.

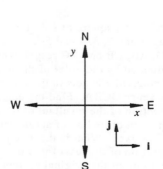

Hence find the least distance between the car and the cyclist and the time at which this occurs.

(AEB)

Solution

The velocity of the cyclist, relative to the car, is given by

$$\mathbf{v}_2 - \mathbf{v}_1 = \left(2\mathbf{i} + 2\sqrt{3}\mathbf{j}\right) - \left(9\mathbf{i} + 3\sqrt{3}\mathbf{j}\right)$$

$$= -7\mathbf{i} - \sqrt{3}\mathbf{j}$$

Integrating, the position vector of the cyclist, relative to the car is given by

$$\mathbf{r}_2 - \mathbf{r}_1 = \left(-7\mathbf{i} - \sqrt{3}\mathbf{j}\right)t + \mathbf{a}$$

Here **a** is a vector constant of integration, which can be determined from the conditions at time $t = 0$. At $t = 0$, you can take

$$\mathbf{r}_2 = 52\mathbf{i} \; , \; \mathbf{r}_1 = \mathbf{0}$$

so $$\mathbf{a} = 52\mathbf{i} - \mathbf{0} = 52\mathbf{i}$$

Hence

$$\mathbf{r}_2 - \mathbf{r}_1 = \left(-7\mathbf{i} - \sqrt{3}\mathbf{j}\right)t + 52\mathbf{i}$$

$$= (52 - 7t)\mathbf{i} - \sqrt{3}t\mathbf{j}$$

Of course, the magnitude of the vector $\mathbf{r}_2 - \mathbf{r}_1$ represents the distance between cyclist and car, say D. That is,

$$D^2 = (52 - 7t)^2 + \left(-\sqrt{3}t\right)^2$$

$$= 52t^2 - 728t + 2704$$

For minimum D^2, differentiating and equating to zero gives

$$104t - 728 = 0 \quad \Rightarrow \quad t = 7$$

and, at $t = 7$,

$$D^2 = 3^2 + \left(-7\sqrt{3}\right)^2$$

$$= 9 + 147$$

$$= 156$$

giving $$D = \sqrt{156} \approx 12.5 \text{ m}$$

It is also useful to use the vector approach for finding the shortest distance between two objects without using calculus as in the example above.

In general, the distance between two objects is

$$\left| \mathbf{r}_A - \mathbf{r}_B \right|$$

where $\mathbf{r}_A$, $\mathbf{r}_B$ are the position vectors of A, B respectively.

Thus, the distance squared between these objects is given by

$$D^2 = \left| \mathbf{r}_A - \mathbf{r}_B \right|^2$$

$$= \left(\mathbf{r}_A - \mathbf{r}_B \right) \cdot \left(\mathbf{r}_A - \mathbf{r}_B \right)$$

Now to find the minimum value of D, differentiate the expression above to give

$$2D\frac{dD}{dt} = \left(\mathbf{v}_A - \mathbf{v}_B \right) \cdot \left(\mathbf{r}_A - \mathbf{r}_B \right) + \left(\mathbf{r}_A - \mathbf{r}_B \right) \cdot \left(\mathbf{v}_A - \mathbf{v}_B \right)$$

$$= 2\left(\mathbf{v}_A - \mathbf{v}_B \right) \cdot \left(\mathbf{r}_A - \mathbf{r}_B \right)$$

So, for $\dfrac{dD}{dt} = 0$, the condition reduces to

$$\boxed{\left(\mathbf{v}_A - \mathbf{v}_B \right) \cdot \left(\mathbf{r}_A - \mathbf{r}_B \right) = 0}$$

This shows that the velocity of A, relative to B, is perpendicular to the position vector of A, relative to B.

Interpret this result where B is at rest.

In the earlier example,

$$\mathbf{v}_2 - \mathbf{v}_1 = -7\mathbf{i} - \sqrt{3}\,\mathbf{j}$$

and

$$\mathbf{r}_2 - \mathbf{r}_1 = (52 - 7t)\mathbf{i} - \sqrt{3}t\,\mathbf{j}$$

so the condition above gives

$$\left(-7\mathbf{i} - \sqrt{3}\,\mathbf{j} \right) \cdot \left((52 - 7t)\mathbf{i} - \sqrt{3}t\,\mathbf{j} \right) = 0$$

$$\Rightarrow \quad -7(52 - 7t) + \sqrt{3}\left(\sqrt{3}\,t \right) = 0$$

$$\Rightarrow \quad 52t = 364$$

$$\Rightarrow \quad t = 7 \quad \text{(as found earlier)}$$

The next two examples show how these concepts can be used to solve problems in kinematics.

Example

A river with long straight banks is 500 m wide and flows with a constant speed of 3 m s^{-1}. A woman rowing a boat at a steady speed of 5 m s^{-1}, relative to the river water, sets off from a point B directly opposite A on the other bank. Find the time taken to cross the river from the point B directly to the point A.

Solution

Whilst you can solve this problem without using vectors, it is often helpful in more complex problems to use vectors.

Vectors are introduced so that

velocity of river $= \mathbf{v}_R = 3\mathbf{i}$

velocity of boat relative to the river $= (-5\sin\theta)\mathbf{i} + (5\cos\theta)\mathbf{j} = \mathbf{v}_B - \mathbf{v}_R$

So the velocity of the boat is given by

$$\mathbf{v}_B = (-5\sin\theta + 3)\mathbf{i} + (5\cos\theta)\mathbf{j}$$

If the boat is to travel directly across the river, this vector must have a zero component in the $\mathbf{i}$ direction.

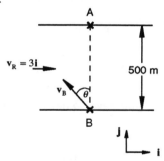

Hence

$$\sin\theta = \frac{3}{5} \quad \left(\text{and}\cos\theta = \frac{4}{5}\right)$$

so that

$$\mathbf{v}_B = 4\mathbf{j}$$

The time taken to reach A is $\dfrac{500}{4} = 125$ s.

Example

At a given instant, a cyclist A passes through a point with position vector $(-9\mathbf{i} - 5\mathbf{j})$ km relative to a fixed point O and is travelling with a constant velocity of $(9\mathbf{i} + 7\mathbf{j})$ km h^{-1}. At the same instant another cyclist B is passing through a point with position vector $(6\mathbf{i}+5\mathbf{j})$ km relative to O and travelling with a constant velocity of $(7\mathbf{i}+6\mathbf{j})$ km h^{-1}. Write down the vector equations of the two cyclists and determine the position vector of the point of intersection of the two paths. Hence, or otherwise, deduce that B passes through this point one hour before A.

Show that, initially, the position vector of B relative to A is $(15\mathbf{i}+10\mathbf{j})$ km and find the position vector of B relative to A at time t hours later. Hence, or otherwise, show that the cyclists are closest together when $t = 8$ and find this minimum separation.

(AEB)

Solution

From the information

$$\mathbf{r}_A = -9\mathbf{i} - 5\mathbf{j} + (9\mathbf{i} + 7\mathbf{j})t$$

and

$$\mathbf{r}_B = 6\mathbf{i} + 5\mathbf{j} + (7\mathbf{i} + 6\mathbf{j})t$$

The point of intersection of the two paths will be given by

$$\mathbf{r}_A = \mathbf{r}_B$$

where for A, $t = \lambda$, say, and for B, $t = \mu$, say.

Why do you have to use different values of t in each equation?

Then

$$(-9+9\lambda)\mathbf{i}+(-5+7\lambda)\mathbf{j}=(6+7\mu)\mathbf{i}+(5+6\mu)\mathbf{j}$$

$$[\mathbf{i}]: \quad -9+9\lambda = 6+7\mu \quad \Rightarrow \quad 9\lambda - 7\mu = 15$$

$$[\mathbf{j}]: \quad -5+7\lambda = 5+6\mu \quad \Rightarrow \quad 7\lambda - 6\mu = 10$$

Solving gives $\mu = 3$ and $\lambda = 4$, so the paths intersect at

$$\mathbf{r} = 27\mathbf{i} + 23\mathbf{j}$$

but, since $\lambda = \mu + 1$, there is a gap of one hour between the two cyclists passing through this point.

Now

$$\mathbf{v}_B - \mathbf{v}_A = (7\mathbf{i} + 6\mathbf{j}) - (9\mathbf{i} + 7\mathbf{j})$$

$$= -2\mathbf{i} - \mathbf{j}$$

At $t = 0$, the position of B relative to A is given by

$$\mathbf{r}_B - \mathbf{r}_A = (6\mathbf{i} + 5\mathbf{j}) - (-9\mathbf{i} - 5\mathbf{j}) = 15\mathbf{i} + 10\mathbf{j}$$

and, at any time $t > 0$,

$$\mathbf{r}_B - \mathbf{r}_A = (6\mathbf{i} + 5\mathbf{j} + (7\mathbf{i} + 6\mathbf{j})t) - \left[(-9\mathbf{i} - 5\mathbf{j}) + (9\mathbf{i} + 7\mathbf{j})t\right]$$

$$= (6 + 7t + 9 - 9t)\mathbf{i} + (5 + 6t + 5 - 7t)\mathbf{j}$$

$$= (15 - 2t)\mathbf{i} + (10 - t)\mathbf{j}$$

Also $\mathbf{v}_B - \mathbf{v}_A = -2\mathbf{i} - \mathbf{j}$

and, using the condition

$$(\mathbf{v}_B - \mathbf{v}_A).(\mathbf{r}_B - \mathbf{r}_A) = 0$$

to find the minimum separation, gives

$$(-2\mathbf{i} - \mathbf{j}).((15 - 2t)\mathbf{i} + (10 - t)\mathbf{j}) = 0$$

$$\Rightarrow \quad -2(15 - 2t) - 1(10 - t) = 0$$

$$\Rightarrow \quad -30 + 4t - 10 + t = 0$$

$$\Rightarrow \quad 5t = 40$$

$$\Rightarrow \quad t = 8$$

and, at $t = 8$

$$\mathbf{r}_A - \mathbf{r}_B = -\mathbf{i} + 2\mathbf{j}$$

giving

$$D^2 = (-1)^2 + 2^2$$

$$= 1 + 4 = 5$$

i.e. $D = \sqrt{5} \approx 2.24 \text{ km}$

Exercise 2C

1. A jet is approaching an airport with velocity $300\mathbf{i}+400\mathbf{j}$. A passenger on the jet sees a helicopter in the distance whose velocity is $50\mathbf{i}-150\mathbf{j}+10\mathbf{k}$.

   (a) What is the velocity of the helicopter relative to the jet?

   (b) What is the velocity of the jet relative to the helicopter?

2. To a cyclist riding with velocity $15\mathbf{i}+15\mathbf{j}$ a steady wind appears to have velocity $3\mathbf{i}-5\mathbf{j}$. What is the actual velocity of the wind?

3. Two particles, A and B, start initially from points with position vectors $2\mathbf{i}-\mathbf{j}$ and $5\mathbf{i}+13\mathbf{j}$ respectively. The velocities of A and B are constant and equal to $2\mathbf{i}-\mathbf{j}$ and $3\mathbf{i}-5\mathbf{j}$.

   (a) Find the velocity of B relative to A.

   (b) Show that the particles collide and find at what time this occurs.

4. Particles A and B start at time $t=0$ s from points with position vectors $(5\mathbf{i}+13\mathbf{j})$ m and $(7\mathbf{i}+\mathbf{j})$ m respectively, relative to a fixed origin. The velocities of A and B are constant and equal to $(3\mathbf{i}-5\mathbf{j})$ m s^{-1} and $(2\mathbf{i}-\mathbf{j})$ m s^{-1} respectively.

   (a) Show that the particles collide and find the position vector of the point of collision.

   (b) Determine the angle between the directions of motion of A and B before collision.

   (AEB)

5. An old man cycles to work each day leaving his home at a point with position vector $(-2\mathbf{i}-8\mathbf{j})$ km relative to an origin O at the centre of the village. The unit vectors $\mathbf{i}$ and $\mathbf{j}$ point east and north respectively. One day he cycles due north at 8 km h^{-1}.

   At the same time, a younger man leaves his home, which has position vector $(-12\mathbf{i}-4\mathbf{j})$ km relative to O, and cycles with velocity $(6\mathbf{i}-6\mathbf{j})$ km h^{-1}. Show that after half an hour the cyclists are closest together and determine this shortest distance between them.

   On that day as the men cycle to work there is a steady wind blowing. To the older man, cycling due north at 18 km h^{-1}, the wind appears to blow **from** the west. To the younger man, cycling with velocity $(6\mathbf{i}-6\mathbf{j})$ km h^{-1}, the wind appears to blow **from** the south. Find the velocity of the wind as a vector.

   (AEB)

6. Two particles A and B are free to move in the plane of the fixed unit vectors $\mathbf{i}$ and $\mathbf{j}$. The velocity of A is $(-3\mathbf{i}+29\mathbf{j})$ m s^{-1} whilst that of B is $v(\mathbf{i}+7\mathbf{j})$ m s^{-1}, where v is a constant. Determine the velocity of B relative to A and find the vector $\overrightarrow{AB}$ at time t s given that, when $t=0$, $\overrightarrow{AB}=(-56\mathbf{i}+8\mathbf{j})$ m.

   Find also the value of v such that the particles collide.

   Show that, when $v=3$, $\overrightarrow{AB}$ at time t s is given by $(6t-56)\mathbf{i}+8(1-t)\mathbf{j}$ and hence find t when A and B are closest together.

   By evaluating a suitable scalar product show that, for your value of t and with $v=3$, $\overrightarrow{AB}$ is perpendicular to the velocity of B relative to A.

   (AEB)

2.4 Miscellaneous Exercises

1. The forces
   $$(3\mathbf{i}+\mathbf{j}+2\mathbf{k})\,\text{N},\quad (6\mathbf{i}+p\mathbf{j}+\mathbf{k})\,\text{N},\quad (2\mathbf{i}-2\mathbf{j}+2\mathbf{k})\,\text{N}$$
   where p is a constant, act through the points with position vectors $(-1+\mathbf{k})$ m, $(8\mathbf{i}+6\mathbf{j}+4\mathbf{k})$ m and $(3\mathbf{j}+\mathbf{k})$ m respectively, relative to an origin O.

   (a) Find the value of p so that the above force system reduces to a single force.

   (b) Find the vector equation of the line of action of this force.

   (c) Find the moment of the force about O.

   (AEB)

2. Forces $\mathbf{F}_1$ and $\mathbf{F}_2$ act at points whose position vectors, relative to a fixed origin, are $\mathbf{r}_1$ and $\mathbf{r}_2$ respectively, where
   $$\mathbf{F}_1=(4\mathbf{i}+3\mathbf{j})\,\text{N},\quad \mathbf{r}_1=(2\mathbf{i}+\mathbf{j})\,\text{m}$$
   $$\mathbf{F}_2=(6\mathbf{i}-3\mathbf{j})\,\text{N},\quad \mathbf{r}_2=(-3\mathbf{j})\,\text{m}$$

   Determine the resultant of these forces.

   Show that the position vector of the point of intersection of the lines of action of the forces $\mathbf{F}_1$ and $\mathbf{F}_2$ is $(-2\mathbf{i}-2\mathbf{j})$ m and hence write down a vector equation of the line of action of the resultant of these forces.

A third force $\mathbf{F}_3 = (-6\mathbf{i} - 5\mathbf{j})$ N acting at the point with position vector $\mathbf{r}_3 = (-2\mathbf{i} - 2\mathbf{j})$ m is now added to the system. When the system of forces, $\mathbf{F}_1$, $\mathbf{F}_2$, $\mathbf{F}_3$, is applied to a lamina it is found that equilibrium can be maintained by applying a force $\mathbf{F}_4$ at the point with position vector $(-\mathbf{i} + 2\mathbf{j})$ m together with a couple $\mathbf{G}$. Find $\mathbf{F}_4$ and $\mathbf{G}$, stating whether $\mathbf{G}$ is clockwise or anticlockwise.   (AEB)

3. A spacecraft is manoeuvring to dock with a space station in deep space when three thruster rockets are fired simultaneously. The rockets are positioned at $(-\mathbf{i} + \mathbf{k})$ m, $(8\mathbf{i} + 6\mathbf{j} + 4\mathbf{k})$ m, and $(3\mathbf{j} + \mathbf{k})$ m, respectively, relative to an origin O, and they exert forces $(3\mathbf{i} + \mathbf{j} + 2\mathbf{k})$ N, $(6\mathbf{i} + p\mathbf{j} + \mathbf{k})$ N and $(2\mathbf{i} - 2\mathbf{j} + 2\mathbf{k})$ N, respectively.

   (a) Find the resultant force acting on the spacecraft, and the resultant couple.

   (b) Explain why, for the value $p = 5$ only, the same effect could be created by placing a single rocket motor producing a force along a suitable direction in the spacecraft.   (AEB)

4. The point A lies in the plane $z = 0$ with $x = 0$ and OA makes an acute angle ϕ with the positive y-axis, where O is the origin.

   The point B is in the region $z > 0$ and AB is parallel to the z-axis. Given that the angle AOB is acute and equal to θ show that a unit vector parallel to OB is $(\cos\theta\sin\phi\,\mathbf{i} + \cos\theta\cos\phi\,\mathbf{j} + \sin\theta\,\mathbf{k})$ and obtain, in a similar form, a unit vector perpendicular to the plane AOB.

   In the particular case when $\cos\theta = \dfrac{3}{5}$ and $\phi = 45°$ there are two forces acting at B. One force is of magnitude F and is perpendicular to OB and in the plane AOB and the other is of magnitude R and is perpendicular to the plane AOB. Show that these forces are parallel to the vectors $(4\sqrt{2}\mathbf{i} + 4\sqrt{2}\mathbf{j} - 6\mathbf{k})$ and $\mathbf{i} - \mathbf{j}$ respectively.

   Given that the component parallel to the vector $\mathbf{i}$ of the total moment of the two forces about O vanishes, find $\left|\dfrac{F}{R}\right|$.

5. The following diagram shows a tetrahedron OABC with $OA = OC = 3a$ and $OB = 4a$. The lines OA, OB and OC are perpendicular to each other and $\mathbf{i}, \mathbf{j}, \mathbf{k}$ denote unit vectors parallel to $\overrightarrow{OA}, \overrightarrow{OB}, \overrightarrow{OC}$ respectively.

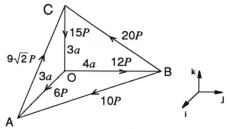

Forces of magnitude $6P$, $12P$, $10P$, $9\sqrt{2}P$, $15P$ and $20P$ act along

$\overrightarrow{OA}$, $\overrightarrow{OB}$, $\overrightarrow{BA}$ $\overrightarrow{AC}$, $\overrightarrow{CO}$ and $\overrightarrow{BC}$ as shown.

Express the forces acting along $\overrightarrow{AC}$, $\overrightarrow{BA}$ and $\overrightarrow{BC}$ in the form $\alpha\mathbf{i} + \beta\mathbf{j} + \gamma\mathbf{k}$, where α, β, γ are to be found in terms of P. Hence, or otherwise, reduce the system of forces to a force $\mathbf{F}$ at O and a couple $\mathbf{G}$ and find $\mathbf{F}$ and $\mathbf{G}$ in the form $\alpha\mathbf{i} + \beta\mathbf{j} + \gamma\mathbf{k}$.

The forces of magnitude $10P$ and $20P$ are now replaced by forces of magnitude $\mathbf{R}$ and $\mathbf{S}$ acting along $\overrightarrow{BA}$ and $\overrightarrow{BC}$ respectively. Find $\mathbf{R}$ and $\mathbf{S}$ so that the system reduces to a couple.   (AEB)

6. The diagram shows a light hollow cube ABCDEFGH of side 4 m.

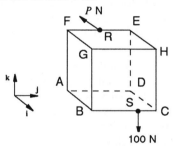

The faces ABCD, EFGH are horizontal and $\mathbf{i}, \mathbf{j}, \mathbf{k}$ denote unit vectors parallel to $\overrightarrow{AB}, \overrightarrow{AD}\ \overrightarrow{AF}$ respectively, with $\mathbf{k}$ being vertically upwards. The point R lies on FE, such that $FR = 1\text{ m}$, and the point S lies on BC such that $BS = 3\text{ m}$.

A force of magnitude P Newtons, parallel to $\overrightarrow{BA}$ acts at R and another force of magnitude 100 N, acts vertically downwards at S. Further forces $(X_A\mathbf{i} + Z_A\mathbf{k})$ and $(X_D\mathbf{i} + Z_D\mathbf{k})$ act at A and D respectively.

(a) Express the position vectors, relative to A, of D, R and S in the form $a\mathbf{i} + b\mathbf{j} + c\mathbf{k}$ where a, b and c are constants to be determined for each point.

(b) Given that the vector sum of all moments about A is zero show that $P = 100$ N and find X_D and Z_D.

(c) Given also that the vector sum of all forces is zero, find X_A and Z_A.   (AEB)

7. A force P in the direction $4\mathbf{i}+3\mathbf{j}$ and of magnitude 10 N acts through the point with position vector $(2\mathbf{j})$ m relative to an origin O. Another force Q in the direction $\mathbf{j}$ and of magnitude 2 N acts through the point with position vector $(4\mathbf{i})$ m relative to O. Find

   (a) P and Q in the form $\alpha\mathbf{i}+\beta\mathbf{j}$ where α, β are scalars to be determined in each case,

   (b) the magnitude of the resultant of P and Q,

   (c) the magnitude of the total moment of P and Q about O. State whether the moment is clockwise or anticlockwise. (AEB)

8. Points A, B and C have position vectors $(8\mathbf{i}+6\mathbf{j})$ m, $(5\mathbf{i}-12\mathbf{j})$ m and $(-3\mathbf{i}-18\mathbf{j})$ m respectively, relative to an origin O. The force $\mathbf{F}_1$, of magnitude 40 N, acts at O along OA and the force $\mathbf{F}_2$, of magnitude 26 N, acts at O along OB. Show that the resultant of these two forces is of the form $\beta\mathbf{i}$ N, and determine β.

   The force $\mathbf{F}_1$ is now replaced by another force $\mathbf{F}_3$, which acts at O along AO. Given that the resultant of $\mathbf{F}_2$ and $\mathbf{F}_3$ acts at O along OC, find $\mathbf{F}_3$ in terms of $\mathbf{i}$ and $\mathbf{j}$.

   A force $\mathbf{F}_4$ is now applied at A. Given that the system of forces $\mathbf{F}_2$, $\mathbf{F}_3$ and $\mathbf{F}_4$ may be reduced to the single force, $\mathbf{F}_1$ through O, together with a couple of magnitude G, find $\mathbf{F}_4$. Find also the magnitude and the sense of the couple G. (AEB)

9. Forces of magnitude P and Q $(\neq 0)$ act along the lines OA and OB respectively, the angle between the positive senses of OA and OB being denoted by θ. Given that the resultant of the forces is also of magnitude P express

   (a) Q in terms of P and θ,

   (b) the angle between OA and the resultant in terms of θ.

   Given that the magnitude of the resultant is unchanged when the magnitude of the force along OA is increased to $\frac{5P}{4}$, find

   (c) Q in terms of P,

   (d) θ correct to the nearest degree,

   (e) the angle, correct to the nearest degree, between OA and this new resultant. (AEB)

10. The position vectors, relative to a fixed origin O, of two buoys A and B in a channel, are $(7\mathbf{i}+9\mathbf{j})$ km and $(5\mathbf{i}+13\mathbf{j})$ km respectively. A ship P, moving with constant velocity $(2\mathbf{i}-3\mathbf{j})$ km h^{-1} passes next to buoy A and five seconds later a ship Q with constant velocity $(3\mathbf{i}-5\mathbf{j})$ km h^{-1} passes next to buoy B.

   (a) Find the velocity of ship Q relative to ship P.

   (b) Find the position vectors of the two ships at a time t seconds after ship Q has passed buoy B. Show that $\overrightarrow{PQ}=(t-12)\mathbf{i}+(19-2t)\mathbf{j}$.

   To avoid collision, ships must ensure that they are never closer than 1 km to each other.

   (c) Find the value of t at which the two ships are closest to each other and show that they do not collide. (AEB)

11. At noon a boat A is 9 km due west of another boat B. To an observer on boat B the boat A always appears to be moving on a bearing of 150° (i.e. S30°E) with constant speed 2.5 m s^{-1}. Find the time at which the boats are closest together and the distance between them at this time. Find also, to the nearest minute, the length of time for which the boats are less than 8 km apart.

   The velocities of B and of a third boat C are given to be $(3\mathbf{i}+4\mathbf{j})$ m s^{-1} and $(5.5\mathbf{i}+2\mathbf{j})$ m s^{-1} respectively, where $\mathbf{i}$ and $\mathbf{j}$ denote unit vectors directed east and north respectively. Express in the form $a\mathbf{i}+b\mathbf{j}$ the velocity of C relative to B. Given that, at noon, C is directly north of A and that the boats B and C are on a collision course, find

   (a) the distance between A and C at noon,

   (b) the time at which B and C would collide. (AEB)

12. Unit vectors $\mathbf{i}$ and $\mathbf{j}$ are defined with $\mathbf{i}$ horizontal and $\mathbf{j}$ vertically upwards. At time $t=0$ a particle P is projected from a fixed origin O with velocity $nu(3\mathbf{i}+5\mathbf{j})$, where n and u are positive constants. At the same instant a particle Q is projected from the point A, where $\overrightarrow{OA}=a(16\mathbf{i}+17\mathbf{j})$ with a being a positive constant, with velocity $u(-4\mathbf{i}+3\mathbf{j})$.

   (a) Find the velocity of P at time t in terms of n, u, g and t. Show also that the velocity of P relative to Q is constant and express it in the form $p\mathbf{i}+q\mathbf{j}$.

   (b) Find the value of n such that P and Q collide.

   (c) Given that P and Q do not collide and that Q is at its maximum height above A when at a point B, find, in terms of u and g, the horizontal and vertical displacements of B from A. (AEB)

3 MODELLING WITH DIFFERENTIAL EQUATIONS

Objectives

After studying this chapter you should

- understand how to formulate simple mathematical models;

- be able to solve simple differential equations, including linear first order equations;

- use initial conditions to find complete solutions;

- appreciate the structure of the solution to linear equations, including second order constant coefficient equations;

- know how to use and apply results from mathematical models, based on differential equations.

3.0   Introduction

In the *Mechanics* module you have met the idea of a mathematical model. Indeed, much of Mechanics is based on the Newtonian model

$$m\frac{d^2\mathbf{r}}{dt^2} = \mathbf{F}$$

Here m is the constant mass of a particle, position vector $\mathbf{r}$, and acted on by a total force $\mathbf{F}$. If action is only in one direction, this equation reduces to

$$m\frac{d^2x}{dt^2} = F$$

and for a given force, F, you have a **second order differential equation** to solve. The form of the force is part of the model.

For example, if motion is in a vertical plane, then F must include gravity but should also include a term which represents air resistance. This is where the model begins to be an approximation to reality, but nevertheless the Newtonian model for motion is one of the most successful models to be used.

It can be used to explain planetary, satellite, rocket, aircraft and land vehicle motions to an excellent degree of accuracy. You will be using this model throughout the rest of the module, but for this chapter you will, on the whole, be looking at other mathematical models.

3.1 Modelling

In this section, you will be looking at two different mathematical models, one of which you may have met in earlier modules. They are included here as they are important models in their own right.

Population models

An English economist, Thomas Malthus, in his 1802 article, *An Essay on the Principle of Population*, formulated the first model which attempted to describe and predict the way in which the magnitude of the human population was changing. In mathematical terms you can summarise his assumptions by introducing the variable $N = N(t)$ to represent the total population, where t is time. In a small time interval, say δt, Malthus argued that both births and deaths are proportional to the population size and the time interval. Hence in time δt, there will be $(\alpha N \delta t)$ births and $(\beta N \delta t)$ deaths where α, β are positive constants, and so the increase in the population size is given by

$$\delta N = \alpha N \delta t - \beta N \delta t = (\alpha - \beta) N \delta t$$

Writing $\alpha - \beta = \gamma$, and dividing by δt gives

$$\frac{\delta N}{\delta t} = \gamma N$$

Taking the limit as $\delta t \to 0$ results in the differential equation

$$\boxed{\frac{dN}{dt} = \gamma N}$$

Added to this is an initial condition; for example, $N = N_0$ at $t = 0$.

This is an example of a 'variables separable' differential equation, since it can be written in the form

$$\frac{1}{N} \frac{dN}{dt} = \gamma$$

and integrating both sides with respect to t,

$$\int \frac{1}{N} \frac{dN}{dt} dt = \int \gamma \, dt$$

$$\int \frac{1}{N} dN = \int \gamma \, dt$$

$$\Rightarrow \quad \ln N = \gamma t + c \quad (c \text{ constant})$$

$$\Rightarrow \quad N = e^{\gamma t + c}$$

$$= e^{\gamma t} e^{c}$$

$$\Rightarrow \quad N = K e^{\gamma t} \quad \left(K = e^{c} \right)$$

But $\quad N = N_0$ at $t = 0$,

giving $\quad N_0 = K e^0 = K$

Hence the complete solution is

$$\boxed{N = N_0 e^{\gamma t}}$$

This solution is illustrated opposite for positive γ.

What does the solution look like when
(a) $\gamma = 0$ **(b)** γ **is negative?**

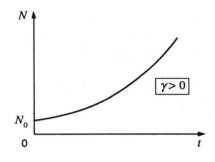

Activity 1

By differentiation check that $N = N_0 e^{\gamma t}$ satisfies the differential equation

$$\frac{dN}{dt} = \gamma N$$

You can see how to use this population model by applying it to the 1790 and 1800 USA population figures shown opposite.

The time $t = 0$ corresponds to 1790, and $t = 1$ to 1800, so

$$N_0 = 3.9$$

The model solution is

$$N(t) = 3.9 e^{\gamma t}$$

Year	USA Population (in millions)
1790	3.9
1800	5.3

and γ is determined by the population value at $t = 1$ (1800). This gives

$$5.3 = 3.9e^{\gamma}$$

$$\Rightarrow \quad e^{\gamma} = \frac{5.3}{3.9}$$

$$\Rightarrow \quad \gamma = \ln\left(\frac{5.3}{3.9}\right) \approx 0.03067$$

and $\boxed{N(t) = 3.9e^{(0.03067)t}}$

What does this model predict for the population if t becomes large? Is this realistic?

Activity 2

Use the model above to predict the USA population for 1810 $(t = 2)$ to 1930 $(t = 14)$. Compare your prediction with the real values given opposite.

Can you explain any discrepancies in the prediction and real values?

Year	USA Population (in millions)
1810	7.2
1820	9.6
1830	12.9
1840	17.1
1850	23.2
1860	31.4
1870	38.6
1880	50.2
1890	62.9
1900	76.0
1910	92.0
1920	106.5
1930	123.2

The model gives a reasonably good fit for quite some time, but eventually predicts a population growing far too quickly.

Why does the model eventually go wrong?

Let us go back to the original assumption and consider what factors have been neglected. The model as it stands predicts the growth of a population in an ideal situation where there are no limits (e.g. food, land, energy) to continued growth. In 1837, Verhulst proposed an extension to the Malthusian model which took into account the 'crowding' factor. In his model, he assumed that the population change was proportional to

(a) the current population level N;

(b) the ratio of unused population resources to total population resources when it is assumed that a maximum population size of N_{∞} can be sustained,

i.e. $\dfrac{(N_{\infty} - N)}{N_{\infty}}$

Thus

$$\frac{dN}{dt} = \gamma N \frac{(N_{\infty} - N)}{N_{\infty}}$$

i.e.

$$\frac{dN}{dt} = \gamma N - \frac{\gamma N^2}{N_\infty}$$

When N is small, γN will be the dominant term on the right hand side, and so we are back with the Malthusian model; but as N becomes large, the $\dfrac{-\gamma N^2}{N_\infty}$ term becomes important.

This is again a first order differential equation, but much more difficult to solve.

*Activity 3

Show, by differentiating the expression below, that the Verhulst model has a solution given by

$$N(t) = \frac{N_\infty}{\left\{ 1 + \left[\dfrac{N_\infty}{N_0} - 1 \right] e^{-\gamma t} \right\}}$$

where $N = N_0$ at $t = 0$.

Use your graphic calculator or a computer program to illustrate the shape of this function. For example, take $\gamma = 0.03$ and

(a) $N_0 = \frac{1}{2} N_\infty$

(b) $N_0 = \frac{1}{4} N_\infty$

(c) $N_0 = 2 N_\infty$

What happens as $t \to \infty$?

Drug doses

The study of the way in which a drug loses its concentration in the blood of a patient is fundamental to **pharmacology**. The 'dose-response' relationship plays a vital role in determining the required dosage level and the interval of time between doses for a particular drug.

Suppose $y = y(t)$ represents the quantity of the drug in the bloodstream at time t. The figure opposite shows some experimental results for penicillin (note that the scale for the concentration is not linear). The simplest way to model such

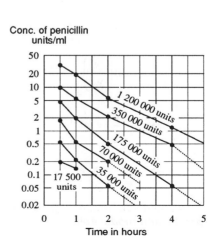

Conc. of penicillin
units/ml

behaviour is to assume that the rate of decrease in the concentration is proportional to the concentration of the drug in the bloodstream. In mathematical terms

$$\frac{dy}{dt} = -ky$$

where k is the positive constant which must be determined experimentally, for the drug under study. Experiments have shown that this equation is a good approximation to reality for many drugs, the most important being penicillin.

Having determined the constant k for a particular drug, you can now take this differential equation as the model. Suppose the patient is given an initial dose y_0, which is assumed to be instantaneously absorbed by the blood at time $t = 0$, resulting in a quantity $y = y_0$ at $t = 0$ in the blood. The actual time for absorption is usually very small compared with the time between doses.

What is the solution of the differential equation subject to $y = y_0$ at $t = 0$?

This differential equation is remarkably similar to the Malthusian population model met earlier in this section.

The solution is given by

$$\int \frac{1}{y} \cdot \frac{dy}{dt}\, dt = \int -k\, dt$$

$$\int \frac{1}{y}\, dy = -kt + A$$

$$\ln y = -kt + A$$

At $t = 0$, $y = y_0$, so $A = \ln y_0$, and

$$\ln y = -kt + \ln y_0$$

$$\Rightarrow \quad \ln\left(\frac{y}{y_0}\right) = -kt$$

$$\Rightarrow \quad \frac{y}{y_0} = e^{-kt}$$

$$\Rightarrow \quad y = y_0\, e^{-kt}$$

How could you have obtained this solution directly from the population model solution?

After a prescribed time, say T, a second dose of quantity y_0 is administered. Just before the dose, at time $t = T_-$, the amount in the blood is given by

$$y(T_-) = y_0 e^{-kT}$$

Just after the dose, at time $T = T_+$,

$$y(T_+) = y_0 + y_0 e^{-kT}$$

$$= y_0\left(1 + e^{-kT}\right)$$

What happens to this new quantity in the blood?

It decays again according to the differential equation model, but now with initial condition

$$y = y_0\left(1 + e^{-kT}\right)$$

Thus for $t \geq T$,

$$y(t) = y_0\left(1 + e^{-kT}\right)e^{-k(t-T)}$$

Hence, as $t \to 2T$,

$$y(2T_-) = y_0\left(1 + e^{-kT}\right)e^{-kT}$$

Again, giving the patient a dose y_0 at $t = 2T$ results in

$$y(2T_+) = y_0\left(1 + e^{-kT} + e^{-2kT}\right)$$

and again solving the differential equation with

$$y = y_0\left(1 + e^{-kT} + e^{-2kT}\right)$$

at $t = 2T$ gives, for $t \geq 2T$,

$$y(t) = y_0\left(1 + e^{-kT} + e^{-2kT}\right)e^{-k(t-2T)}$$

Thus $\qquad y(3T_-) = y_0\left(1 + e^{-kT} + e^{-2kT}\right)e^{-kT}$

and after a dose y_0 at $t = 3T$,

$$y(3T_+) = y_0\left(1 + e^{-kT} + e^{-2kT} + e^{-3kT}\right)$$

Continuing in this way,

$$y(nT_+) = y_0\left(1 + e^{-kT} + e^{-2kT} + \ldots + e^{-nkT}\right)$$

for $n = 1, 2, \ldots$

What is the sum of the G.P. in the formula above?

The common ratio is e^{-kT} and there are $(n+1)$ terms, so

$$y(nT_+) = y_0\frac{\left(1 - e^{-(n+1)kT}\right)}{\left(1 - e^{-kT}\right)}$$

What happens as n gets larger?

Denoting the long term saturation level by y_s, then the sum to infinity gives

$$y_s = \frac{y_0}{\left(1 - e^{-kT}\right)}$$

This formula plays a key role. It can be used for determining

(a) the required time interval, T, between doses for a given dose y_0 and prescribed final level y_s;

(b) the dose level y_0 required to obtain a final dose level y_s with a prescribed interval between doses, T.

One disadvantage of this method is the slow build-up to the required drug level y_s. Another approach is to start with a large initial dose, say the required final level y_s itself, and then at time T

$$y(T_-) = y_s e^{-kT}$$

The patient is now given a 2nd dose, say y_d, which brings the level up to y_s again;

i.e.　　　　$y_s = y(T_+) = y_s e^{-kT} + y_d$

This gives

$$y_d = y_s\left(1 - e^{-kT}\right) = y_0$$

So we are back to giving a dose y_0 at every time interval T after the initial boost. These methods of accumulation are illustrated opposite.

The second method has the great advantage of reaching the required level immediately, but for many drugs this can have

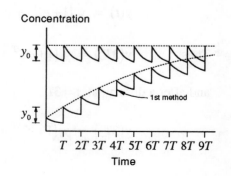

unpleasant side effects on the body. Often in practice a compromise is made between the two methods illustrated above.

The patient starts with a double initial dose, $2y_0$, followed by regular doses y_0. In this way, the advantages of each method are used and the disadvantages minimised.

Activity 4

Consider the effect of one initial double dose, $2y_0$, followed by regular doses, y_0.

Exercise 3A

1. (a) The population of USSR was 209 million in 1959, and it was estimated to be growing exponentially at a rate of 1% per year. This means

    $$\frac{dP}{dt} = (0.01)P$$

    Find the predicted population after 1959. What is the value predicted for 1980 and when will the population be double that of 1959?

    (b) The population of New Zealand is given in the table below.

Year	Population
1921	1.218×10^6
1926	1.344×10^6

    Modelling the change in population by the differential equation

    $$\frac{dP}{dt} = kP,$$

    use the data above to estimate the value of k. Predict the population in 1936, 1945, 1953 and 1977, and compare with the actual data given below.

Year	Population
1935	1.491×10^6
1945	1.648×10^6
1953	1.923×10^6
1977	3.140×10^6

    What conclusions regarding the suitability of your model can you reach?

2. A building society advertises that interest will be compounded continuously at a rate of 10% per year. This means that if P is the balance in an account at time t,

    $$\frac{dP}{dt} = (0.1)P$$

    If P_0 is invested on the first day of a year, find how much is in the account at the end of the first year. What is the 'effective' yearly interest rate? How long will it take an investment of £100 to double itself?

3. In a fasting experiment, the weight of a volunteer decreased from 180 lbs to 155 lbs in 30 days. It was noted that the weight loss per day was approximately proportional to the weight of the volunteer.

    Determine a differential equation to describe this behaviour and estimate how long it will take the volunteer to reach 130 lbs.

3.2 First order differential equations: variables separable

All the mathematical models discussed in the last section were first order differential equations. A general first order differential equation can be written in the form

$$\frac{dy}{dx} = f(x,y)$$

where f is a given function of x and y. The **general solution** of this equation, which requires integrating once, will contain **one** arbitrary constant (essentially the constant of integration).

Specifying one condition, say $y = y_0$ at $x = x_0$, will in principle be sufficient to solve for the arbitrary constant, and this will give a **complete solution** – that is, one particular solution which satisfies a given condition.

The following simple example illustrates these ideas.

Example

Find the general solution of the differential equation

$$\frac{dy}{dx} = \cos x$$

and the solution which satisfies $y = 2$ when $x = \frac{3\pi}{2}$.

Solution

This is a very simple equation to solve, since you can write

$$\int \frac{dy}{dx}\, dx = \int \cos x\, dx$$

i.e.
$$\int dy = \int \cos x\, dx$$

This gives

$$y = \sin x + K$$

where K is an arbitrary constant. This is the general solution, and some typical solutions are illustrated opposite.

Applying the condition

$$y = 2 \quad \text{when} \quad x = \frac{3\pi}{2}$$

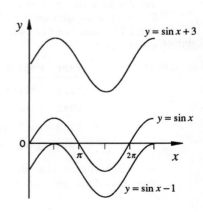

will define exactly one of these solution curves

$$2 = \sin \frac{3\pi}{2} + K$$

$$= -1 + K$$

Hence $K = 3$ and the complete solution for these conditions is

$$y = \sin x + 3$$

This differential equation, and those met in Section 3.1, are all special cases of what is called **variables separable** first order differential equations. These take the form

$$\boxed{\frac{dy}{dx} = f(x)\, g(y)}$$

where the right hand side of the differential equation can be separated into two distinct functions, one in y and one in x. The advantage of this type of differential equation is that it can, in principle at least, always be solved. The method of solution is straightforward:

$$\frac{1}{g(y)} \frac{dy}{dx} = f(x)$$

$$\Rightarrow \quad \int \frac{1}{g(y)} \frac{dy}{dx}\, dx = \int f(x)\, dx$$

$$\Rightarrow \quad \boxed{\int \frac{1}{g(y)}\, dy = \int f(x)\, dx}$$

Example

Find the general solution of the differential equation

$$\frac{dy}{dx} = e^{x-y}$$

Solution

This can be rewritten as

$$\frac{dy}{dx} = e^x e^{-y}$$

$$\Rightarrow \quad e^y \frac{dy}{dx} = e^x$$

$$\Rightarrow \quad \int e^y \frac{dy}{dx}\, dx = \int e^x dx$$

$$\Rightarrow \quad e^y = e^x + K \quad (K \text{ constant})$$

$$\Rightarrow \quad y = \ln\left(e^x + K\right)$$

There are many mathematical models from all sorts of disciplines that lead to first order variables separable differential equations. Three further applications will be discussed below.

Response to a stimulus

Our sensory organs are responsive to a wide range of stimuli. For example, the ear can detect sound ranging in intensity from a pressure of 0.0002 units of force (dynes) per square centimetre to a pressure of 2000 dynes per cm². This means that the ear can detect sounds from as low as a ticking watch a few metres away to noises as loud as a jet aircraft.

The first mathematical model to describe the response, R, to a stimulus S, was due to the German physiologist Gustav Fechner (1801–1887). The model can be written in differential form

$$\boxed{\frac{dR}{dS} = \frac{k}{S}}$$

where k is some positive constant. This equation implies that the increment in the reaction for an equal increment in stimulus decreases as the magnitude of the stimulus increases. For example, a small noise heard when you are lying awake at night, when the background noise is low, is quite significant, whereas the same noise would not be heard during the daytime when the background noise level is much higher.

The governing differential equation is variables separable and can be readily solved

$$\int \frac{dR}{dS} \, dS = \int \frac{k}{S} \, dS$$

$$R = k \ln S + A$$

where A is the constant of integration.

Now let S_0 be the lowest level of the stimulus which can be consistently detected. This is called the **threshold value** or **detection threshold**. An example would be the tick of a watch at 6 metres under quiet conditions. Other examples of detection thresholds are given opposite.

Stimulus	Detection threshold
Light	The flame of a candle 30 miles away on a dark night
Taste	Water diluted with sugar in the ratio of 1 teaspoon to two gallons
Smell	One drop of perfume diffused into the volume of three average size rooms
Touch	The wing of a bee dropped on your cheek at a distance of 1 centimetre

Activity 5

Suggest other detection thresholds, e.g. detection of a personal stereo with headphones in a public place, etc.

So, at $S = S_0$, $R = 0$,

giving $\qquad 0 = k \ln S_0 + A$

$\Rightarrow \qquad A = -k \ln S_0$

$\Rightarrow \qquad R = k \ln S - k \ln S_0$

$\Rightarrow \qquad \boxed{R = k \ln\left(\dfrac{S}{S_0}\right)}$

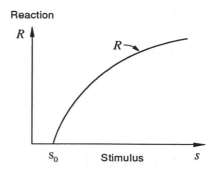

A typical solution is illustrated opposite.

Interpret the prediction that an increment in reaction becomes smaller with stronger stimulus.

A possible example to illustrate this concept is that of being in an average sized room with just one 50 watt bulb in one lamp. An increase of 50 watts to 100 watts would produce a dramatic improvement in the quality of the light provided; but the same increase of 50 watts to 150 watts would make only a small improvement. The **Weber–Fechner Law** essentially tells us that sensations only increase in an arithmetic form in response to logarithmic changes in the stimulation. This explains the remarkable capacity of the ear to respond efficiently to such a wide range of stimuli.

For some time this model was regarded as a basis for physio-physics; but in the early 1950's new methods were devised for measuring sensory perception. These were largely conceived by S. Stevens (1906–1973) and he first showed that the Weber–Fechner Law was inadequate. He formulated his own law, which is based on the differential equation

$$\boxed{\dfrac{dR}{dS} = n\,\dfrac{R}{S}}$$

where n is a positive constant.

This is similar to the earlier model except for the extra R multiplier on the right hand side.

Can you predict the effect that this extra R multiplier will have on the solution?

Activity 6

Show that the solution to Stevens' model is of the form

$$R = KS^n$$

This is known as **Stevens' Power Law** and predicts that equal stimulus ratios correspond to equal reaction ratios. The constant K is determined by the choice of units whilst the exponent n varies with the source of sensation. The power law for three types of physiological sensations

(a)   perceived electric shock,

(b)   apparent visual length,

(c)   brightness,

is illustrated opposite. Stevens' data appears to demonstrate that his power law accurately describes the relationship between stimulation and sensation.

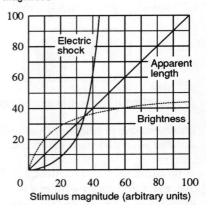

Water flow: Torricelli's Law

This is a law that is used to predict the flow of water from a container through a small hole. You will be able to verify it through a simple experiment as described in the next activity.

Activity 7

Take a transparent plastic bottle (e.g. a squash bottle) which has vertical sides for at least 10 cm. Make a hole about 2 mm in diameter in the side of the bottle near its base. Fix a scale to the side of the bottle, fill the bottle, leave it uncapped and time the flow of water for every cm lost in height. Repeat the experiment three or four times and take the average of the readings.

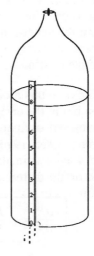

Some typical average times from the initial height of 12 cm are given in the table below.

Height (cm)	11	10	9	8	7	6	5	4	3	2	1
Average time (s)	6.5	17.3	29.0	41.3	53.7	67.7	83.5	101.0	120.7	146.5	179.7

In formulating a mathematical model to describe this situation, the important variables must be defined, namely

t = time since water started to flow

h = height of water in the bottle above the outlet hole

V = volume of water in the bottle

v = volume rate of flow through the hole

If we consider the flow of water through the hole it is clear that V and v are connected by

$$\frac{dV}{dt} = -v$$

Also, $V = V_0 + Ah$, where V_0 is the volume of water in the bottle beneath the hole and A is the cross-sectional area.

Hence $\quad A\dfrac{dh}{dt} = -v$

To proceed further, the form of v must be considered. From the experiment it is clear that v is a function of h.

What is the simplest form to take for v ?

So, taking $v = ah$ gives the differential equation for height, h, as

$$\frac{dh}{dt} = -\lambda h$$

where $\lambda = \dfrac{a}{A}$ is constant.

What is the general solution of the equation?

Following the usual analysis gives

$$\boxed{h = Ke^{-\lambda t}} \quad (K \text{ constant})$$

To validate this model, you must see if the test data is a good fit with the theoretical prediction.

As you do not know the value of λ, a suitable method of validation is to take logarithms throughout the equation above;

i.e. $\qquad \ln h = \ln K - \lambda t$

and then plot values of $\ln h$ against t. The theoretical model shows that this should be a straight line.

What conclusions can you draw from this graph?

Although the points are not far from a straight line, it would also appear likely that a downward bending curve would provide a better fit!

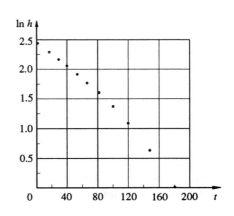

What assumptions in the model need to be reconsidered?

The obvious one is the functional relationship between v and h, where it was assumed to be linear for the model.

There is in fact a physical principle, known as **Torricelli's Law**, that can help us.

> For a non-viscous fluid flowing in a jet from a hole in a container, where the area of the hole is much smaller than the area of the free fluid surface, the velocity of the jet at the hole, u, is given by
>
> $$u^2 = 2gh$$
>
> where h is the height of the fluid surface above the hole and g is the acceleration due to gravity.

Now if k is the area of the hole, then

$$v = ku$$

and so

$$v = k(2gh)^{\frac{1}{2}}$$

The governing differential equation becomes

$$\boxed{\frac{dh}{dt} = -\mu h^{\frac{1}{2}}}$$

where

$$\mu = \frac{k(2g)^{\frac{1}{2}}}{A}$$

This is again a variables separable differential equation which can be written as

$$\int \frac{dh}{h^{\frac{1}{2}}} = \int -\mu \, dt$$

$$\Rightarrow \quad 2h^{\frac{1}{2}} = -\mu t + B \qquad (B \text{ is an arbitrary constant})$$

$$\Rightarrow \quad \boxed{h^{\frac{1}{2}} = \frac{\mu t}{2} + C} \qquad \left(C = \frac{B}{2}\right)$$

So the theoretical prediction now is that plotting $h^{\frac{1}{2}}$ against t should produce a **straight line**. The plot of experimental data is shown opposite.

The straight line agreement is good except for small h. Here the water is no longer issuing as a jet so it is no surprise that the prediction is no longer accurate.

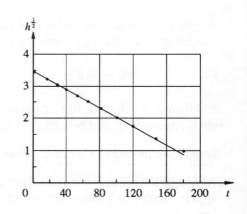

Exercise 3B

1. (a) **Loewenstein Equation**

   The differential equation for this model is

   $$\frac{dR}{dS} = \frac{R}{(1 + \alpha S)S}$$

   where S is the stimulus, R is the reaction, and α is a positive constant. Determine R as a function of S and interpret the solution.

   (b) **Extension of Stevens' Model**

   Consider the model described by the equation

   $$\frac{dR}{dS} = \frac{cR^\alpha}{S^\beta}$$

   where c, α and β are positive constants. Solve for R as a function of S and show that both Stevens' Law and the Weber–Fechner Law are special cases of this model.

2. Using the notation of Section 3.2, assume that

   $$\frac{dh}{dt} = -\lambda h^\alpha, \quad 0 < \alpha < 1$$

   Deduce the predicted form for h. What quantities give a predicted straight line graph?

   For $\alpha = \frac{1}{3}$, test the model against the experimental data found in Section 3.2.

3. Investigate the inhibited population model described by the differential equation

   $$\frac{dN}{dt} = \gamma N \left[1 - \left(\frac{N}{N_\infty} \right)^{\alpha - 1} \right]$$

   where $\alpha > 1$. Find an equation satisfied by N and sketch typical solutions.

4. A model of seasonal growth is given by

   $$\frac{dx}{dt} = r x \cos(\omega t)$$

   where r and ω are constants. Illustrate the behaviour of the solution x of this equation.

5. In a model of epidemics, a single infected individual is introduced into a community containing n individuals susceptible to the disease. Define $x(t)$ to be the number of uninfected individuals in the population at time t. Assuming that the infection spreads to all those susceptible, then $x(t)$ decreases from its initial value, $x(0) = n$, to zero. A possible equation for $x(t)$ is

   $$\frac{dx}{dt} = -r x (n + 1 - x)$$

   where r is a positive constant which measures the rate of infection. Determine the solution of this first order equation. When is the infection rate a maximum?

3.3 First order differential equations: linear

This is another very special and very important class of differential equations. They take the form

$$\boxed{\frac{dy}{dx} + P(x)y = Q(x)}$$

where P and Q are given functions of x. Note that the equation is

linear in y and $\frac{dy}{dx}$ but not in x.

There is a set method of solving equations of this type and the process is described below, together with an example.

1. Write the equation in the form:

   Equation $\dfrac{dy}{dx} + P(x)y = Q(x)$

   Example $\dfrac{dy}{dx} + xy = 2x$ $(P(x)=x, \;\; Q(x)=2x)$

2. Evaluate $e^{\int P(x)\,dx}$ (the integrating factor).

   Equation $e^{\int P(x)\,dx}$

   Example $e^{\int x\,dx} = e^{\frac{1}{2}x^2}$

3. Multiply throughout by integrating factor.

   Equation $e^{\int P(x)\,dx}\dfrac{dy}{dx} + e^{\int P(x)\,dx}P(x)y = e^{\int P(x)\,dx}Q(x)$

   Example $e^{\frac{1}{2}x^2}\dfrac{dy}{dx} + e^{\frac{1}{2}x^2}(xy) = e^{\frac{1}{2}x^2}2x$

4. The L.H.S. can now be written as a differential of
   $(y \times$ integrating factor).*

   Equation $\dfrac{d}{dx}\left(ye^{\int P\,dx}\right) = e^{\int P\,dx}Q(x)$

   Example $\dfrac{d}{dx}\left(ye^{\frac{1}{2}x^2}\right) = 2xe^{\frac{1}{2}x^2}$

5. Integrate both sides (remembering to bring in an arbitrary constant).

   Equation $ye^{\int P\,dx} = \int e^{\int P\,dx}Q\,dx + K$

   Example $ye^{\frac{1}{2}x^2} = 2e^{\frac{1}{2}x^2} + K$

6. Divide by the integrating factor.

   Equation $y = e^{-\int P\,dx}\int e^{\int P\,dx}Q\,dx + Ke^{-\int P\,dx}$

   Example $y = 2 + Ke^{-\frac{1}{2}x^2}$

*Note that P is written now for $P(x)$ and this result follows since

$$\frac{d}{dx}\left(ye^{\int P\,dx}\right) = \frac{dy}{dx}e^{\int P\,dx} + ye^{\int P\,dx}\frac{d}{dx}(\int P\,dx)$$

$$= \frac{dy}{dx}e^{\int P\,dx} + P(x)ye^{\int P\,dx}$$

Why is $\dfrac{d}{dx}\int P(x)\,dx = P(x)$**?**

One further example is given to illustrate the method

Example
Find the general solution of the differential equation, for $x > 1$,

$$x \ln x \frac{dy}{dx} + y = 2\ln x$$

Solution
Following the steps as defined above,

Step 1 $\qquad \dfrac{dy}{dx} + \dfrac{1}{x\ln x}\,y = \dfrac{2}{x}$

Step 2 $\qquad e^{\int \frac{1}{x\ln x}\,dx} = e^{\ln(\ln x)} \quad \left(\text{since } \dfrac{d}{dx}\big(\ln(\ln x)\big) = \dfrac{1}{x}\times\dfrac{1}{\ln x}\right)$

$$= \ln x$$

Step 3 $\qquad \ln x \dfrac{dy}{dx} + \dfrac{1}{x}\,y = \dfrac{2\ln x}{x}$

Step 4 $\qquad \dfrac{d}{dx}\big(y\ln x\big) = \dfrac{2\ln x}{x}$

Step 5 $\qquad y\ln x = \displaystyle\int \dfrac{2\ln x}{x}\,dx = (\ln x)^2 + c$

Step 6 $\qquad y = \ln x + \dfrac{c}{\ln x}$

The real importance of linear differential equations will be seen in Chapter 4, when second order equations will be used to model vibrational systems. First order linear differential equations also have interesting and varied applications, as you will see in the next two models.

Art forgeries

After the liberation of Belgium in World War II, an extensive search was started for Nazi collaborators. Numerous works of art had been sold to the Germans, and a third rate Dutch painter, H. A. Van Meegeran, was arrested in May 1945 for collaborating with the enemy in selling Goering a 17th century Vermeer painting, *Woman Taken in Adultery*.

On 12th July 1945, Van Meegeran surprised the art world by announcing from his prison cell that he was the painter of *Woman*

Taken in Adultery and also of the very famous and beautiful
Disciples at Emmaus, four other presumed Vermeers and two
de Hooghs.

His claims were not at first taken seriously, so while in prison he
began to forge the Vermeer painting, *Jesus Amongst the Doctors*,
in order to show just how good a forger he was. When the work
was nearing completion, he learned that the charge of collaborating
was to be changed to that of forgery and so he refused to 'age' the
painting.

So in order to settle the question of whether the paintings were
forgeries, an international panel of distinguished art historians,
physicists and chemists was appointed. After some months of
work, the panel unanimously concluded that the paintings were
indeed forgeries. The main reasons for their conclusion were

(a) the paintings tended to resist water and ethyl alcohol like 17th
     century paintings, but also resisted strong alkalis and acids,
     very unlike 17th century paintings;

(b) evidence was found of how Van Meegeran had tried to
     produce the 'age' crackle of an old painting;

(c) the colour cobalt blue, which was not known in the 17th
     century, was found in two of the paintings;

(d) the medium used in the paintings was an artificial resin of the
     phenolformaldehyde group first discovered at the end of the
     19th century.

On this evidence Van Meegeran was convicted on 12th October
1947, and sentenced to one year in prison. However, on 30th
December 1947 he suffered a heart attack and died.

Despite this evidence, many art experts did not believe that the
famed *Disciples at Emmaus* was a forgery. In fact it was certified
by a noted art historian, A. Bredius, and bought by the Rembrandt
Society for $170 000. A thoroughly scientific and conclusive
proof that *Disciples at Emmaus* **was** a forgery was eventually
achieved in 1967 by scientists at Carnegie Mellon University. The
basis of their method is described below.

White lead $\left(Pb^{210}\right)$ is a radioactive substance with a half-life of
22 years. It is a pigment of major importance in paintings, and it is
manufactured from ores which contain uranium and elements to
which uranium decays. One of these elements is Radium 226
$\left(Ra^{226}\right)$ which has a half-life of 1600 years, and decays to Pb^{210}.

While still part of the ore, the amount of Ra^{226} decaying to Pb^{210}
is equal to the amount of Pb^{210} disintegrating per unit time,
i.e. Pb^{210} and Ra^{226} are in a **radioactive equilibrium**.

In the manufacture of the pigment, however, the radium and most of its descendants are removed. The Pb^{210} decays and continues to do so until it reaches an 'equilibrium' with the smaller amount of Ra^{226} that survived the chemical process.

The key variables are

$$t \quad = \quad \text{time}$$

$$y(t) = \quad \text{amount of Pb}^{210} \text{ per gram of ordinary lead at time } t$$

$$t_0 \quad = \quad \text{time of manufacture}$$

$$y_0 \quad = \quad y(t_0)$$

$$r(t) = \quad \text{number of disintegrations of Ra}^{226} \text{ per minute per gram of ordinary lead}$$

Then the differential equation model for radioactive decay is used;

i.e. $$\boxed{\frac{dy}{dt} = -\lambda y + r(t)}$$

where λ is constant for Pb^{210}. This equation, without the $r(t)$ term, was introduced in the *Pure Mathematics* module and used in carbon dating techniques.

Activity 8

Use the integrating factor method to show that the general solution of the equation above is given by

$$y(t) = e^{-\lambda t} \int e^{\lambda t} r(t) dt + A e^{-\lambda t}$$

No further progress can be made until a form for r is assumed. Taking the simplest possible model as $r(t) = r$, constant, gives

$$y(t) = e^{-\lambda t} r \left(\frac{e^{\lambda t}}{\lambda} \right) + A e^{-\lambda t}$$

$$y(t) = \frac{r}{\lambda} + A e^{-\lambda t}$$

Now $$y(t_0) = y_0,$$

so $$y_0 = \frac{r}{\lambda} + A e^{-\lambda t_0},$$

giving $$A = e^{\lambda t_0} \left(y_0 - \frac{r}{\lambda} \right)$$

So, finally,

$$y(t) = \frac{r}{\lambda} + \left(y_0 - \frac{r}{\lambda}\right)e^{-\lambda(t-t_0)}$$

Is it reasonable to take r as constant?

The half-life of Ra^{226} is 1600 years, and we are dealing with paintings of about 400 years old. So very little Ra^{226} has decayed in 400 years and so the number of disintegrations of Ra^{226} can be approximated by a constant. You can now use the above equation for we can measure both y and r today. λ is known and you want to know $(t - t_0)$. Unfortunately, you still do not know y_0.

Since the original quantity of Pb^{226} was in equilibrium with the larger quantity of radium in the ore from which the pigment was manufactured, then

$$\lambda y_0 = R$$

where R denotes the number of disintegrations of Ra^{226} per minute per gram of ordinary lead. But measurements for R from a variety of ores over the earth's surface give values in the range 0–200.

Hence (λy_0) is in this range but this is not sufficient to obtain an estimate of the date of origin. However, you can still make progress, for suppose the painting in question was **not** a forgery but was painted about 300 years ago. Then with $t - t_0 = 300$ in the equation for $y(t)$, you can find λy_0,

i.e.

$$\lambda y_0 = \lambda y e^{300\lambda} - r\left(e^{300\lambda} - 1\right)$$

and $\lambda = 3.151 \times 10^{-2}$. This number, λy_0, should be in the range 0–200. So any painting giving a value of (λy_0) much greater than 200 will almost certainly be a forgery.

For the *Disciples at Emmaus* painting, $\lambda y = 8.5$ and $r = 0.8$, (actually, Polonium 210 is measured, which is approximately the value of Lead 210). The equation for y_0 gives

$$\lambda y_0 = 98\,147$$

This is unacceptably large for a genuine 17th century painting, and so it can be concluded that *Disciples at Emmaus* is indeed a forgery.

Fish growth

As well as models for population growth of species the key concept with fish is their weight. One model that is frequently used is known as the **von Bertaluffy Growth Model**

$$\frac{dw}{dt} = \alpha w^{\frac{2}{3}} - \beta w$$

Here $w(t)$ is the weight of a fish at time t, and α and β are constants. The first term is the increase in weight due to nutrients and is taken as proportional to surface area; the second term is the rate of loss of weight due to respiration and is taken as proportional to the weight.

This equation can be rewritten as

$$\frac{dw}{dt} + \beta w = \alpha w^{\frac{2}{3}}$$

but it is not **linear**, since there is a $w^{\frac{2}{3}}$ on the right hand side. There is, though, a substitution which can transfer this to a linear differential equation; this is

$$x = w^{\frac{1}{3}}$$

Using this definition of x,

$$\frac{dx}{dt} = \frac{1}{3} w^{-\frac{2}{3}} \frac{dw}{dt}$$

$$= \frac{1}{3} w^{-\frac{2}{3}} \left(\alpha w^{\frac{2}{3}} - \beta w \right)$$

$$= \frac{1}{3}\alpha - \frac{1}{3}\beta w^{\frac{1}{3}}$$

$$= \frac{1}{3}\alpha - \frac{1}{3}\beta x$$

So

$$\frac{dx}{dt} + \frac{1}{3}\beta x = \frac{1}{3}\alpha$$

and this is a linear differential equation.

Activity 9

Use integrating factor methods to solve for x and show that the solution for w is given by

$$w(t) = \left(\frac{\alpha}{\beta} \right)^3 \left(1 + C\frac{\beta}{\alpha} e^{-\frac{\beta t}{3}} \right)^3$$

where C is an arbitrary constant.

What is the predicted behaviour of w as $t \to \infty$?

A sketch of possible fish growth is shown opposite, indicating the limits to growth inherent in this model.

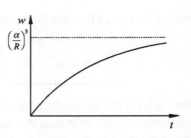

Exercise 3C

1. Find the general solution of the following differential equations.

   (a) $5\dfrac{dy}{dx} - 3y = 0$

   (b) $x^2\left(y^2 + 1\right) + y\sqrt{x^3 + 1}\ \dfrac{dy}{dx} = 0$

   (c) $\sqrt{2xy}\ \dfrac{dy}{dx} = 1$

   (d) $y\dfrac{dy}{dx} - x^2 = x^2 y$

2. Find the general solutions of the following first order differential equations.

   (a) $x\dfrac{dy}{dx} + y = x^2$

   (b) $(x+1)\dfrac{dy}{dx} + 2y = 4(x+1)^2$

   (c) $\dfrac{dy}{dx} + 2y\tan x = 3$

   (d) $x\ln x\ \dfrac{dy}{dx} + y = x\ln x$

   (e) $\cos x\ \dfrac{dy}{dx} + y\sin x = \cos 2x$

3. Use the model in this section to determine from the data given below whether the following paintings are forged Vermeers.

Picture	Disintegrations Polonium 210	Disintegrations Radium 226
Washing of Feet	12.6	0.26
Woman Reading Music	10.3	0.3
Woman Playing Mandolin	8.2	0.17
Lace Maker	1.5	1.48

3.4 Structure of solutions to linear differential equations

There is one important aspect concerning the structure of the general solution of linear first order differential equations that is of fundamental importance when you move on to second order linear differential equations (in Chapter 4). Returning to the first example of the last section, the solution of

$$\frac{dy}{dx} + xy = 2x$$

was found to be

$$y = 2 + Ke^{-\frac{1}{2}x^2}$$

The two terms in the formula for y are both significant. Consider first

$$y_c = Ke^{-\frac{1}{2}x^2}$$

Then
$$\frac{dy_c}{dx} = Ke^{-\frac{1}{2}x^2} \frac{d}{dx}\left(-\frac{1}{2}x^2\right)$$

$$= -Kxe^{-\frac{1}{2}x^2}$$

Thus
$$\frac{dy_c}{dx} + xy_c = -Kxe^{-\frac{1}{2}x^2} + xKe^{-\frac{1}{2}x^2}$$

$$= 0$$

So, it has been shown that y_c is a solution of

$$\frac{dy}{dx} + xy = 0;$$

indeed it is the general solution, since it contains one arbitrary constant.

This second equation, derived from the first by putting zero in the right hand side, is referred to as the **associated homogeneous equation**.

Now consider the other term, $y_p = 2$. Note that

$$\frac{dy_p}{dx} + xy_p = 0 + x \times 2 = 2x$$

so $y_p = 2$ is one particular solution of the full equation.

This example illustrates the general result that

$$\left[\begin{array}{c}\text{The general solution of a} \\ \text{linear differential equation} \\ \frac{dy}{dx} + Py = Q\end{array}\right] \equiv \left[\begin{array}{c}\text{The general solution,} \\ y_c, \text{ of the associated} \\ \text{homogeneous equation} \\ \frac{dy}{dx} + Py = 0\end{array}\right] + \left[\begin{array}{c}\text{One particular} \\ \text{solution, } y_p, \text{ of} \\ \text{the full equation}\end{array}\right]$$

(y_c is sometimes referred to as the **complementary function** whilst y_p is a **particular solution**.)

Activity 10

Show that the solution, $y = \ln x + \dfrac{C}{\ln x}$, of the differential

equation, $x\ln x \dfrac{dy}{dx} + y = 2\ln x$, obeys the framework given

above. (Hint: put $y_c = \dfrac{C}{\ln x}$ and $y_p = \ln x$)

*Activity 11

For the solution of the general linear first order differential equation, define

$$y_p = e^{-\int P dx} \int e^{\int P dx} Q \, dx, \quad y_c = K e^{-\int P dx}$$

and again show that the solution agrees with the above rule, i.e. y_p is one particular solution and y_c is the general solution of the associated homogeneous equation.

As a foretaste of what is to come in Chapter 4, the next example shows how second order linear differential equations can be solved.

Example

Solve the differential equation

$$\frac{d^2y}{dx^2} + \frac{dy}{dx} - 6y = 3$$

Solution

As given above, the structure of the solution is

$$y(x) = y_c(x) + y_p(x)$$

where $y_c(x)$ is the general solution of the associated homogeneous equation and $y_p(x)$ is one particular solution.

$$\boxed{y_c(x)}$$

This is the general solution of

$$\frac{d^2y}{dx^2} + \frac{dy}{dx} - 6y = 0$$

Looking for solutions of the form $y = e^{mx}$, gives

$$\frac{dy}{dx} = m e^{mx}$$

$$\frac{d^2y}{dx^2} = m^2 e^{mx}$$

and substituting in the differential equation

$$m^2 e^{mx} + m e^{mx} - 6 e^{mx} = 0$$

$$\Rightarrow \quad e^{mx}\left(m^2 + m - 6\right) = 0$$

$$\Rightarrow \quad \left(m^2 + m - 6\right) = 0 \qquad (\text{as } e^{mx} \neq 0 \text{ for all } x)$$

$$\Rightarrow \quad (m-2)(m+3) = 0$$

$$\Rightarrow \quad m = 2, \ -3$$

Thus both $y = e^{2x}$ and $y = e^{-3x}$ are solutions of the equation; and since the equation is linear,

$$y = A e^{2x} + B e^{-3x}$$

is a solution. In fact it is the general solution since it contains two arbitrary constants (see Activity 12 below).

$$\boxed{y_p(x)}$$

This is one particular solution of the full equation

$$\frac{d^2 y}{dx^2} + \frac{dy}{dx} - 6y = 3$$

and, since the right hand side is a constant, you can spot that

$$y_p(x) = \frac{1}{2}$$

is in fact one solution.

Combining these two components gives the general solution

$$y(x) = A e^{2x} + B e^{-3x} + \frac{1}{2}$$

Activity 12

Show that the function $y(x)$ defined above does in fact satisfy the full differential equation.

Exercise 3D

1. For at least two of the solutions to problems in Question 2, Exercise 3C, show that they are of the form

   $$y = y_c + y_p$$

   where y_c is the complementary function and y_p is one particular solution.

2. Solve the following second order differential equations:

   (a) $\dfrac{d^2y}{dx^2} - \dfrac{dy}{dx} + 2y = 0$

   (b) $\dfrac{d^2y}{dx^2} + 7\dfrac{dy}{dx} + 12y = 12$

   (c) $\dfrac{d^2y}{dx^2} + y = 0$

   (d) $\dfrac{d^2y}{dx^2} - y = 4x$

3.5 Resistive motion

Consider a particle of mass m, moving upwards in the positive x-direction and subject to

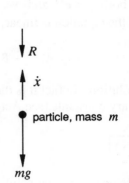

R

$\dot{x}$

particle, mass m

mg

(a) gravitational force, mg, downwards;

(b) resistive force (due to air, etc.) which opposes motion.

The differential equation governing the motion (for constant mass, m) is

$$m\frac{d^2x}{dt^2} = -mg - R$$

where the particle is moving upwards in the positive x-direction.

There are many models that can be taken for the resistive force. For example

(i) $R = 0$

This is often used, but it is probably not a good model unless you are on the moon.

(ii) $R = mkv \quad \left(v = \dfrac{dx}{dt}\right)$

Again this is a well-used model, and in many cases close to reality.

(iii) $R = mkv^2$

This has a strong effect for large values of v.

Unfortunately, experimental evidence points to a model of the form $R = mkv^{1.1}$ but analytically this is a difficult function to cope with.

In this section, the cases (ii) and (iii) given above will be considered.

Linear resistance

In this case $R = mkv$ and the governing differential equation becomes

$$m\frac{dv}{dt} = -mg - mkv$$

or

$$\boxed{\frac{dv}{dt} + kv = -g}$$

You should recognise this as a linear first order differential equation. To solve, first find the integrating factor

$$e^{\int k\,dx} = e^{kt}$$

Multiply through by e^{kt} to give

$$e^{kt}\frac{dv}{dt} + e^{kt}kv = -e^{kt}g$$

$$\Rightarrow \quad \frac{d}{dt}\left(ve^{kt}\right) = -e^{kt}g$$

Integrating

$$ve^{kt} = -g\int e^{kt}dt + A \qquad (A \text{ is an arbitrary constant})$$

$$\Rightarrow \quad ve^{kt} = -\frac{g}{k}e^{kt} + A$$

$$\Rightarrow \quad v = -\frac{g}{k} + Ae^{-kt}$$

If, at $t = 0$, $x = 0$ and $v = u$, then

$$u = -\frac{g}{k} + A$$

and

$$v(t) = -\frac{g}{k} + \left(u + \frac{g}{k}\right)e^{-kt}$$

What is the behaviour of v as t increases?

To complete the analysis, note that

$$\frac{dx}{dt} = -\frac{g}{k} + \left(u + \frac{g}{k}\right)e^{-kt}$$

which can be integrated to obtain

$$x(t) = -\frac{g}{k}t + \left(u + \frac{g}{k}\right)\frac{e^{-kt}}{(-k)} + B \text{ (B is an arbitrary constant)}$$

Since at $t = 0$, $x = 0$, so

$$0 = 0 - \frac{1}{k}\left(u + \frac{g}{k}\right) + B$$

$$\Rightarrow \quad B = \frac{1}{k}\left(u + \frac{g}{k}\right)$$

$$\Rightarrow \quad x(t) = -\frac{gt}{k} + \frac{1}{k}\left(u + \frac{g}{k}\right)\left(1 - e^{-kt}\right)$$

What is the behaviour of x as t increases?

At what time does the particle come to rest instantaneously?

Activity 13

With the values

$$g = 9.8 \text{ m s}^{-2}, \quad k = 0.01 \text{ s}^{-1}, \quad u = 10 \text{ m s}^{-1},$$

use a graphic calculator (or graph package on a computer) to find the characteristics of the solution $x(t)$.

Speed squared resistance

In this case $R = mkv^2$, so that the governing equation becomes

$$\boxed{\frac{dv}{dt} + kv^2 = -g}$$

Although this is still a first order differential equation, it is **not** linear, and not so easy to solve. One method is to solve for v as a function of x, so that

$$\frac{dv}{dt} = \frac{dv}{dx}\frac{dx}{dt} = v\frac{dv}{dx}$$

Hence, $\qquad v\dfrac{dv}{dx} = -\left(kv^2 + g\right)$

and this is a variables separable equation

$$\int \frac{v\,dv}{\left(k\,v^2 + g\right)} = \int -dx$$

Integrating,

$$\frac{1}{2k} \ln\left(k\,v^2 + g\right) = -x + A \quad (A \text{ is a constant of integration})$$

and, as before, at $t = 0$, $x = 0$ and $v = u$, then

$$\frac{1}{2k} \ln\left(k\,u^2 + g\right) = A$$

So

$$\boxed{x = \frac{1}{2k} \ln\left(\frac{k\,u^2 + g}{k\,v^2 + g}\right)}$$

How far will the particle have travelled before it comes to rest instantaneously?

Example

A particle of mass 0.2 kg is moving in a straight line under the action of a resistive force which, when the particle has speed v m s^{-1}, is of magnitude $k\,v^3$ N, where k is a constant. Given that the force is of magnitude 80 N when $v = 2$, find k. Show that, at time t seconds, v satisfies

$$\frac{dv}{dt} = -50v^3$$

Find the time taken for the speed to decrease from 2 m s^{-1} to 1 m s^{-1}.

Solution

Resistive force, R, is of the form

$$R = kv^3$$

When $v = 2$, $R = 80$, giving

$$80 = k \times 2^3 \quad \Rightarrow \quad k = 10$$

Thus $\qquad R = 10v^3$

and the differential equation for motion is

$$m\frac{dv}{dt} = -R$$

$\Rightarrow \qquad 0.2\frac{dv}{dt} = -10v^3$

$\Rightarrow \qquad \frac{dv}{dt} = -50v^3$

Integrating

$$\int \frac{dv}{v^3} = \int -50\,dt$$

$\Rightarrow \qquad -\frac{1}{2v^2} = -50t + A \quad (A \text{ is a constant of integration})$

If $v = 2 \text{ m s}^{-1}$ at $t = 0$,

$$-\frac{1}{8} = A$$

and $\qquad \dfrac{1}{2v^2} = 50t + \dfrac{1}{8}$

The time taken for the speed to reduce to 1 m s^{-1} is given by

$$\frac{1}{2} = 50t + \frac{1}{8}$$

$\Rightarrow \qquad 50t = \dfrac{3}{8}$

$\Rightarrow \qquad t = \dfrac{3}{400} = 0.0075 \text{ s}$

Exercise 3E

1. A particle moves along a straight line under the action of a resistive force. When the particle has speed $v\,\mathrm{ms^{-1}}$, the retardation is of magnitude $kv^2\,\mathrm{ms^{-2}}$, where k is constant. Given that the particle has an initial speed of $2\,\mathrm{ms^{-1}}$, show that its speed at time t seconds later is given by

   $$v = \frac{2}{1+2kt}.$$

   Given also that the speed is halved after 4 seconds, find k. (AEB)

2. At time t hours the speed of a glider moving horizontally in a straight line is $v\,\mathrm{km\,h^{-1}}$. When $\frac{1}{v}$ is plotted against t, the resulting graph is a straight line. Show that $\frac{dv}{dt} = -kv^2$, where k is a constant.

   At $t=0$ the speed of the glider is $80\,\mathrm{km\,h^{-1}}$ and after it has travelled 2 km its speed is $65\,\mathrm{km\,h^{-1}}$. Find the additional distance travelled by the glider before its speed is reduced to $40\,\mathrm{km\,h^{-1}}$. (AEB)

3. A particle of mass 0.1 kg is projected from an origin O with a velocity whose horizontal and vertical components are $7\,\mathrm{ms^{-1}}$ and $14\,\mathrm{ms^{-1}}$ respectively. The particle moves under the action of gravity and of a force equal to $-0.7\mathbf{v}$ N where $\mathbf{v}\,\mathrm{ms^{-1}}$ is the velocity of the particle.

   The horizontal and vertical displacements of the particle from O at a time t seconds after projection are denoted by x m and y m respectively.

   Show that $\frac{d^2x}{dt^2} = -7\frac{dx}{dt}$ and, taking $g=9.8\,\mathrm{ms^{-2}}$, write down the differential equation satisfied by y.

   Hence show that,

   $$x = 1-e^{-7t}, \quad y = 2.2\left(1-e^{-7t}\right) - 1.4t$$

   (AEB)

4. The speed $v\,\mathrm{ms^{-1}}$ of a particle moving on the x-axis is such that, at time t seconds,

   $$\frac{dv}{dt} = \left(3 - 5e^{-1}\right).$$

   Given that $v=1$ when $t=0$, find v at any subsequent time. Show also that the minimum value of v is approximately 0.53. (AEB)

5. A particle moves in a horizontal line such that its speed v at time t is given by the differential equation $\frac{dv}{dt} = f - kv$, where f and k are positive constants. Suggest a possible physical cause for each of the terms on the right hand side of this equation.

   Given that $f = 100\,\mathrm{ms^{-2}}$ and $k=1\,\mathrm{s^{-1}}$, find the time taken for the speed of the particle to increase from $25\,\mathrm{ms^{-1}}$ to $50\,\mathrm{ms^{-1}}$.

   Given that the particle starts from rest, determine how far it travels before it attains a speed of $90\,\mathrm{ms^{-1}}$. Determine the terminal speed, v_0, of the particle (i.e $v \to v_0$ as $t \to \infty$).

   (AEB)

3.6 Miscellaneous Exercises

1. During the intial stages of the growth of yeast cells in a culture, the rate of increase in the number of cells is proportional to the number of cells present.

   If $n = n(t)$ represents the number of cells at time t, show that

   $$\frac{dn}{dt} = kn$$

   for some constant k. If the cells double in unit time, determine k, and solve for n in terms of t and the initial number of cells, n_0.

2. A particle falls vertically through a resistive medium, the resistance being directly proportional to the speed of the particle. When the particle is moving with speed w, the resistive force is equal to half the force of gravity on the particle.

   Denoting the speed of the particle at time t by v, show that

   $$\frac{dv}{dt} = g\left(1 - \frac{v}{2w}\right)$$

   Hence find, in terms of g and w, the time taken for the speed of the particle to increase from zero to w. (AEB)

3. (a) Past data on world oil production (in millions of metric tons) is given in the table below.

Year	Production
1960	1091
1962	1259
1964	1458
1966	1693

Assuming that the rate of growth of production is proportional to the production, estimate the production in 1968, 1970 and 1972. Compare your predictions with the actual values given below.

Year	Production
1968	1986
1970	2340
1972	2550

(b) US petrol consumption (in 1000 barrels per day) is given below.

Year	Consumption
1946	2015
1950	2724
1955	3655
1960	4130

Formulate a differential equation model to describe the growth in petrol consumption and use it to estimate the 1965 and 1970 values. These values are actually 4853 and 6083 respectively. If you think your model is a reasonable one, estimate the 1972 value.

[The actual 1972 value is 6668.]

4. (a) In a chemical reaction, two substances, C_1 and C_2, combine in equal amounts to produce a compound, C_3. Suppose that a and b are the initial concentrations (at $t=0$) of C_1 and C_2. Define $x(t)$ to be the concentration of C_3 at time t. The rate of increase of the concentration of C_3 is

$$\frac{dx}{dt} = r(a-x)(b-x)$$

where r is a positive constant.

(i) If $x(0)=0$, determine the concentration of C_3 as a function of time for $t>0$.

(ii) If $a=10$ and $b=15$ (in appropriate units), determine the limiting concentration of C_3.

(b) In some chemical reactions, certain products may catalyse their own formation. If $x(t)$ is the amount of such a product at time t, a possible model for such a reaction is given by the differential equation

$$\frac{dx}{dt} = r x(c-x)$$

where r and c are positive constants.

In this model, the reaction is completed when $x=c$, because one of the chemicals of the reaction is used up.

(i) Determine the general solution in terms of the constants r and c, and $x(0)$.

(ii) For $r=1$, c=100 and $x(0)=20$, draw a graph of $x(t)$ for $t>0$.

5. Nutrients flow across cell walls to determine the growth, survival and reproduction of the cells. This suggests that, during the early stages of a cell's growth, the rate of increase of the weight of the cell will be proportional to its surface area. If the shape and density of the cell do not change during growth, the weight $x(t)$ of the cell at time t will be proportional to the square of the radius.

(a) Verify that $x(t)$ satisfies the first order equation

$$\frac{dx}{dt} = cx^{\frac{2}{3}}$$

during the early stages of growth. (c is a positive constant.)

(b) In terms of the constant c and the initial weight $x(0)$ determine the weight $x(t)$ of the cell at time t.

(c) If $c=3$ and $x(0)=1$ (in appropriate units), determine the length of time for the weight of the cell to double.

6. A body of mass m, travelling in a straight line, is acted upon by a force whose rate of working mP is constant, and by a resistive force mkv^2, where v is the speed and k is a positive constant.

Show that the distance travelled by the body as its speed increases from

$$\frac{1}{4}\sqrt[3]{\left(\frac{P}{k}\right)} \quad \text{to} \quad \frac{1}{2}\sqrt[3]{\left(\frac{P}{k}\right)}$$

is $\left(\frac{1}{3k}\right)\ln\left(\frac{9}{8}\right)$. (AEB)

7. A disease is spreading through an isolated population. At time t, p denotes the proportion of the population which has the disease. The model for the epidemic assumes that the rate of change of p is proportional to the product of p and $(1-p)$, the proportion which does not have the disease.

   (a) Form the differential equation for this model in terms of p and t.

   (b) Explain the rationale on which this model is based.

   (c) Given that when $p = \frac{1}{2}$, $\frac{dp}{dt} = \frac{1}{2}$, show that

   $$\frac{dp}{dt} = 2p(1-p)$$

   (d) Solve the differential equation in (c) given that $p = \frac{1}{2}$ at time $t = 0$.

   [You may use the identity

   $$\frac{1}{p(1-p)} = \frac{1}{p} + \frac{1}{1-p}$$

   without proof.]

   Sketch the behaviour of p for $t > 0$.

   What happens to p as t gets large?   (AEB)

8. A particle moving in a straight line is subject to a resistance per unit mass which, when the particle is moving with speed v, is $au^2v + bv^3$, where a, b and u are positive constants. The particle is moving with speed u when it passes through a fixed point O on the line.

   Find the distance from O of the point at which the particle comes to rest.

   Show, using the identity

   $$\frac{au^2}{au^2v + bv^3} = \frac{1}{v} - \frac{bv}{au^2 + bv^2}$$

   that

   $$\left\{ \frac{1}{v} - \frac{bv}{au^2 + bv^2} \right\} \frac{dv}{dt} = -au^2.$$

   Hence show that the speed of the particle is reduced from u to $\frac{1}{2}u$ in time $\frac{1}{2au^2} \ln\left(\frac{4a+b}{a+b} \right)$.

   If, instead, $a = 0$, find the time taken for the speed of the particle to be reduced from u to $\frac{1}{2}u$.

9. A bullet of mass 0.1 kg moving horizontally with speed 100 ms^{-1} strikes a wooden block of mass 1 kg which is lying at rest on a smooth plane. Given that the bullet remains embedded in the block find the speed of the block when

   (a) the bullet comes to rest relative to the block,

   (b) the bullet is moving at one half of its initial speed.

   When the bullet is moving within the block with speed v ms^{-1} relative to the block, the magnitude of the force exerted by the block on the bullet is such that at time t seconds after the bullet enters the block, $\frac{dv}{dt} = -11v^3$.

   Find

   (c) the time taken from when the bullet enters the block until the speed of the bullet relative to the block has decreased from 100 ms^{-1} to 2 ms^{-1}.

   (d) the distance in centimetres travelled by the bullet within the block during that time.

4 HARMONIC MOTION

Objectives

After studying this chapter you should

- understand how to model a vibrating system;

- be able to solve the differential equations for forced and damped harmonic motion;

- be able to solve the equation for resonance and understand its significance.

4.0 Introduction

You have already met the equation for simple harmonic motion in the *Mechanics* text. Here you will first revise these concepts and then introduce a damping term in the equation which provides a more realistic model. The general characteristics of the solutions will be considered, and the added complications of a forcing function will be dealt with. The solutions will rely heavily on the methods of solving differential equations outlined in the previous chapter.

4.1 Simple harmonic motion

In the *Mechanics* text you were introduced to the concept and mathematics of simple harmonic motion (S.H.M.). A simple example is illustrated opposite where a particle of mass m is suspended in a vertical plane at one end of a spring, which is fixed at its other end. In equilibrium, the forces acting on the particle balance; i.e.

$$T_0 = mg$$

You have also seen that the tension in a spring is normally modelled by Hooke's Law, giving

$$\boxed{T_0 = \frac{\lambda e}{\ell}}$$

Here e is the extension of the spring in its equilibrium position, ℓ its natural (unstretched) length and λ its **modulus of elasticity**.

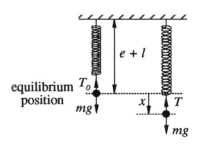

Thus

$$mg = \frac{\lambda e}{\ell}$$

and, if needed, this can be solved to find the extension, namely

$$e = \frac{mg\ell}{\lambda}$$

What happens if the mass of the particle, m, is increased?

What happens if the particle is pulled down a further distance and then released?

Suppose, for example, the particle is pulled down a further distance x from its equilibrium position and then released.

The tension, T, in the spring has now increased, so that the particle is no longer in equilibrium, and, using Newton's second law of motion,

$$m\frac{d^2x}{dt^2} = mg - T$$

$$= mg - \frac{\lambda(e+x)}{\ell} \quad \text{(the total extension is now } (e+x)\text{)}$$

$$= \left(mg - \frac{\lambda e}{\ell}\right) - \frac{\lambda x}{\ell}$$

$$= -\frac{\lambda x}{\ell}, \ \text{ since } \ mg = \frac{\lambda e}{\ell}$$

So, the governing differential equation for the motion is

$$\frac{d^2x}{dt^2} + \omega^2 x = 0$$

where $\qquad \omega^2 = \dfrac{\lambda}{m\ell}$

There are two equivalent forms for the general solution of this second order linear differential equation; namely

(1) $\qquad x = A\cos\omega t + B\sin\omega t$

Check that this is in fact a solution of the differential equation.

The initial conditions are, at $t = 0$,

$\qquad x = a$ (assuming it has been extended a further distance a)

$\qquad \dot{x} = 0$ (assuming it is released from rest)

The first condition gives

$$a = A\cos 0 + B\sin 0 = A \implies A = a$$

and, since

$$\dot{x} = -A\omega\sin\omega t + B\omega\cos\omega t,$$

the second condition gives

$$0 = B\omega \implies B = 0$$

The complete solution is

$$x = a\cos\omega t$$

This shows that the particle oscillates with **period** $\dfrac{2\pi}{\omega}$, about its equilibrium position.

The length a is known as the **amplitude** of the motion. The graph opposite illustrates the motion.

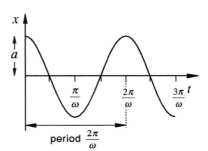

period $\dfrac{2\pi}{\omega}$

(2) $x = A\cos(\omega t + \alpha)$

This alternative form can sometimes be a more useful way of expressing the general solution.

Check that this is in fact a solution of the differential equation.

Applying the initial conditions, at $t = 0$,

$$x = a \implies a = A\cos\alpha$$

and, since

$$\dot{x} = -A\omega\sin(\omega t + \alpha)$$

at $t = 0$, $\dot{x} = 0$ gives

$$0 = -A\omega\sin\alpha$$

The second equation gives $\alpha = 0$ (since $A = 0$ would give no solution), and the first equation now gives $A = a$. So, as before, the complete solution is given by

$$x = a\cos\omega t$$

This model predicts that the vibration continues in the same way for evermore.

What will actually happen in practice?

How can the model be adapted to be more realistic?

Clearly, the assumptions behind the model, namely Hooke's Law and gravity, do not fully represent reality. Although the oscillations will continue, there will be a damping effect, with the oscillations slowly dying out. This aspect will be covered in the next section.

Example

A particle moves along the x-axis and describes simple harmonic motion of period 16 seconds about the origin O as centre. At time $t = 4$ s, $x = 12$ cm and the particle is moving towards O with

speed $\dfrac{5\pi}{8}$ cm s^{-1}. Given that the displacement, x, at any time, t,

may be written as

$$x = a\cos(\omega t + \phi)$$

find a, ω and ϕ.

Solution

Since the period is given by $\dfrac{2\pi}{\omega}$,

$$16 = \frac{2\pi}{\omega} \implies \omega = \frac{\pi}{8}$$

At $t = 4$, $x = 12$ gives

$$12 = a\cos\left(\frac{\pi}{2} + \phi\right)$$

$$\implies \quad \sin\phi = -\frac{12}{a}$$

Also, $\qquad \dot{x} = -a\omega\sin(\omega t + \phi)$

and, at $t = 4$, $\dot{x} = -\dfrac{5\pi}{8}$ (the negative sign shows that it is moving towards O)

so $\qquad -\dfrac{5\pi}{8} = -a\dfrac{\pi}{8}\sin\left(\dfrac{\pi}{2} + \phi\right)$

This gives

$$5 = a\sin\left(\frac{\pi}{2} + \phi\right)$$

$$\implies \quad \cos\phi = \frac{5}{a}$$

Now

$$\cos^2\phi + \sin^2\phi = 1$$

$$\Rightarrow \quad 144 + 25 = a^2$$

$$\Rightarrow \quad a = 13$$

and ϕ is such that $\sin\phi = -\dfrac{12}{13}$, $\cos\phi = \dfrac{5}{13}$, which gives

$$\phi \approx -1.176 \text{ radians}$$

Exercise 4A

1. A particle P performs simple harmonic oscillations of amplitude 4 cm and period 8 s. Find

    (a) the maximum speed of P,

    (b) the maximum magnitude of the acceleration of P,

    (c) the speed of P when it is 2 cm from the centre of the oscillations.   (AEB)

2. Show that $x = A\sin(\omega t + \varepsilon)$, where A, ω and ε are constants, satisfies the differential equation

    $$\frac{d^2x}{dt^2} + \omega^2 x = 0 \,.$$

    A particle moves on a straight line with simple harmonic motion about the point O as centre. At time $t = 0$ the particle passes through a point D, where $OD = 3\,cm$, moving away from O. The particle next passes through D at time $t = 4$ seconds, moving towards O, and it passes through D for the third time after a further 12 seconds. Find ω and show that the amplitude is $3\sqrt{2}$ cm.   (AEB)

3. A particle P of mass 8 kg describes simple harmonic motion with O as centre and has a speed of 6 m/s at a distance of 1 m from O and a speed of 2 m/s at a distance of 3 m from O.

    (a) Find

        (i)   the amplitude of the motion,

        (ii)   the period of the motion.

        (iii) the maximum speed of P,

        (iv) the time taken to travel from O directly to one extreme point B of the motion.

    (b) Determine the magnitude of

        (i)   the acceleration of P when at a distance of 2 m from O,

        (ii)   the force acting on P when at a distance of 2 m from O.

    (c) Write down an expression for the displacement of P from O at any time t, given that P is at O at $t = 0$. Hence, or otherwise, find the time taken to travel directly from O to a point C between O and B and at a distance of 1 m from O. Find also the time taken to go directly from C to the point D between O and B and at a distance of 2 m from O.

    (Answers may be left in a form involving inverse trigonometric functions.)   (AEB)

4. A particle P is free to move in a straight line OA, where O and A are fixed points on the line. The acceleration of P at time t seconds is $12\sin 2t \text{ ms}^{-1}$ in the direction OA. When $t = 0$, the particle P passes through O moving with speed $u \text{ ms}^{-1}$ towards A. Find

    (a) the velocity of P at time t seconds,

    (b) the displacement of P from O at t seconds,

    (c) the value of u so that the motion is simple harmonic.

    The acceleration of P in the direction OA is changed to $12|\sin 2t| \text{ ms}^{-2}$. Given also that, when $t = 0$, the particle passes through O with speed 8 ms^{-1} in the direction OA, find the displacement of P from O when $t = \pi$.   (AEB)

5. A particle P is attached to one end of a light
    elastic spring of natural length 1 m. The other
    end of the spring is attached to a fixed point O.
    Initially the particle hangs in equilibrium at the
    point B where OB = 1.098 m. It is then depressed
    a distance of 0.1 m below B and released from
    rest. Show that x, the vertical displacement, in
    metres, of P and B satisfies

    $$\frac{d^2x}{dt^2} + 100x = 0.$$

    Find

    (a) the time taken until P is next at a distance of
        0.1 m below B,

    (b) the time taken until P first reaches the point
        C at a distance of 0.05 m below B,

    (c) the speed of P at C.

    (Take $g = 9.8 \text{ ms}^{-2}$)   (AEB)

6. The end A of a light elastic spring AB of natural
    length 1 m is held fixed. A particle P is attached
    at B and when P hangs vertically in equilibrium
    AB = 1.4 m. The spring is placed on a smooth
    horizontal table with P still attached to B and the
    end A held fixed. The particle P is then set in
    motion in the line AB so that at time t s the
    distance AB is equal to $(1+x)$ m. Show, by
    taking g to be 10 ms^{-2}, that

    $$\frac{d^2x}{dt^2} + 25x = 0,$$

    and find the positive constant ω so that

    $$x = a\cos(\omega t - \alpha)$$

    satisfies this equation for all constants a and α.

    Find a and $\tan\alpha$ given that, when $t = 0$, $x = 0.3$,
    and that P is moving in the direction AB with
    speed 2 ms^{-1}. Determine also the maximum
    value of x and the maximum speed of P.   (AEB)

4.2   Damped motion

Returning to our first example, a particle is attached to the end of a
spring and oscillates in the vertical plane. To attempt to model
reality more accurately, a 'damping' term will be added which
reflects the effect that factors such as air resistance might have on
the particle.

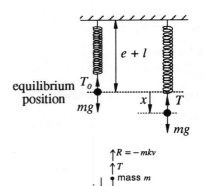

Since air resistance opposes motion, it is assumed to take the form

$$\boxed{R = -mkv}$$

Here k is a constant, and the constant of proportionality, mk, is
chosen to be of this form for mathematical convenience.

The full equation of motion is now

$$m\frac{d^2x}{dt^2} = mg - T - R$$

$$= mg - \lambda\frac{(e+x)}{\ell} - mk\frac{dx}{dt}$$

$$= -\frac{\lambda x}{\ell} - mk\frac{dx}{dt} \qquad \left(mg = \frac{\lambda e}{\ell}\right)$$

$$\boxed{\frac{d^2x}{dt^2} + k\frac{dx}{dt} + \omega^2 x = 0} \qquad (\text{where } \omega^2 = \frac{\lambda}{m\ell})$$

This is the governing differential equation for the motion. Note that, if there is no resistance, $k = 0$ and the usual equation for S.H.M. is recovered.

As before the initial conditions, at $t = 0$, are $x = a$, $\dot{x} = 0$.

Activity 1

Investigate solutions of the governing differential equation. For simplicity take $\omega = \dfrac{1}{2}$, and then find the form of the general solution for $k = 0, \dfrac{1}{2}, 1, 2$.

From Chapter 3, you will note that the solution of a **linear second order differential equation**

$$\frac{d^2x}{dt^2} + a\frac{dx}{dt} + bx = f(t)$$

is of the form

$$x = x_c(t) + x_p(t)$$

Here $x_c(t)$ is the **complementary function**, which is the general solution of the associated homogeneous differential equation

$$\frac{d^2x}{dt^2} + a\frac{dx}{dt} + bx = 0$$

and $x_p(t)$ is one **particular solution** of the full differential equation.

Now, for our differential equation, namely

$$\frac{d^2x}{dt^2} + k\frac{dx}{dt} + \omega^2 x = 0$$

there is no right hand side (i.e. $f(t) = 0$) so that you require only the complementary function. This is found by substituting

$$x = e^{mt} \qquad (m \text{ constant})$$

in the differential equation. This gives

$$\frac{dx}{dt} = me^{mt} \quad \text{and} \quad \frac{d^2x}{dt^2} = m^2 e^{mt}$$

and substituting

$$m^2 e^{mt} + k\left(me^{mt}\right) + \omega^2 e^{mt} = 0$$

$$\left(m^2 + mk + \omega^2\right)e^{mt} = 0$$

Why can you deduce that $\left(m^2 + mk + \omega^2\right) = 0$**?**

Since $e^{mt} \neq 0$ for all t,

$$\boxed{m^2 + mk + \omega^2 = 0}$$

How many distinct solutions does this quadratic equation have?

The solutions for m are given by

$$m = \frac{-k \pm \sqrt{k^2 - 4\omega^2}}{2}$$

and so clearly depend on the sign of $k^2 - 4\omega^2$.

There are three possible cases:

$$k^2 - 4\omega^2 < 0 \quad - \quad \text{two complex roots}$$
$$k^2 - 4\omega^2 = 0 \quad - \quad \text{one (repeated) real root}$$
$$k^2 - 4\omega^2 > 0 \quad - \quad \text{two real distinct roots}$$

and each case will be considered.

$$\boxed{k^2 - 4\omega^2 < 0}$$

Writing $\alpha^2 = 4\omega^2 - k^2$, the roots can now be written as

$$m = \frac{-k \pm \sqrt{-\alpha^2}}{2}$$

$$= -\frac{k}{2} \pm i\frac{\alpha}{2}$$

So the roots are given by

$$m_1 = -\frac{k}{2} + i\frac{\alpha}{2} \quad \text{and} \quad m_2 = -\frac{k}{2} - i\frac{\alpha}{2}$$

(If you are not familiar with complex numbers, you can jump to Activity 2.)

The general solution is now given by

$$x = Ae^{m_1 t} + Be^{m_2 t} \quad (A, B \text{ are arbitrary constants})$$

94

This can be simplified, using the properties of indices and complex numbers:

$$x = Ae^{\left(-\frac{k}{2}+i\frac{\alpha}{2}\right)t} + Be^{\left(-\frac{k}{2}-i\frac{\alpha}{2}\right)t}$$

$$= Ae^{-\frac{kt}{2}}e^{i\frac{\alpha t}{2}} + Be^{-\frac{kt}{2}}e^{-i\frac{\alpha t}{2}}$$

$$= e^{-\frac{kt}{2}}\left(Ae^{i\frac{\alpha t}{2}} + Be^{-i\frac{\alpha t}{2}}\right)$$

$$= e^{-\frac{kt}{2}}\left[A\left(\cos\frac{\alpha t}{2} + i\sin\frac{\alpha t}{2}\right) + B\left(\cos\left(-\frac{\alpha t}{2}\right) + i\sin\left(-\frac{\alpha t}{2}\right)\right)\right]$$

$$= e^{-\frac{kt}{2}}\left[(A+B)\cos\frac{\alpha t}{2} + i(A-B)\sin\frac{\alpha t}{2}\right]$$

and writing new arbitrary constants

$$C = A + B$$

$$D = i(A - B)$$

finally gives the solution

$$\boxed{x = e^{-\frac{kt}{2}}\left(C\cos\frac{\alpha t}{2} + D\sin\frac{\alpha t}{2}\right), \quad \alpha = \sqrt{4\omega^2 - k^2}}$$

What are the main characteristics of this solution?

Activity 2

By differentiating twice, show that the formula for x given above satisfies the governing differential equation

$$\frac{d^2x}{dt^2} + k\frac{dx}{dt} + \omega^2 x = 0$$

Activity 3

Use a graphic calculator (or computer with a graph-drawing package) to investigate the form of the solution for x given above.

For simplicity take $\omega = \frac{1}{2}$, $k = \frac{1}{2}$ (or $\frac{1}{4}$) and vary the values of C and D.

To complete the solution, the initial conditions must be applied.

At $t = 0$, $x = a$,

so $\qquad a = C$

Also, $\qquad \dfrac{dx}{dt} = -\dfrac{k}{2} e^{-\frac{kt}{2}} \left(C \cos \dfrac{\alpha t}{2} + D \sin \dfrac{\alpha t}{2} \right)$

$$+ e^{-\frac{kt}{2}} \left(-C \dfrac{\alpha}{2} \sin \dfrac{\alpha t}{2} + D \dfrac{\alpha}{2} \cos \dfrac{\alpha t}{2} \right)$$

and, at $t = 0$,

$$0 = -\dfrac{k}{2} C + D \dfrac{\alpha}{2}$$

Thus $\qquad D = \dfrac{ka}{\alpha}$

and the complete solution is given by

$$\boxed{\; x = a e^{-\frac{kt}{2}} \left(\cos \dfrac{\alpha t}{2} + \dfrac{k}{\alpha} \sin \dfrac{\alpha t}{2} \right) \;}$$

In Activity 3, you should have already observed that

(a) the particle still oscillates but with reduced period

$$\dfrac{2\pi}{\left(\dfrac{\alpha}{2} \right)} = \dfrac{4\pi}{\sqrt{4\omega^2 - k^2}}$$

$$= \dfrac{2\pi}{\sqrt{\omega^2 - \dfrac{1}{4} k^2}}$$

$\left(\text{note, again, that if } k = 0, \text{ the result returns to } \dfrac{2\pi}{\omega} \right)$;

(b) the amplitude, due to the $e^{-\frac{kt}{2}}$ term, decreases with time.

The graph opposite illustrates the motion.

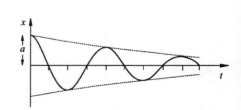

Example

Find the general solution of the differential equation governing damped harmonic motion when

$$\dfrac{d^2 x}{dt^2} + \dfrac{1}{2} \dfrac{dx}{dt} + \dfrac{1}{4} x = 0$$

Solution

You can go straight to the general solution given above, and substitute in $k = \frac{1}{2}$, $\omega^2 = \frac{1}{4}$, but the full procedure is illustrated below.

Let

$$x = e^{mt}$$

$$\Rightarrow \quad \frac{dx}{dt} = me^{mt}, \quad \frac{d^2x}{dt^2} = m^2 e^{mt}$$

Substituting in the differential equation gives

$$m^2 e^{mt} + \frac{1}{2} me^{mt} + \frac{1}{4} e^{mt} = 0$$

$$\left(m^2 + \frac{1}{2} m + \frac{1}{4}\right) e^{mt} = 0$$

This gives

$$m^2 + \frac{1}{2} me + \frac{1}{4} = 0$$

$$m = \frac{-\frac{1}{2} \pm \sqrt{\frac{1}{4} - 1}}{2}$$

$$= -\frac{1}{4} \pm \frac{1}{2} \sqrt{-\frac{3}{4}}$$

$$= -\frac{1}{4} \pm \frac{1}{4} \sqrt{3}\, i$$

So the roots are $m_1 = -\frac{1}{4} + \frac{1}{4} \sqrt{3}\, i$ and $m_2 = -\frac{1}{4} - \frac{1}{4} \sqrt{3}\, i$,

and the solution is of the form

$$x = Ae^{\left(-\frac{1}{4} + \frac{1}{4}\sqrt{3}i\right)t} + Be^{\left(-\frac{1}{4} - \frac{1}{4}\sqrt{3}i\right)t}$$

$$\Rightarrow \quad x = e^{-\frac{1}{4}t}\left(C\cos\frac{\sqrt{3}}{4}t + D\sin\frac{\sqrt{3}}{4}t\right)$$

(using the same analysis as before).

This type of damping is sometimes referred to as **light damping**. Although the form of the solution is changed, the particle still oscillates, but with its amplitude reducing to zero.

$$\boxed{k^2 - 4\omega^2 = 0}$$

This time, the roots of

$$m^2 + mk + \omega^2 = 0$$

are given by $m = -\dfrac{k}{2}$, but this root is repeated, and the general solution is of the form

$$\boxed{x = e^{-\frac{kt}{2}}(A + Bt)}$$

Activity 4

By differentiating with respect to time show that the function x given above satisfies the governing differential equation provided that $k^2 - 4\omega^2 = 0$.

As before, to find the complete solution, the initial conditions must be satisfied.

At $t = 0$, $x = a$, so

$$a = A$$

Differentiating

$$\frac{dx}{dt} = -\frac{k}{2}e^{-\frac{kt}{2}}(A + Bt) + e^{-\frac{kt}{2}}B$$

At $t = 0$, $\dot{x} = 0$,

giving $\qquad 0 = -\dfrac{k}{2}A + B$

Hence $\qquad B = \dfrac{ka}{2}$

and the complete solution is given by

$$x = ae^{-\frac{kt}{2}}\left(1 + \frac{k}{2}t\right)$$

or, in terms of ω,

$$x = ae^{-\omega t}(1 + \omega t)$$

Activity 5

Choose values of ω and a and use a graphic calculator or computer with a graph-drawing package to illustrate the form of the solution.

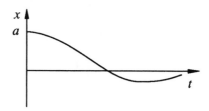

You should find that x no longer oscillates, but it tends to zero as t increases. A graph of a typical solution is shown opposite.

Example

Find the general solution of the differential equation

$$\frac{d^2x}{dt^2} + \frac{dx}{dt} + \frac{1}{4}x = 0$$

Solution

As before, substitute $x = e^{mt}$ in the differential equation, to give

$$m^2 e^{mt} + m e^{mt} + \frac{1}{4} e^{mt} = 0$$

$$\Rightarrow \quad \left(m^2 + m + \frac{1}{4}\right) e^{mt} = 0$$

$$\Rightarrow \quad m^2 + m + \frac{1}{4} = 0$$

$$\Rightarrow \quad \left(m + \frac{1}{2}\right)^2 = 0$$

Hence $m = -\frac{1}{2}$ (repeated), and the general solution is of the form

$$x = Ae^{-\frac{1}{2}t} + Bte^{-\frac{1}{2}t}$$

$$\Rightarrow \quad x = e^{-\frac{1}{2}t}(A + Bt)$$

This type of damping is referred to as **critical damping**, since it is the critical value of k which eradicates the oscillations. For smaller values of k, when $k^2 < 4\omega^2$, there will still be oscillations, whilst for larger values, when $k^2 > 4\omega^2$, as you will see, there is no oscillation at all.

$$\boxed{k^2 - 4\omega^2 > 0}$$

In this case, the roots of

$$m^2 + mk + \omega^2 = 0$$

will be of the form

$$m = \frac{-k \pm \sqrt{k^2 - 4\omega^2}}{2}$$

giving $\qquad m_1 = -\frac{k}{2} + \frac{1}{2}\sqrt{k^2 - 4\omega^2}$

and $\qquad m_2 = -\frac{k}{2} - \frac{1}{2}\sqrt{k^2 - 4\omega^2}$

You can immediately see that $m_2 < 0$.

What is the sign of m_1?

The general solution is of the form

$$\boxed{x = Ae^{m_1 t} + Be^{m_2 t}}$$

where both m_1 and m_2 are negative. To find the complete solution for x, again apply the initial conditions, $x = a$, $\dot{x} = 0$ at $t = 0$.

This gives

$$a = A + B$$

and, since

$$\frac{dx}{dt} = Am_1 e^{m_1 t} + Bm_2 e^{m_2 t}$$

$\dot{x} = 0$ gives

$$0 = Am_1 + Bm_2$$

Solving, $\qquad a = A + \left(-A\frac{m_1}{m_2}\right)$

$\Rightarrow \qquad A = \frac{am_2}{(m_2 - m_1)}$

and $\qquad B = \frac{am_1}{(m_1 - m_2)}$

Example

Solve the differential equation

$$\frac{d^2x}{dt^2} + 3\frac{dx}{dt} + \frac{5}{4}x = 0$$

Solution

Substituting $x = e^{mt}$ gives

$$m^2 + 3m + \frac{5}{4} = 0$$

$$\Rightarrow \quad m = \frac{-3 \pm \sqrt{9 - 5}}{2}$$

$$= \frac{-3 \pm 2}{2}$$

$$= -\frac{1}{2} \text{ or } -\frac{5}{2}$$

Hence the general solution is given by

$$x = Ae^{-\frac{1}{2}t} + Be^{-\frac{5}{2}t}$$

Activity 6

For a variety of values of A and B, determine the form of the graph of x against t. What happens as $t \to \infty$?

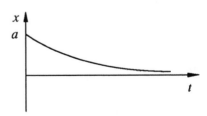

Since both the terms in x are **negative exponential**, it is clear that x tends to zero as t increases. A graph of a typical solution is illustrated opposite.

This is the case of **heavy damping** (or overdamping) in which the magnitude of the damping effect, modelled by the constant k, is so large that there is absolutely no oscillating motion at all.

Example

A particle P is attached to one end of a light elastic spring. The other end of the spring is attached to a fixed point O on a smooth horizontal table. The particle moves on the table along the line of the spring and, in addition to the force exerted by the spring, it is also acted on by a resistive force which is directly proportional to its speed. When the extension of the spring is 0.1 m and the particle is moving in the sense from O to P with speed 0.2 ms^{-1}, the total force on it in the direction $\overrightarrow{OP}$ is -0.09 N. When the spring is compressed by an amount of 0.1 m and the particle is moving in the sense from O to P with speed 0.25 ms^{-1}, the force acting on it is zero. Given that the mass of P is 0.1 kg, show that the extension x metres of the spring at any time t seconds satisfies

$$\frac{d^2x}{dt^2} + 2\frac{dx}{dt} + 5x = 0$$

Given also that the spring has natural length 1.2 m, find its modulus of elasticity.

When $t = 0$ the extension of the spring is 0.2 m and P is moving with speed 0.4 ms^{-1} in the sense from O to P. Find x for all values of t. (AEB)

Solution

In the first position, assuming the resistive force is of the form $R = k\dot{x}$

$$T + k\dot{x} = 0.09$$

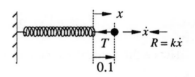

and $\qquad T = \dfrac{\lambda(0.1)}{\ell}, \quad \dot{x} = 0.2$

giving $\qquad (0.1)\dfrac{\lambda}{\ell} + k(0.2) = 0.09$

In the second position, since the spring is in compression, and the particle is in equilibrium,

$$T = k\dot{x}$$

giving $\qquad (0.1)\dfrac{\lambda}{\ell} = k(0.25)$

Using these two equations,

$$0.25k + 0.2k = 0.09 \implies k = 0.2$$

and, since $\ell = 1.2$,

$$\lambda = \frac{(0.2) \times (0.25) \times (1.2)}{(0.1)} = 0.6$$

The differential equation for motion is

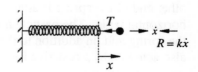

$$m\frac{d^2x}{dt^2} = -T - R = -\frac{\lambda x}{\ell} - k\dot{x}$$

$$\Rightarrow \quad 0.1\frac{d^2x}{dt^2} + 0.2\frac{dx}{dt} + \frac{0.6}{1.2}x = 0$$

$$\frac{d^2x}{dt^2} + 2\frac{dx}{dt} + 5x = 0$$

The solution of this equation is found by substituting

$$x = e^{mt}$$

in the differential equation, giving

$$m^2 + 2m + 5 = 0$$

Solving, $\quad m = \dfrac{-2 \pm \sqrt{4 - 20}}{2}$

$$= -1 \pm 2i$$

So $\quad x = Ae^{(-1+2i)t} + Be^{(-1-2i)t}$

$$\Rightarrow \quad x = e^{-t}(C\cos 2t + D\sin 2t)$$

Applying the conditions, at $t = 0$, $x = 0.2$ and $\dot{x} = 0.4$;

so $\quad 0.2 = C$

and, since

$$\dot{x} = -e^{-t}(C\cos 2t + D\sin 2t) + e^{-t}(-2C\sin 2t + 2D\cos 2t)$$

at $t = 0$,

$$0.4 = -C + 2D$$

Solving,

$$C = 0.2 \text{ and } D = 0.3$$

giving the complete solution for x as

$$x = e^{-t}(0.2\cos 2t + 0.3\sin 2t)$$

Exercise 4B

1. Solve the differential equation of damped harmonic motion

$$\frac{d^2x}{dt^2} + k\frac{dx}{dt} + x = 0$$

when

(a) $k = \sqrt{5}$ (b) $k = 2$ (c) $k = \sqrt{3}$

In each case find the complete solution which satisfies $x = 0$, $\dot{x} = 1$ at $t = 0$ and sketch each solution.

2. The three points A, O, B, in that order, are in a straight line on a smooth horizontal table, with $AO = OB = 2a$. One end of each of two light elastic strings of natural length a and modulus $5mn^2a$ (where n is a positive constant) is attached to a particle P of mass m and the other ends of the strings are fastened to A and B respectively. The particle moves along the line AB and is subject to a resistive force of magnitude $2mn$ times its speed. Assuming that both strings remain taut, show that the displacement, x, of P from O at time t will satisfy

$$\frac{d^2x}{dt^2} + 2n\frac{dx}{dt} + 10n^2x = 0$$

Given that, at $t = 0$, $x = a$ and $\frac{dx}{dt} = -10na$, find x at any subsequent time t. Draw a sketch graph showing the behaviour of the speed of the particle with time for $0 \le t \le \frac{\pi}{2n}$. (AEB)

3. A particle P of mass m is attached to one end of a light spring of modulus $2mn^2a$ and natural length a, where n is a constant. The other end of the spring is attached to a fixed point O. The particle is in equilibrium at a point B directly below O, and at time $t = 0$ an impulse is applied to P so that it starts to move down with speed u. The particle is also subject to a resistive force of magnitude $2mn$ times its speed. Show that x, its downward displacement from B at time t, satisfies

$$\frac{d^2x}{dt^2} + 2n\frac{dx}{dt} + 2n^2x = 0.$$

Find x in terms of n, u and t.

The particle first comes to instantaneous rest at a point Q_1 below B and then moves upwards through B, coming next to instantaneous rest at a point Q_2 above B and then moving downwards through B. Find $\frac{BQ_2}{BQ_1}$. (AEB)

4.3 Forced motion

Having analysed the effect that a natural damping factor has on harmonic motion, you are now in a position to take the analysis of vibratory systems one important step forward, by including an external forcing function, $F(t)$, on the system.

So, for a particle, lying on a smooth horizontal plane, attached at one end of a spring and the other end being fixed (as in the diagram opposite), which is extended a distance x, the equation of motion takes the form

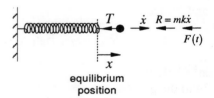

equilibrium position

$$m\frac{d^2x}{dt^2} = -T - R + F(t)$$

Here R is the resistive force, taken, as before, as $mk\dot{x}$, T is the tension in the spring, again, as before, assumed to obey Hooke's Law, namely,

$$T = \frac{\lambda x}{\ell}$$

and $F(t)$ is the **forcing** function. Writing $f(t) = \frac{F(t)}{m}$, so that $f(t)$ is the forcing function per unit mass, and substituting for T, you obtain

$$\frac{d^2x}{dt^2} + k\frac{dx}{dt} + \omega^2 x = f(t)$$

What is the form of the general solution of this second order differential equation?

The general solution is made up of two parts, namely,

$$x = x_c(t) + x_p(t)$$

where $x_c(t)$ is the general solution of the associated homogeneous equation (i.e. R.H.S. = 0),

$$\frac{d^2x}{dt^2} + k\frac{dx}{dt} + \omega^2 x = 0,$$

(and, from the previous section, you can solve this), and $x_p(t)$ is one particular solution of the full equation.

In degree courses for engineers, physicists and mathematicians, a method called **Laplace Transformations** is used, which can in principle solve all equations of this type. In this module, the right hand side will be restricted to forcing functions of the form

$$at^n \quad \text{or} \quad b\sin(\omega t + \varepsilon) \quad \text{or} \quad ce^{\alpha t}$$

and a method of 'trial and test' will be used.

The following example illustrates this method.

Example

Find the general solution of the governing differential equation for forced damped harmonic motion where

$$\frac{d^2x}{dt^2} + 3\frac{dx}{dt} + 2x = t + 1$$

What are the characteristics of this solution?

Solution

The general solution is made up of two parts.

$$\boxed{x_c(t)}$$

This is the general solution of

$$\frac{d^2x}{dt^2} + 3\frac{dx}{dt} + 2x = 0$$

As before, you look for solutions of the form

$$x = e^{mt}$$

and substituting in the differential equation gives

$$m^2 e^{mt} + 3me^{mt} + 2e^{mt} = 0$$

$$\Rightarrow \quad \left(m^2 + 3m + 2\right)e^{mt} = 0$$

$$\Rightarrow \quad \left(m^2 + 3m + 2\right) = 0$$

$$\Rightarrow \quad (m+2)(m+1) = 0$$

$$\Rightarrow \quad m = -2 \text{ or } -1$$

Thus $\qquad x_c(t) \ = \ Ae^{-2t} + Be^{-t} \qquad (A, B \text{ are arbitrary constants})$

$\boxed{x_p(t)}$

This is one particular solution of the full equation,

$$\frac{d^2 x}{dt^2} + 3\frac{dx}{dt} + 2x \ = \ t + 1$$

The 'trial and test' method used here first requires you to guess the form of a particular solution. This clearly depends on the form of the function on the right hand side. In the case of a polynomial of degree n, a general polynomial of degree n is tried. Here, assume that x_p takes the form

$$x_p = at + b \quad (a, b \text{ constants to be determined})$$

Hence $\qquad \dfrac{dx_p}{dt} = a, \quad \dfrac{d^2 x_p}{dt^2} = 0$

and substituting in the differential equation gives

$$0 + 3a + 2(at + b) = t + 1$$

$$2at + (3a + 2b) = t + 1$$

Comparing coefficients,

$$\begin{matrix} \text{[constant]} & 3a + 2b = 1 \\ \text{[}t\text{]} & 2a = 1 \end{matrix} \Big\} \quad a = \frac{1}{2}, b = -\frac{1}{4}$$

This gives

$$x_p(t) = \frac{1}{2}t - \frac{1}{4}$$

The general solution of the equation is now given by

$$x(t) = Ae^{-2t} + Be^{-t} + \frac{1}{2}t - \frac{1}{4}$$

Finally, the general characteristic of the solution can be readily determined by noting the behaviour of x for large t. The first two terms tend to zero, but the particular solution clearly increases with t; in other words,

$$x(t) \sim \frac{1}{2}t$$

for large t.

Does this result make sense in the light of the forcing function being applied?

Activity 7

Find the general solution of

$$\frac{d^2x}{dt^2} + 3\frac{dx}{dt} + 2x = t^2$$

Clearly the key part of this method of solution is in choosing the appropriate form of the particular solution. This, of course, depends on the form of the forcing function on the right hand side of the equation.

The following table gives suggestions to try for the form of the particular solution.

R.H.S. (forcing function)	Try
Polynomial of degree n	General polynomial of degree n
(e.g. $t^2 + 1$)	(try $at^2 + bt + c$)
$e^{\alpha t}$	$ae^{\alpha t}$ (or $ate^{\alpha t}$)*
$\sin \omega t$	$a\sin \omega t + b\cos \omega t$
$\cos \omega t$	$a\sin \omega t + b\cos \omega t$

* this is a special case, which you will meet later.

The following example illustrates a number of these methods.

Example

Find the general solution of

$$\frac{d^2x}{dt^2} + 3\frac{dx}{dt} + 2x = f(t)$$

where

(a) $f(t) = e^t$

(b) $f(t) = \sin \omega t$

(c) $f(t) = e^{-t}$

Solution

In each case, the first part of the solution is $x_c(t)$ and, from the previous example, is given by

$$x_c(t) = Ae^{-2t} + Be^{-t}$$

(a) When $f(t) = e^t$, the suggested form of $x_p(t)$ is

$$x_p(t) = a e^t$$

where the constant is found by satisfying the differential equation. Substituting x_p in the full differential equation

$$a e^t + 3a e^t + 2a e^t = e^t$$

$$6a e^t = e^t$$

and this is satisfied by taking $6a = 1$; i.e. $a = \frac{1}{6}$. Thus a

particular solution is $x_p(t) = \frac{1}{6}e^t$, and the general solution

is

$$x(t) = Ae^{-2t} + Be^{-t} + \frac{1}{6}e^t$$

(b) Since $f(t) = \sin \omega t$ the suggested form of $x_p(t)$ is

$$x_p(t) = a\sin \omega t + b\cos \omega t$$

where constants a and b are to be determined so that $x_p(t)$ is a solution of the full differential equation. Now

$$\frac{dx_p}{dt} = a\omega \cos \omega t - b\omega \sin \omega t$$

$$\frac{d^2x_p}{dt^2} = -a\omega^2 \sin \omega t - b\omega^2 \cos \omega t$$

and substituting in the full differential equation gives

$$-a\omega^2 \sin \omega t - b\omega^2 \cos \omega t + 3(a\omega \cos \omega t - b\omega \sin \omega t)$$
$$+ 2(a \sin \omega t + b \cos \omega t) = \sin \omega t$$

$$(-a\omega^2 - 3b\omega + 2a) \sin \omega t + (-b\omega^2 + 3a\omega + 2b) \cos \omega t = \sin \omega t$$

To satisfy this equation, you need to take

$$-a\omega^2 - 3b\omega + 2a = 1$$

$$-b\omega^2 + 3a\omega + 2b = 0 \implies b = \frac{3a\omega}{(\omega^2 - 2)}$$

and $\quad a(2 - \omega^2) - \dfrac{9a\omega^2}{(\omega^2 - 2)} = 1$

$$\implies \quad a(-\omega^4 + 4\omega^2 - 4 - 9\omega^2) = \omega^2 - 2$$

$$\implies \quad a = \frac{2 - \omega^2}{\omega^4 + 5\omega^2 + 4}, \quad b = \frac{-3\omega}{\omega^4 + 5\omega^2 + 4}$$

and the particular solution is

$$x_p(t) = \frac{(2 - \omega^2) \sin \omega t - 3\omega \cos \omega t}{\omega^4 + 5\omega^2 + 4}$$

The general solution is then given by

$$x(t) = x_c(t) + x_p(t)$$

i.e. $\quad x(t) = Ae^{-2t} + Be^{-t} + \dfrac{(2 - \omega^2) \sin \omega t - 3\omega \cos \omega t}{\omega^4 + 5\omega^2 + 4}$

(c) When $f(t) = e^{-t}$, the first suggestion for $x_p(t)$ is

$$x_p(t) = ae^{-t}$$

Thus $\quad \dfrac{dx_p}{dt} = -ae^{-t}, \quad \dfrac{d^2x_p}{dt^2} = ae^{-t}$

and substituting in the differential equation

$$ae^{-t} + 3(-ae^{-t}) + 2ae^{-t} = e^{-t}$$

But L.H.S. $= 0$, so it can never equal the right hand side; that is, there is not a particular solution of the form ae^{-t}.

Why is it obvious that $x_p = ae^{-t}$ would not work?

Note that e^{-t} is part of the solution $x_c(t)$, and so it automatically satisfies L.H.S. $=0$.

The table now recommends trying

$$x_p = ate^{-t}$$

Thus

$$\frac{dx_p}{dt} = ae^{-t} - ate^{-t}$$

$$\frac{d^2x_p}{dt^2} = -2ae^{-t} + ate^{-t}$$

and substituting in the differential equation gives

$$-2ae^{-t} + ate^{-t} + 3\left(ae^{-t} - ate^{-t}\right) + 2ate^{-t} = e^{-t}$$

$$\Rightarrow \quad ae^{-t} = e^{-t} \quad \text{(since } te^{-t} \text{ terms cancel)}$$

$$\Rightarrow \quad a = 1$$

and a particular solution is given by

$$x_p = te^{-t}$$

The general solution is then given by

$$x_p = Ae^{-2t} + Be^{-t} + te^{-t}$$

Activity 8

Find the general solution of

$$\frac{d^2x}{dt^2} + \omega^2 x = \sin pt$$

when $p \neq \omega$. Is your solution valid for $p = \omega$?

The example given in the activity represents an oscillating (vibrating) system (with no damping) with a harmonic forcing function. A particular example is given below.

Example

Solve the vibrational differential equation

$$\frac{d^2x}{dt^2} + \omega^2 x = \cos pt$$

with initial conditions $x = a$, $\dot{x} = 0$ when $t = 0$, and

(a) $p \neq \omega$

(b) $p = \omega$

In both cases, describe the motion.

Solution

The solution for x is given by

$$x(t) = x_c(t) + x_p(t)$$

where $x_c(t)$ is the general solution of

$$\frac{d^2x}{dt^2} + \omega^2 x = 0$$

As you have seen in Section 4.1, this has general solution

$$x_c(t) = A\cos\omega t + B\sin\omega t$$

(a) For a particular solution, try

$$x_p(t) = a\sin pt + b\cos pt$$

Thus $\dfrac{dx_p}{dt} = ap\cos pt - bp\sin pt$

$$\frac{d^2x_p}{dt^2} = -ap^2\sin pt - bp^2\cos pt$$

and substituting in the differential equation gives

$$-ap^2\sin pt - bp^2\cos pt + \omega^2(a\sin pt + b\cos pt) = \cos pt$$

$$a(\omega^2 - p^2)\sin pt + b(\omega^2 - p^2)\cos pt = \cos pt$$

To satisfy these equations, you must take

$$[\sin pt] \quad a(\omega^2 - p^2) = 0$$

$$[\cos pt] \quad b(\omega^2 - p^2) = 1$$

Since $\omega \neq p$, $a = 0$ and $b = \dfrac{1}{\omega^2 - p^2}$, giving

111

$$x_p(t) = \frac{1}{\left(\omega^2 - p^2\right)} \cos pt$$

and general solution

$$x(t) = A\cos\omega t + B\sin\omega t + \frac{1}{\left(\omega^2 - p^2\right)}\cos pt$$

The initial condition gives

$$x = a \ \text{at} \ t = 0 \ \Rightarrow \ a = A + \frac{1}{\left(\omega^2 - p^2\right)}$$

and since

$$\dot{x}(t) = -A\omega\sin\omega t + B\omega\cos\omega t - \frac{p}{\left(\omega^2 - p^2\right)}\sin pt,$$

at $t = 0$, $\dot{x} = 0$, giving $0 = B$

So, the complete solution is given by

$$x(t) = \left(a - \frac{1}{\left(\omega^2 - p^2\right)}\right)\cos\omega t + \frac{1}{\left(\omega^2 - p^2\right)}\cos pt$$

This predicts an oscillating solution for $x(t)$, since it combines two oscillating functions.

(b)   You can see that when $p = \omega$, the solution found above breaks down. So a particular solution of

$$\frac{d^2 x}{dt^2} + \omega^2 x = \cos\omega t$$

is required. This is not covered in the table, since the suggested try $(a\sin\omega t + b\cos\omega t)$ will not work.

Why can you be sure that this try for x_p will not work?

In fact, the form of $x_p(t)$ will include a 't' multiplier: so try

$$x_p(t) = at\sin\omega t + bt\cos\omega t$$

Hence

$$\frac{dx_p}{dt} = a\sin\omega t + a\omega t\cos\omega t + b\cos\omega t - bt\omega\sin\omega t$$

$$= (a - bt\omega)\sin\omega t + (a\omega t + b)\cos\omega t$$

and $\dfrac{d^2x_p}{dt^2} = -b\omega \sin \omega t + \omega (a - bt\omega) \cos \omega t$

$$+ a\omega \cos \omega t - \omega (a\omega t + b) \sin \omega t$$

$$= -\omega (a\omega t + 2b) \sin \omega t + \omega (2a - bt\omega) \cos \omega t$$

Substituting in the differential equation gives

$$-\omega (a\omega t + 2b) \sin \omega t + \omega (2a - bt\omega) \cos \omega t$$

$$+ \omega^2 (at \sin \omega t + bt \cos \omega t) = \cos \omega t$$

$$\Rightarrow \qquad -2b\omega \sin \omega t + 2a\omega \cos \omega t = \cos \omega t$$

This equation is satisfied by

$$2a\omega = 1 \text{ and } 2b\omega = 0$$

$$\Rightarrow \qquad a = \dfrac{1}{2\omega} \ , \ b = 0$$

and $\quad x_p(t) = \dfrac{t}{2\omega} \sin \omega t$

The general solution is given by

$$x(t) = A \cos \omega t + B \sin \omega t + \dfrac{t}{2\omega} \sin \omega t$$

Applying the initial conditions,

$$x = a, t = 0 \ \Rightarrow \ a = A$$

and, since

$$\dot{x}(t) = -A\omega \sin \omega t + B\omega \cos \omega t + \dfrac{1}{2\omega} \sin \omega t + \dfrac{t}{2} \cos \omega t$$

at $\ t = 0, \dot{x} = 0 \ $ giving

$$0 = B\omega \ \Rightarrow \ B = 0$$

So the complete solution is

$$x(t) = a \cos \omega t + \dfrac{t}{2\omega} \sin \omega t$$

Again this has oscillating behaviour but note the '*t*' multiplier which will give an increasing amplitude.

Activity 9

Investigate, using a graphic calculator or computer with a graph-drawing package, the behaviour of the solution of the above problem, when $\omega \neq p$, namely

$$x(t) = \left(a - \frac{1}{\left(\omega^2 - p^2 \right)} \right) \cos \omega t + \frac{1}{\left(\omega^2 - p^2 \right)} \cos pt$$

for varying values of ω and p (take $a = 1$ for simplicity).

Activity 10

Investigate the behaviour of the solution, when $\omega = p$, namely

$$x(t) = a \cos \omega t + \frac{t}{2\omega} \sin \omega t$$

for larger values of t.

The two distinct solutions in Activities 9 and 10 are very different in their behaviour for large values of t. The solution in Activity 9 ($\omega \neq p$) continues to exhibit oscillatory motion, with finite amplitude, whilst in Activity 10 ($\omega = p$), the amplitude increases linearly.

A typical solution in Activity 10 is illustrated opposite.

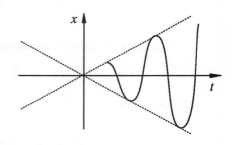

The phenomenon illustrated is known as **resonance** and occurs when the natural frequency, ω, of a vibrating system, equals the forcing frequency, p, of the applied force. In this case the amplitude of the oscillation increases without limit – it is a very dangerous situation in practice. Marching armies break step as they cross a bridge since the frequency of their step might equal one of the natural frequencies of the bridge.

There are very many famous cases where resonance has caused problems, such as

(a) Tacoma Bridge in the USA, in which the frequency of the wind equalled one of the natural frequencies of the bridge, with the result that it completely disintegrated as oscillations increased in amplitude.

(b) original turbines in the QE2, which caused all sorts of problems until the resonance was controlled.

*Activity 11

The complete model of a damped vibrating system is

$$\frac{d^2x}{dt^2} + k\frac{dx}{dt} + \omega^2 x = \cos pt$$

For $k < 4\omega^2$, find the form of the particular solution, and interpret the behaviour of x for large t. Is the solution still valid when $p = \omega$?

Exercise 4C

1. Solve the differential equation of forced harmonic motion when

$$\frac{d^2x}{dt^2} + 4\frac{dx}{dt} + 3x = f(t) \;, \text{ and}$$

   (a) $f(t) = c$, constant   (b) $f(t) = e^t$

   (c) $f(t) = e^{-t}$

   In each case, find the behaviour of x for large t.

2. Solve the equation of harmonic motion

$$\frac{d^2x}{dt^2} + 4x = \sin pt; \quad x = a, \ \dot{x} = 0 \text{ at } t = 0;$$

   when   (a) $p = 1$ (b) $p = 2$

3. A body of mass m, which is suspended on the end of an elastic spring, moves such that its vertical displacement, x, from its equilibrium position is given by

$$\ddot{x} + 4n^2 x = an^2 \cos nt \;,$$

   where a and n are positive constants. Given that $x = 0$ and $\dot{x} = 0$ when $t = 0$, find the displacement at any time t.   (AEB)

4. A light spring AB of natural length a and modulus mn^2a lies straight and slack on a rough horizontal table. A particle mass m is attached to the spring at B. The coefficient of friction between the table and the particle is μ.

   Initially the particle is at rest and the end A is then made to move with constant speed u in the direction BA.

   Find the extension in the spring when the particle starts to move.

   At a time t after the particle starts to move, its distance from its original position is denoted by x.

   Show that, while x is increasing,

$$\frac{d^2x}{dt^2} + n^2 x = n^2 ut$$

   Find x at time t and also the maximum speed of the particle.   (AEB)

4.4   Miscellaneous Exercises

1. A particle of mass m moves along the x-axis and is attracted towards the origin O by a force of magnitude $5m\omega^2$ times its distance from O, where ω is a constant. The particle is resisted by a force of magnitude $4m\omega$ times its speed. No other forces act. Write down the differential equation for the particle's displacement, x, along the line from O, and show that, at time t,

$$x = e^{-2\omega t}(A\cos \omega t + B\sin \omega t)$$

   where A and B are constants.   (AEB)

2. A particle P of mass m, free to move in the xy plane, has position vector $\mathbf{r}$ relative to a fixed origin O. The particle is acted on by the force $-6mn^2\mathbf{r} - 5mn\mathbf{v}$, where n is a constant and $\mathbf{v}$ is the velocity of P. Show that, at time t,

$$\frac{d^2x}{dt^2} + 5n\frac{dx}{dt} + 6n^2 x = 0 \;.$$

   At time $t = 0$ the particle starts from the point $(a, 0)$ and moves into the region $y > 0$ with speed na in a direction making an angle of 60° with the positive x-axis. Find x at any subsequent time t. Obtain, similarly, an expression for y at time t.   (AEB)

3. A particle of mass m moves along the x-axis and is attracted towards the fixed origin O by a force of magnitude $5m\omega^2|x|$, where ω is a constant. In addition, the motion of the particle is resisted by a force of magnitude $4m\omega v$ where v is the speed of the particle at time t. Write down an equation of motion of the particle and hence show that, at any time t, $x = Ce^{-2\omega t}\cos(\omega t + \phi)$, where C and ϕ are constants.

   Given that, at $t = 0$, $x = 3a$ and the particle is moving towards O with speed $2a\omega$, where a is a constant, find C and ϕ.

   Sketch the graph of x against t, paying particular attention to the behaviour of x near $t = 0$ and as t becomes large. (AEB)

4. At time t, a particle of mass m is moving along the x-axis in the direction Ox. The particle is subject to a force of attraction towards O of magnitude $m\omega^2 x$ (where ω is a constant) and a forcing function $mf(t)$ away from O. Show that x, the distance of the particle from O in the positive direction, satisfies

$$\frac{d^2x}{dt^2} + \omega^2 x = f(t)$$

   (a) Find the general solution for x when

   (i) $f(t) = 0$

   (ii) $f(t) = a\sin\omega t$ (a is a constant)

   (b) In (a)(ii) the particle is initially at rest at the origin.

   (i) Find x in terms of ω, a and t.

   (ii) Give a sketch of the solution curve $x = x(t)$ and describe its main characteristics. (AEB)

5. A particle of mass m is tied to one end of a light elastic string and the other end is attached to a fixed point O. Given that the natural length of the string is a, and the stretched length, when the particle hangs in equilibrium, is $\frac{5a}{3}$, find the modulus of the string.

   The particle is now held at rest at O and released. Find the particle's speed at the instant when the string becomes taut. Show that, in the subsequent motion, the acceleration of the particle at time t later is given by

$$\ddot{x} = -\frac{3g}{2a}\left(x - \frac{2a}{3}\right),$$

   where x is measured downwards from the position at which the string becomes taut.

Verify that solutions of this equation are given by

$$x - \frac{2a}{3} = A\cos\left\{\sqrt{\left(\frac{3g}{2a}\right)}\,t + \phi\right\}$$

and determine the constants A and ϕ for the particle's motion. Hence find the total time which elapses before the particle first comes instantaneously to rest. (AEB)

6. One end of an elastic spring of modulus of elasticity $18mn^2 a$ and natural length a is attached to a particle P of mass m. The other end is fastened to a point O on a horizontal table. The particle is free to move on the table in the line OP. At time t there is a force $9mn^2 a e^{-3nt}$ acting on P in the sense from O to P and the motion of P is opposed by a frictional force of magnitude $6mn$ times its speed. Show that x, the extension of the spring, satisfies the differential equation

$$\frac{d^2x}{dt^2} + 6n\frac{dx}{dt} + 18n^2 x = 9n^2 a e^{-3nt}$$

   Given that at $t = 0$, $x = 0$ and $\frac{dx}{dt} = 0$, find x in terms of a, n and t and show that x never becomes negative. (AEB)

7. A particle of mass m is moving along a straight line and is attracted towards a fixed point O by a force $2m\omega^2 x$ where x is the distance of the particle from O at time t and ω is a constant. In addition the motion of the particle is resisted by a force of magnitude $2m\omega\dot{x}$ where $\dot{x}$ is the speed of the particle at time t. Write down a differential equation to determine the motion of the particle and hence show that

$$x = Ce^{-\omega t}\cos(\omega t + \alpha),$$

   where C and α are constants.

   Given that $t = 0$, $x = a$ and $\dot{x} = \left(\sqrt{3} - 1\right)a\omega$, where a is a constant, find C and α. Also find the times at which the particle is instantaneously at rest.

   Sketch the graph of x against t, showing clearly the behaviour of x as t becomes large. (AEB)

8. [In this question take g to be $10\ \text{ms}^{-2}$]

   A particle P is attached to one end of a light elastic spring of natural length 0.5 m. The other end of the spring is held at a fixed point A and the particle hangs in equilibrium at the point B directly below A, where AB = 0.525 m. The equilibrium is disturbed by the upper end of the spring being made to oscillate in a vertical line so that, at time t seconds after the motion has been started, the downward displacement of the upper end of the spring from A is

$$0.02\sin 10t \text{ metres.}$$

Show that x metres, the downward displacement of P from B at time t seconds, satisfies

$$\ddot{x} + 400x = 8\sin 10t$$

Find x in terms of t. (AEB)

9. A particle moves in a straight line such that its displacement from a fixed point O at time t is given by

$$x = a\cos(\omega t - \phi)$$

where a, ω and ϕ are positive constants. It is observed that the period of the motion is 16 s and that at a certain time the particle is 5 m from O and that 4 s later it is still on the same side of O but 12 m from O. Find a, ω and ϕ.

Show that after a further four seconds the particle is on the other side of O and at a distance 5 m from O. Find the speed and acceleration of the particle in this position and state whether it is travelling towards or away from O. Also, find the time which elapses before the particle next passes through this position. (AEB)

10. A particle of mass m is attached to one end of a light spring of natural length a and modulus $5m\omega^2 a$, where $\omega > 0$. The other end of the spring is attached to a fixed point O on a horizontal plane. At time $t = 0$, the particle is released from rest at a point A on the plane, where $OA = 3a$.

Given that the particle experiences a resistance to motion of magnitude $2m\omega$ times its speed together with a driving force $10m\omega^2 a\cos\omega t$ in the direction OA, show that the extension, x, of the spring beyond its natural length at time t satisfies the equation

$$\ddot{x} + 2\omega\dot{x} + 5\omega^2 x = 10\omega^2 a\cos\omega t$$

Find x in terms of a and ωt and show that for large values of t the motion of the particle is approximately simple harmonic with amplitude $\sqrt{5}\,a$. (AEB)

5 IMPULSIVE MOTION

Objectives

After studying this chapter you should

*   be able to solve problems where sharp blows are applied to bodies, e.g. in tennis and cricket;
*   be able to solve problems involving collisions between bodies where they move together after colliding, e.g. in a car crash;
*   be able to solve problems involving collisions between bodies where they bounce apart after colliding, e.g. in snooker.

5.0   Introduction

Collisions occur in many everyday situations such as car accidents and ball games; this chapter explores the relationship between the situation before and after a collision. The variables that can influence the outcome of a collision include the mass and velocity of the items which are colliding. Another factor affecting any impact is the actual material of the items in contact – consider the difference between dropping a hard rubber on to a carpet and on to a concrete floor.

The work follows on from the considerations of One-dimensional Motion (Chapter 2) and Work and Energy (Chapter 6) of the *Mechanics* text.

5.1   Sharp blows

In practically all ball games a ball comes into contact with some object (bat, racket, wall) for a short period of time and then moves off again. You will try and model what happens during this contact period, starting with problems where the motion is always in the same straight line.

In the diagram opposite, a cricket ball of mass 0. 5 kg is moving horizontally with speed 15 m s^{-1} when it is struck by a cricket bat so that, immediately after leaving the bat, it is moving horizontally with speed 25 m s^{-1} away from the bat.

What happens during contact?

15 m s^{-1} 25 m s^{-1}

Obviously there will be a force acting on the ball in the direction away from the bat and this is modelled as a constant force of magnitude F N acting for a small time T. The acceleration of the ball during the contact period is therefore

$$\frac{F}{0.5} \text{ m s}^{-2}$$

and from the constant acceleration formula $(v = u + at)$,

$$25 = -15 + \frac{FT}{0.5}$$

since the initial velocity in the direction away from the bat is -15 m s^{-1}

i.e. $\qquad FT = 0.5(25 + 15) = 20$

The product of F and T is finite and therefore, since T is assumed to be small, F has to be taken to be large. Therefore a simple model of a sharp blow is a large constant force acting for a very short time so that the product of force and time is finite. For the case when the force is constant this product is called the **impulse** of the force but, as you will see later, this is not true for a force which varies with time.

The positive direction has been taken as the direction away from the wall so 0.5×25 N s represents the momentum of the ball after collision and -0.5×15 N s represents the momentum before collision. Therefore $0.5(25 + 15)$ N s is the change in momentum of the ball. The above equation shows that

$$\boxed{\begin{array}{ccc} \text{impulse} & & \text{change of momentum} \\ \text{(in a particular direction)} & = & \text{(in that direction)} \end{array}}$$

The units of impulse are the same as that of momentum, i.e. N s.

In order to avoid confusion when dealing with circular and rigid body motion, it is necessary to be a little more precise about the use of the word 'momentum'. The product of the mass and velocity of a particle, which has been referred to as momentum, is actually called the **linear momentum**; later on you will come across **angular momentum**. In problems involving motion on a line it is necessary to pick a positive direction for velocity, and therefore linear momentum.

What happens if the force is not constant?

It is very unlikely that the contact force will be constant throughout contact and therefore you should look for some more general quantity associated with a force so that this would always be equal to the change of linear momentum.

Taking the positive direction of v to be away from the bat, Newton's law of motion gives

$$m\frac{dv}{dt} = F$$

The change of linear momentum between $t = 0$ and $t = T$ can be found by integrating the left hand side of the above equation from $t = 0$ to $t = T$, giving

$$(mv)_{t=T} - (mv)_{t=0} = \int_0^T F\, dt$$

What is the value of the RHS of this equation when F is constant?

Now the impulse of a force F acting for a time T can, in general,

be defined as $\qquad\qquad \displaystyle\int_0^T F\, dt$

so that, by construction, impulse is equal to change of linear momentum; this is a fundamental principle of Mechanics.

The impulse–momentum principle for a particle

When a force is applied to a particle over a period then the change of linear momentum of the particle, measured in the direction of the force, is equal to the impulse of the force over that period.

In mathematical terms,

$$(mv)_{t=T} - (mv)_{t=0} \;=\; \text{impulse}$$

5.2   Modelling a sharp blow

In modelling a sharp blow, the precise form of the force is not considered; it is simply said that an 'impulse' is applied so that there is an **instantaneous** change of linear momentum equal to the impulse. The model is therefore one where it is assumed that there are large forces acting for effectively infinitesimal periods of time so that the impulse is finite.

During any sharp blow there will obviously be forces like gravity acting but, in the limit of zero time, these do not make a contribution to the impulse. This is also true of the tension in an elastic spring or string, neither of which can sustain an impulsive tension. The forces which make a contribution in the limit as time tends to zero are referred to as **impulsive forces** and normally their detailed behaviour is not known.

Some impulsive forces can be modelled by relatively simple formulae.

Activity 1

Draw the graph of $F = \dfrac{T}{t^2 + T^2}$ against T for $T = 0.1,\ 0.01,\ 0.001$.

Also evaluate the integral of this function from $t = 0$ to T.

Does it give a reasonable example of a force acting for a small period of time to give a finite impulse?

Example

A ball of mass 0.06 kg hits a vertical wall with a speed of 12 m s^{-1}, the direction of motion being perpendicular to the wall. The ball rebounds back with a speed of 6 m s^{-1}. Find the impulse exerted by the wall on the ball.

Solution

Assume that the positive direction of linear momentum you choose is that away from the wall as shown in the diagram. The linear momentum of the ball immediately after impact is

$$0.06 \times 6 \text{ N s} = 0.36 \text{ N s}$$

the linear momentum immediately before impact is

$$0.06 \times (-12) \text{ N s} = -0.72 \text{ N s}$$

The impulse is therefore $0.36 - (-0.72) \text{ N s} = 1.08 \text{ N s}$

As would be expected, the impulse is acting away from the wall. (By Newton's third law there will be an equal and opposite impulse acting on the wall.)

Exercise 5A

1. An impulse of magnitude 1.6 N s is applied to a particle of mass 0.4 kg. The particle is free to move along the x-axis and the impulse is applied in this direction. Find the resulting speed of the particle.

2. A railway truck of mass 1200 kg, moving along a straight horizontal track at 5 m s^{-1}, runs into fixed buffers and rebounds with a speed of 2 m s^{-1}. Find the impulse on the truck.

3. A roller skater whose total mass is 75 kg receives a horizontal impulse of magnitude 225 N s when standing at rest. Find the initial speed of the skater and, given that the total resistance is 25 N, determine the total distance moved across the rink.

4. A tennis ball of mass 0.07 kg is moving horizontally with speed 6 m s^{-1} when it is hit by a racket and leaves the racket horizontally with a speed of 12 m s^{-1}. Calculate the magnitude of the impulse on the ball.

5. Assuming that the ball and racket in Question 4 are in contact for 0.06 s, find the force acting, assuming

   (a) that it is constant,

   (b) that it is of the form ct, where t is time in seconds, measured from impact.

6. A cricket ball of mass 0.15 kg moving horizontally with speed 15 m s^{-1} just as it reaches a batsman, is hit straight back horizontally with a speed of 25 m s^{-1}. Find the impulse of the bat on the ball.

7. Assuming that the bat and the ball in Question 6 are in contact for 0.05 s, find the form of the force exerted by the bat on the ball. Assume that it can be modelled as a quadratic equation in time and that it vanishes at the start and end of the period of contact.

8. A concrete slab of mass 3 kg falls from rest at a vertical height of 12 m above firm horizontal ground from which it does not rebound. Calculate, taking $g = 9.8$ m s^{-2}, the impulse on the ground due to the slab and state the units in which your answer is measured.

9. A ball of mass 0.2 kg falls vertically on to a horizontal floor. The ball strikes the floor with a speed 12 m s^{-1} and bounces to reach a height of 2.5 m above the floor. Taking $g = 9.8$ m s^{-2}, show that the impulse on the floor is 3.8 N s.

5.3 Interactions between particles

You have concentrated on the effect of the impulse on the ball but, since by Newton's third law action and reaction are equal and opposite, there will be an opposite impulse acting on the bat, and therefore, on the batsman. This should affect the momentum but normally the batsman would exert a further impulse on the ground to stay at rest. This kind of reaction is particularly obvious in the case of shooting a rifle, when there is a recoil. There are, however, many problems involving sharp blows between bodies where one body does not compensate in the way that a human ball player does, and motion of both bodies is possible. Obvious examples include snooker balls or cars colliding.

Consider these types of problems by looking at two cars driving directly towards each other as in the diagram opposite.

During the collision there will be impulsive forces acting between the cars. By Newton's third law the forces exerted by car 2 on car 1 during collision are equal and opposite to those exerted by car 1 on car 2. Since impulse is the integral of the force, the impulses acting on the cars are equal and opposite; the impulse on car 1 due to car 2 can be denoted as I and that of car 2 due to car 1 as $-I$ (i.e. I to the left).

The positive direction is taken to be towards the right so that by the impulse–momentum principle

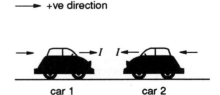

+ve direction

car 1   car 2

change in linear momentum of car $1 = I$

change in linear momentum of car $2 = -I$

Adding,

change in total linear momentum of cars 1 and $2 = 0$

This is the principle of **conservation of linear momentum** which you have already met.

Imagine a more complicated kind of collision where external impulses J and K act on cars 1 and 2 as shown opposite. (There could be other cars or a wall, this does not really matter for the present.)

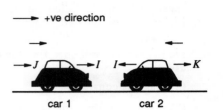

Applying the impulse–momentum principle then gives

change in linear momentum of car $1 = J + I$

change in linear momentum of car $2 = K - I$

Adding these gives

change in total linear momentum of cars 1 and $2 = K + J$

The right hand side is the sum of the external impulses applied to the two cars (i.e. excluding the interactive impulses).

You could carry on and include more cars and would find out that, however many cars (i.e. particles) were involved, the change of linear momentum is equal to the total impulse.

This gives

The impulse–momentum principle for a system of particles

The total change, in any period, of the linear momentum of a system of particles moving in a line is equal to the total external impulse (i.e. excluding the impulses between the particles) acting on the system during that period.

If there are no external impulses acting then you will obtain the **principle of conservation of linear momentum** which says that during any period when there are no external impulses acting on the system, the **total linear momentum remains constant**.

Though you have concentrated on collisions you should note that the principle of conservation of linear momentum holds for **all** periods when there are no impulses acting and, since impulse is the integral of force, the principle can be restated as

> The total linear momentum of a system of interacting particles on which there are no external forces acting remains constant.

For any kind of interaction or collision between two bodies moving in a line, the impulse–momentum principle or the principle of conservation of linear momentum, will give one relation between the velocities before and after collision. Therefore more information is generally needed to find the separate velocities. However, when the interacting bodies move together after collision or interaction, there will be enough information to find both velocities.

Example

Two cars of mass 1000 kg and 1600 kg are moving directly towards each other with speeds of 15 m s^{-1} and 10 m s^{-1} respectively. The heavier car is brought to rest by the collision. Find the velocity of the other car immediately after collision.

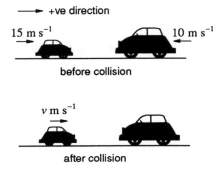

Solution

Take the positive direction to the right so that the linear momentum of the lighter car is 15 000 N s whilst that of the heavier car is −16 000 N s. The linear momentum before collision is therefore −1000 N s. The heavier car is brought to rest and the other car is assumed to have a velocity v m s^{-1} to the right. Conservation of linear momentum gives

$$1000v = 15000 - 16000$$

$$= -1000$$

so the lighter car moves backwards with speed 1 m s^{-1}.

Example

Solve the previous example assuming now that, after collision, the cars move together.

Solution

If both cars move together, after collision, with speed v m s^{-1},

total linear momentum after collision $= 2600v$ N s

total linear momentum before collision $= -1000$ N s

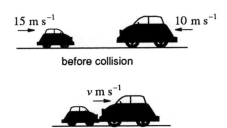

Hence

$$2600v = -1000$$

giving $\qquad v = -\dfrac{5}{13} \text{ m s}^{-1}$

So the cars move to the left with speed $\dfrac{5}{13}$ m s^{-1}.

Example

Car A in the diagram is about to tow car B; the tow rope is slightly slack so that car A can reach a speed of 2 m s^{-1} before the rope tightens. Determine the motion of the cars immediately after the rope tightens. The masses of cars A and B are 1000 kg and 1200 kg respectively.

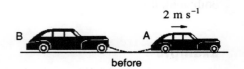

Solution

Initially the tow rope is assumed to be slightly slack so that car A can reach a speed of 2 m s^{-1} before the rope tightens.

Immediately after the rope tightens the cars will be moving at the same speed of u m s^{-1}.

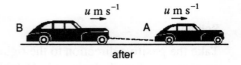

Now

$\qquad$ linear momentum 'before' $= 1000 \times 2$ N s

$\qquad$ linear momentum 'after' $\quad = (1000u + 1200u)$ N s

so the principle of conservation of linear momentum gives

$$2000 = 1000u + 1200u \;\Rightarrow\; u = \dfrac{10}{11}$$

[Since car B moves there is an impulse acting on it. This impulse is due to the rope and is called the impulsive tension even though it is not a force. The impulsive tension in the rope is $1200u$ N s and this is approximately 1091 N s.]

Example

Two particles A and B of mass m and $4m$ lie in a straight line, joined by an inextensible string, which is just taut. An impulse of magnitude $10mU$ is applied to B in the sense from A to B. Determine the subsequent motion.

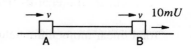

Solution

You only consider possible motion along the string. Since the string is inextensible both particles move with the same speed v. The total linear momentum after the particles start moving is

$$mv + 4mv = 5mv$$

The impulse–momentum principle gives

$$5mv = 10mU$$

so that

$$v = 2U$$

The impulsive tension acts on A towards B and this can be denoted by I. Applying the impulse–momentum principle to A gives

$$I = mv = 2mU$$

Equally, you could have applied the principle to B, remembering that the impulse would then be acting towards A.

What would have happened if, in the example above, the impulse on B had been from B to A?

A relatively small change in the conditions can produce a very different problem.

Example

Answer the previous example when the string is replaced by an elastic spring of modulus $20mn^2a$ and natural length a, where n is a constant.

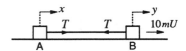

Solution

There is no impulsive tension in the spring and therefore particle A will not be jerked into motion and, even when it moves, it will not necessarily move with the same speed as B. It is therefore necessary to consider the motion of the particles separately and to assign coordinates x and y to them respectively. Choose x and y to be the displacements of the particles, in the sense from A to B, from their original positions.

Applying the impulse–momentum principle to B shows that it moves off with speed $\dot{y}$ given initially by

$$4m\dot{y} = 10mU$$

$$\dot{y} = 2.5U$$

and the initial speed of A is zero.

Their subsequent motion is governed by their equations of motion.

The only force acting is the tension T in the spring. It acts in opposite directions on the two particles, giving

$$m\ddot{x} = T, \ 4m\ddot{y} = -T$$

Dividing the first equation by m and the second by $4m$ gives

$$\ddot{y} - \ddot{x} = -\frac{5T}{4m}$$

The extension of the spring is $y - x - a$, and using Hooke's Law

$$T = 20mn^2 (y - x - a)$$

Therefore

$$\ddot{y} - \ddot{x} = -25n^2 (y - x - a)$$

This is the simple harmonic equation in the variable $y - x$, which, from Chapter 4, you should know how to solve.

Activity 2

Using the formulae for S.H.M. show that the extension in the spring in the above example at time t after being set in motion is

$\dfrac{U}{2n} \sin 5nt$, and that $x = -\dfrac{2U}{5n} (\sin 5nt - 5nt)$.

Exercise 5B

1. A railway truck of mass 15 tonnes moving with speed 2 m s^{-1} collides with a stationary truck of mass 10 tonnes. The trucks move together immediately on impact. Find their common speed.

2. Car B, which is of mass 1300 kg, is initially stationary and is struck by car A, of mass 1200 kg, moving with speed 20 m s^{-1}. The cars become entangled and move together immediately after collision. Find their common speed after collision.

3.

ram
400 kg

pile
200 kg

The diagram shows a pile being driven into the ground by dropping a heavy weight (the ram) on to it from a height.

The ram weighs 400 kg and the pile weighs 200 kg. Given that the ram is dropped from a height of 1.6 m and does not rebound off the pile, find the common speed of the ram and pile immediately after impact.

(Assume that $g = 9.81$ m s^{-2}.)

4.

4 km h^{-1} 2 km h^{-1}

B   A

A railway goods wagon A of total mass of 25 tonnes is moving along the horizontal track in a railway yard at a speed of 2 km h^{-1}. A second goods wagon B with a total mass of 35 tonnes and moving with speed 4 km h^{-1} collides with wagon A and is coupled to it. Find the common velocity v of the two wagons as they move together after being coupled.

5. A 0.045 kg rifle bullet is fired horizontally with a velocity of 400 m s^{-1} into a 6 kg block of wood which can move freely in the horizontal direction. Determine the final velocity of the block.

6. Two swimmers are about to dive from the end of an initially stationary boat of mass 200 kg. Immediately after leaving the boat, a swimmer has a horizontal velocity of 6 m s^{-1} relative to the boat. The swimmers are of mass 60 kg and 50 kg respectively.

   Find the final velocity of the boat assuming

   (a) both swimmers dive simultaneously;

   (b) the heavier swimmer dives first;

   (c) the lighter swimmer dives first.

7. A girl of mass 44 kg runs and, when her horizontal velocity is 4 m s^{-1}, jumps on a 12 kg toboggan. The girl and toboggan travel a distance of 21 m horizontally on snow before coming to rest. What is the coefficient of friction between the toboggan and the snow? Take $g = 9.81$ m s^{-2}.

8. A porter at an airport throws a 12 kg package with a horizontal velocity of 2 m s^{-1} on to a luggage trolley weighing 36 kg. The trolley is initially at rest and can roll freely so that its subsequent motion can be modelled as sliding on a smooth surface. Find the velocity of the trolley after the package has stopped sliding relative to the trolley.

9. Tom, of mass 79 kg, and Lucy, of mass 70 kg, are standing on ice directly facing each other. Tom throws a 1 kg ball which moves with a horizontal speed of 10 m s^{-1} to Lucy who catches it and throws it back to Tom with the same horizontal speed. Modelling the ice as perfectly smooth, find the speeds of Tom and Lucy immediately after the ball has been returned to Tom.

10. A 50 tonne railway engine moving at 3 km h^{-1} strikes a stationary 10 tonne flatbed railway wagon which is carrying a 15 tonne load. The load can slide along the floor of the wagon towards the engine. Immediately after collision the engine and wagon move together. Find the speed of the engine

    (a) immediately after the coupling;

    (b) after the load has slid to a stop relative to the wagon.

5.4   Problems involving pulleys

Impulse problems involving particles on a string passing over a pulley sometimes occur. In some ways they can be treated as particles moving on a straight string but they have to be handled carefully. The following examples are typical of those that may occur.

Example

Two particles of mass 0.2 kg and 0.4 kg, attached one at each end of an inextensible string passing over a smooth pulley as shown in the diagram, are set in motion. At the instant when the particles have a common speed of 2 m s^{-1} the heavier particle hits a horizontal surface off which it does not rebound. (The surface is referred to as being inelastic.) Find the speed with which the heavier particle is first jerked into motion.

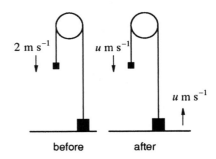

before   after

Solution

Once the heavier particle has stopped, the lighter one continues upwards under gravity to its highest point and then falls, reaching the point where the string is about to become taut with speed again

2 m s^{-1}. This is because the lighter particle's energy remains

constant and, since the potential energy has not changed, neither will the speed (only the direction will change).

When the string becomes taut there will be an impulsive tension T in the string and the heavier particle will be jerked off the horizontal surface. Suppose that both particles move with a common speed u m s^{-1}.

Applying the impulse–momentum principle to the heavier particle gives

$$T = 0.4u$$

The impulsive tension acting on the lighter particle will be upwards; the velocity of the particle will have changed from 2 m s^{-1} downwards to u m s^{-1} downwards. Therefore the change in linear momentum downwards is $0.2(u-2)$ and this is equal to $-T$.

Thus

$$0.2(u-2) = -T = -0.4u$$

$$0.2u - 0.4 = -0.4u$$

$$0.6u = 0.4$$

$$u = \frac{2}{3}$$

So the particle is jerked into motion with speed $\frac{2}{3}$ ms^{-1}.

(Note that the equation for u is exactly the same as if the two particles had been in a straight line.)

Example

When the same particles are moving freely with a speed of 2 m s^{-1} as shown in the diagram, the lighter particle picks up a mass 0.5 kg which is lying on a fixed ring through which the particle passes. Find the common speed of the system immediately after the mass has been picked up.

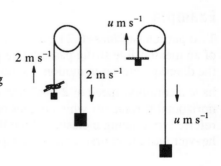

Solution

Let the particles move with a new unknown speed u m s^{-1}.

There will be an impulsive tension T in the string and this is the impulse acting on the combined particle so, applying the impulse–

momentum principle to this particle

$$T = (0.5 + 0.2)u - 2 \times 0.2$$

The velocity of the heavier particle, downwards, will change from 2 m s^{-1} to u m s^{-1} so the change in its linear momentum downwards gives

$$-T = 0.4u - 0.4 \times 2$$

Eliminating T,

$$0.7u - 0.4 = -0.4u + 0.8$$

$$\Rightarrow \quad 1.1u = 1.2$$

$$\Rightarrow \quad u = \frac{12}{11} \approx 1.09 \text{ m s}^{-1}$$

5.5 Motion not in the same line

So far only situations where the motion of the particles is in the same straight line have been considered. Problems where a sharp blow causes a change in motion from one line to another will now be examined. Common examples are again in ball games. A ball thrown against a wall will often change direction; returns of service in tennis are rarely in the direction of the original delivery and the same is true in cricket.

When the motion is not along a line the idea of linear momentum generalises to the product of the mass and velocity. This makes its vector nature more explicit.

In the above examples there has been a change of momentum and you need to generalise the previous work to cope with a vector situation. If you assume a force F acting for a time T, then integrating the vector equation of motion

$$m\frac{d\mathbf{v}}{dt} = \mathbf{F}$$

from $t = 0$ to $t = T$

gives

$$(m\mathbf{v})_{t=T} - (m\mathbf{v})_{t=0} = \int_0^T \mathbf{F}\,dt$$

Comparing this equation with that found for a cricket ball moving in a line you will see that, by defining the impulse as the vector $\int_0^T \mathbf{F}\,dt$, the result

$$\boxed{\text{change of momentum } = \text{ impulse}}$$

still holds.

So the impulse–momentum principle holds in all circumstances where impulse is a vector and the impulse of a force **F** acting for a time T is $\displaystyle\int_0^T \mathbf{F}\,dt$.

A sharp blow can again be modelled by saying that 'impulsive' forces are applied so that the impulse is equal to the change of linear momentum. The only difference is that you are now dealing with vector quantities.

Example

The diagram opposite shows a ball, of mass 0.4 kg, moving horizontally. It hits a wall at an angle and rebounds horizontally in a different direction. The view is of the ball from above. Immediately before impact the components of the velocity of the ball parallel to and towards the wall are 3 m s^{-1} and 4 m s^{-1}. Immediately after impact the components of velocity parallel to and away from the wall are 2 m s^{-1} and 3 m s^{-1}. Find the impulse exerted by the wall on the ball.

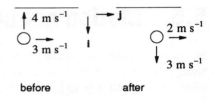

before   after

Solution

Since you are dealing with vectors, the first step is to introduce unit vectors. Use the unit vectors **i** and **j** shown in the diagram, **i** in the direction away from the wall and **j** parallel to it .

The velocities before and after impact are $-4\mathbf{i}+3\mathbf{j}$ m s^{-1} and $3\mathbf{i}+2\mathbf{j}$ m s^{-1}. The linear momentum before impact is

$$0.4(-4\mathbf{i}+3\mathbf{j}) \text{ N s}$$

and that after impact is

$$0.4(3\mathbf{i}+2\mathbf{j}) \text{ N s}$$

The impulse is given by

$$0.4(3\mathbf{i}+2\mathbf{j}) - 0.4(-4\mathbf{i}+3\mathbf{j}) = (2.8\mathbf{i}-0.4\mathbf{j}) \text{ N s}$$

What is the impulse exerted by the ball on the wall in the last example?

Instead of expressing the impulse in vector form its magnitude and direction could be given.

Example

A tennis ball of mass 0.06 kg is moving horizontally with speed 10 m s^{-1} when it is struck by a racket and is returned so that, immediately after impact, it is moving with speed 18 m s^{-1} in the same horizontal plane at an angle of 25° to its original line of motion. Find the magnitude and direction of the impulse acting on the ball.

Solution

The safest way of working out the impulse, even in problems where the data is not given explicitly in terms of unit vectors, is to pick suitable perpendicular unit vectors and refer everything to them.

Referring to the diagram, one suitable unit vector $\mathbf{i}$ is along the original line of flight but away from the racket. (It could be towards the racket but you know that the impulse will be roughly in the direction away from the racket and it avoids sign problems to take this into account.) The other unit vector, $\mathbf{j}$, is perpendicular to $\mathbf{i}$ as shown. The momentum (in N s) before collision is $-0.06 \times 10\mathbf{i}$ and that after collision is

$$0.06 \times (18\cos 25\mathbf{i} + 18\sin 25\mathbf{j})$$

The impulse (in N s) is therefore

$$0.06 \times (18\cos 25\mathbf{i} + 18\sin 25\mathbf{j}) + 0.06 \times 10\mathbf{i} = 1.58\mathbf{i} + 0.46\mathbf{j}$$

and has magnitude

$$\sqrt{1.58^2 + 0.46^2} \approx 1.65 \text{ N s}$$

acting at an angle of

$$\arctan\left(\frac{0.46}{1.58}\right) = 16.2° \text{ to the original line.}$$

Exercise 5C

1. A particle of mass 0.2 kg moving with velocity $(2\mathbf{i} + 5\mathbf{j})$ m s^{-1} is struck so that its velocity becomes $(5\mathbf{i} + \mathbf{j})$ m s^{-1}. Find the impulse applied to the particle.

2. An impulse $(5\mathbf{i} + 7\mathbf{j})$ N s is applied to a particle of mass 0.5 kg moving with velocity $(3\mathbf{i} + 11\mathbf{j})$ m s^{-1}. Find the velocity of the particle immediately after the impulse is applied.

3. A cricket ball of mass 0.15 kg is moving horizontally along the line of the wickets with speed 20 m s^{-1} when it is struck by the batsman so that immediately afterwards it moves towards square leg (perpendicular to the line of the wickets) with speed 30 m s^{-1}.

    Find the magnitude and direction of the impulse applied by the batsman.

4.

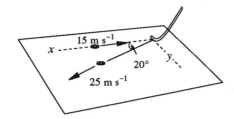

The diagram shows an ice hockey puck, of mass 0.20 kg, moving with speed 15 m s^{-1} and just about to be struck by a hockey stick. After being struck the puck moves in the direction shown with a velocity of 25 m s^{-1}. Find the magnitude and direction of the impulse due to the hockey stick.

5.

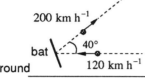

The diagram shows a baseball, of mass 0.15 kg, travelling with a horizontal speed of 120 km h^{-1} just before being struck by the bat. Just after the impact the velocity of the ball is 200 km h^{-1} in the direction 40° above the horizontal as shown. Determine, in N s, the horizontal and vertical components of the impulse acting on the ball.

6.

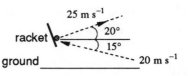

The tennis player strikes the ball with the racket while the ball is still rising as shown in the diagram. The speeds of the ball before and after impact are 20 m s^{-1} and 25 m s^{-1} and the directions are shown in the figure. Given that the mass of the ball is 0.06 kg, find the horizontal and vertical components of the impulse on the ball.

5.6   Interacting particles

The next step is to see how to tackle problems involving connected and colliding particles when motion is not along a line.

In general, you may assume, as shown in the diagram, that you have two particles A and B (modelling finite bodies such as cars or snooker balls) in contact instantaneously so that B exerts an impulse **I** on A and therefore, by Newton's third law, A exerts an impulse – **I** on B. It is also assumed that at the instant of interaction (collision) there are other external impulses **J** and **K** acting on A and B respectively.

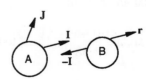

Therefore

> change of linear momentum of A = **J** + **I**

> change of linear momentum of B = **K** − **I**

Adding these gives

> total change of linear momentum of A and B = **J** + **K**

that is, the total external impulse acting on the bodies.

This can be generalised to cover any number of particles giving the most general form of the impulse–momentum principle.

In any interaction between any number of particles the total change in linear momentum of the system is equal to the total external impulse acting on it.

This simplifies when there are no external impulses (i.e. forces) to the **principle of conservation of momentum** .

In any interaction between particles in which the total external (applied) force, and therefore impulse, is zero then the total linear momentum is conserved.

Example

Two particles A and B of mass m and $2m$, are at rest on a smooth horizontal table and are attached one to each end of an inextensible string which is just taut. An impulse of magnitude J is applied to B at an angle α to the line AB produced.

Determine the motion immediately after the impulse has been applied.

Solution

The initial motion of particle A will be along the line of the string and its speed v will be equal to the component of the velocity of B along the string. Applying the impulse–momentum principle along the string gives

$$3mv = J \cos \alpha$$

so that
$$v = \frac{J \cos \alpha}{3m}$$

Particle A will have no initial velocity perpendicular to the string. Applying the impulse–momentum principle perpendicular to the string gives the speed u of B to be such that $2mu = J \sin \alpha$; so

$$u = \frac{J \sin \alpha}{2m}$$

The subsequent motion of the particles is rather complicated and requires the use of the idea of the centre of mass. This problem is examined again when considering the centre of mass in Chapter 7.

Example

Car A of mass 1100 kg travelling north at 45 km h^{-1} collides with
car B of mass 1400 kg travelling west at 30 km h^{-1} as shown in the
diagram. The two cars become entangled and move together as
one after the crash. Find the magnitude of their common velocity
and the angle between the subsequent direction and the north.

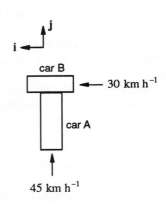

Solution

There are no external impulses and therefore the principle of
conservation of linear momentum applies.

Unit vectors **i** and **j** are chosen in the westerly and northerly
directions respectively.

Car A has linear momentum 49 500**j** and car B has linear
momentum 42 000**i**. (The units of momentum have not been
specified in this case; multiplying by $\dfrac{5}{18}$ to convert from km h^{-1}
to m s^{-1} would give the linear momentum in N s but you do not
need to change units if you take the units of the combined velocity
to be in km h^{-1}.)

Denoting the common velocity by **v** km h^{-1}, the principle of
conservation of linear momentum gives

$$2500\mathbf{v} = 42\,000\mathbf{i} + 49\,500\mathbf{j}$$

The common velocity is therefore $(16.8\mathbf{i} + 19.8\mathbf{j})$ km h^{-1}, and is
of magnitude 25.97 km h^{-1} at an angle 40.3° to the northerly
direction.

Example

The diagram opposite shows an inextensible string of length $2a$,
lying on a smooth horizontal table, carrying particles of mass $5m$ at
its end points and a particle of mass $15m$ at its midpoint. Initially
the system is as shown in the diagram with the strings each making
an angle α with the bisector of the angle between them where

$\cos\alpha = \dfrac{3}{5}$. An impulse of magnitude $31mV$ is then applied to the

heaviest particle along the bisector of the angle and in the sense
which will cause the particles to move immediately. Find the
velocities of the particles immediately after impact.

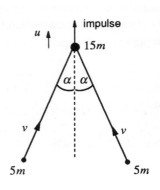

Solution

The first step in problems like this is to picture what happens and
choose variables appropriately. Since the blow is along the

bisector, it follows by symmetry that both of the lighter particles will have the same velocity v and that it will be along the string, and that the heaviest particle will move in the direction of the impulse with speed u.

The impulse–momentum principle can be applied to the whole system to give

$$15mu + 5mv\cos\alpha + 5mv\cos\alpha = 15mu + 6mv = 31mV$$

i.e. $\qquad 15u + 6v = 31V$

This gives only one equation and you have two unknowns and will need a second condition. The only dynamical principle possible has been applied without bringing in new variables (e.g. the impulsive tension) so a kinematic condition has to be used. This is provided by noticing that the string being inextensible means that the velocity components along the string at the ends and middle must be the same

i.e. $\qquad u\cos\alpha = v$

giving $\qquad 3u = 5v$

Solving the two equations gives

$$v = V \quad \text{and} \quad u = \frac{5V}{3}$$

[Note that if symmetry was not used, then you would have had to introduce three more variables, namely the two components of the velocities of the lighter particles perpendicular to the string, and the component of the velocity of the heaviest particle perpendicular to the impulse.

Since there is no impulse perpendicular to the string at the ends, applying the impulse–momentum principle perpendicular to the string at its end points, shows that the components of velocity perpendicular to the string are zero. Applying the impulse–momentum principle perpendicular to the impulse, for the whole system, gives that there is no velocity perpendicular to the impulse.

You would also have had to assume that the velocity components along the string were different and the kinematic condition about the velocities at the ends would then have shown the components along the string to be the same. Using symmetry therefore avoids a great deal of extra work!]

Exercise 5D

1. Two particles of mass 0.2 kg and 0.3 kg moving with velocities $(2\mathbf{i}+5\mathbf{j})$ m s^{-1} and $(3\mathbf{i}-3\mathbf{j})$ m s^{-1} respectively, collide and move as one particle. Find the velocity of this composite particle immediately after the collision.

2. A boy standing on ice and of mass 35 kg catches a ball which, when it reaches him, is moving with a speed of 4 m s^{-1} at an angle of 60° above the horizontal. Given that the ball is of mass 1 kg, find the speed with which the boy moves horizontally.

3.

   The diagram shows an old cannon of mass 2000 kg. The cannon fires a cannon ball of mass 8 kg with an initial velocity of 400 m s^{-1} at an angle of 60° to the horizontal. The cannon is on a horizontal surface and free to move horizontally. Find the speed with which the cannon recoils.

4. Car A moving eastwards and a similar car B moving northwards, collide at a crossroads and get entangled so that they move together after collision. The tangle of cars moves in a direction 57.3° east of north. Both drivers claim they were moving at 30 mph before the collision. Are these claims likely to be correct?

5. In Question 4, skid marks suggest that, after collision, the two cars started moving off with speed 25.6 mph. What were the speeds of the two cars immediately before collision?

6.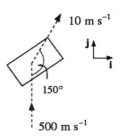

   The diagram shows a bullet of mass 0.05 kg, moving with speed 500 m s^{-1}, just about to enter a wooden block of mass 3 kg moving with speed 10 m s^{-1} at an angle of 150° to the direction of motion of the bullet. Find, using the unit vectors shown, the velocity of the block and bullet immediately after the bullet has stopped moving relative to the block.

7. Three particles A, B, C of masses $3m$, $2m$ and m respectively, lie on a smooth horizontal plane. Particles A and B are joined by a light inelastic string as are particles B and C. Initially the particles are at rest with the strings straight and taut and the angle ABC equal to 135°. An impulse of magnitude J is applied to C along the line BC. Find the initial speed of C.

   (Initially, A will move along AB and C will move along BC. B will have two components of velocity, one along and one perpendicular to AB. The component along AB will be the same as the speed of A and the other component has to be chosen so that the component of the velocity of B along BC will be the same as the speed of C. The impulse–momentum principle should be applied to the whole system along and perpendicular to BC.)

5.7   Problems involving bouncing

In many collision situations, such as snooker balls hitting each other or a ball hitting a wall, the colliding bodies do not stick together, but bounce apart.

There are effectively two different situations, one where one body remains fixed (e.g. ball hitting a wall) and the other where both bodies can move (e.g. balls on a snooker table).

One body fixed

Normally you do not know the impulse applied by a wall or any fixed body and have no theoretical method of finding the speed after collision.

In fact to do this, you will have to use observation to carry out some simple experiments, for example, dropping a ball on a floor.

Activity 3

Drop a ball from a height h on to a floor and measure, as carefully as you can, the height h' to which it bounces. Applying the formula $v^2 = u^2 + 2as$ to the downwards motion gives the speed u with which the ball reaches the floor as $\sqrt{2gh}$ and the speed v with which it leaves as $\sqrt{2gh'}$. You can now estimate the ratio $\dfrac{u}{v}$ from your experiments.

Repeat with different heights and then with different balls. You should find that for each ball, the ratio is roughly constant.

This is effectively Newton's experimental law, which states

$$\boxed{\frac{\text{speed after collision}}{\text{speed before collision}} = \text{constant}}$$

The constant is normally denoted by e and is called the **coefficient of restitution**. It satisfies the conditions $0 \le e \le 1$. The lower limit refers to a perfectly plastic, or inelastic collision, where the ball sticks to the floor. The upper limit corresponds to a perfectly elastic collision.

If the speed before collision is v, then the law gives the speed after collision as ev and, for a ball of mass m, there is an energy loss of $\frac{1}{2}mv^2(1-e^2)$. There is therefore an energy loss in any collision for $e < 1$; some of the energy loss is dissipated as heat (e.g. a squash ball gets very warm during a game of squash).

What other examples illustrate energy loss due to heat dissipation?

Your experiments have only involved a ball hitting a plane at right angles, but Newton's experimental law is effectively valid for collisions at an angle with a plane. It takes the slightly more general form

$$\boxed{\frac{\text{normal speed after collision}}{\text{normal speed before collision}} = e}$$

The effect of the collision against a rigid surface is to reverse the direction of motion. It is useful, particularly when you come to look at collisions involving two moving bodies, to rewrite Newton's law in a slightly different form which takes care of the reversal of direction.

The velocity component after collision in a direction normal to the surface is given by $-e \times$ velocity component in the same direction before collision.

For oblique collisions with a plane, Newton's law has to be supplemented by some condition parallel to the plane and you can only consider smooth planes. This means that there can be no impulse parallel to the plane and therefore no change in linear momentum.

Example

A ball is dropped vertically downwards on to a smooth plane from a height of 1.2 m. Given that the coefficient of restitution between the ball and plane is 0.4 find (taking $g = 9.8 \text{ m s}^{-2}$)

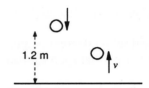

(a)   the height to which the ball first bounces,

(b)   the time taken from dropping the ball to it reaching the top of its first bounce.

Solution

The formula $v^2 = u^2 + 2gh$ gives the speed, in m s^{-1}, of the ball when it first reaches the plane as

$$\sqrt{2 \times 9.8 \times 1.2} = 4.85$$

The speed of rebound is, from Newton's experimental law,

$$-0.4 \times 4.85 = -1.94 \quad \text{(the negative sign indicating that the ball is now travelling upwards)}$$

Applying $v^2 = u^2 + 2gh$ again gives the height, in m, to which the ball rises as

$$\frac{(-1.94)^2}{2 \times 9.8} = 0.19$$

Applying the formula $v = u + gt$ gives the time, in seconds, of the downwards motion as

$$\frac{4.85}{9.8} = 0.49$$

Applying the formula to the upwards motion gives the time to the top of the bounce as

$$\frac{1.94}{9.8} = 0.20$$

The total time is therefore 0.69 s.

Example

A ball is projected obliquely so that it hits a smooth floor at an angle of 30° to the horizontal and with a speed of 12 m s^{-1}. Given that the coefficient of restitution is $\frac{1}{3}$, find the magnitude and direction of the velocity of rebound.

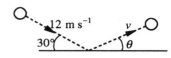

Solution

The vertical speed, in m s^{-1}, of the ball immediately before impact is $12\sin 30° = 6$, and so, by Newton's experimental law, the normal speed of rebound is 2 m s^{-1}.

The horizontal speed **before** collision is

$$12\cos 30° = 5\sqrt{3} \text{ m s}^{-1}$$

Since the plane is smooth, this is unchanged by the collision.

The speed **after** collision is therefore

$$v = \sqrt{75+4} = 8.89 \text{ m s}^{-1}$$

This velocity is at an angle

$$\theta = \arctan\left(\frac{2}{5\sqrt{3}}\right) = 13° \text{ to the horizontal.}$$

Example

A ball is projected horizontally from a point above a smooth floor so that it bounces as shown. The coefficient of restitution is given as 0.75. Given that the length of the first bounce is observed to be 0.4 m, find the length of the second bounce.

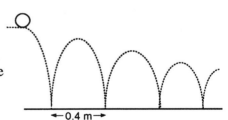

Solution

If the vertical component of velocity of the ball at the start of a bounce is v, then the time taken to reach the top of the bounce can be shown to be $\frac{v}{g}$ and the total time for the bounce is twice this.

Since the floor is smooth, the horizontal component of velocity, u, is unchanged and the length of the bounce is $u \times$ time of flight, and therefore proportional to the vertical component of velocity, v, at the start of the bounce. But v decreases by a factor $e = 0.75$ at each bounce, so the length of the second bounce is
$$0.75 \times 4 = 0.3 \text{ m}$$

Why is the time to reach the top of the bounce $\frac{v}{g}$?

Exercise 5E

(In numerical questions take $g = 9.8 \text{ m s}^{-2}$)

Questions 1 to 4 refer to a small ball dropped from rest at a height h on to a smooth plane, the coefficient of restitution being e and h_1 being the height reached after the first bounce.

1. $h = 4$ m, $e = 0.2$. Find h_1.

2. $h = 4$ m, $h_1 = 1$ m. Find e.

3. $h = 1$ m, $e = \frac{1}{3}$. Find the total distance travelled by the ball before it comes to rest.

4. $h = 1.8$ m. $e = 0.2$. Given that the ball is of mass 0.2 kg, find the magnitude of the impulse on the ball at the first bounce.

5. A tennis ball is projected vertically downwards from a height of 1.4 m on to a tennis court. Given that the coefficient of restitution is 0.6, find the speed of projection in order that the ball just returns to the point of projection after bouncing once.

6. A ball is thrown against a smooth vertical wall and immediately before impact it is moving in a vertical plane perpendicular to the wall with speed 10 m s^{-1} at an angle of 30° to the horizontal. Given that the coefficient of restitution is 0.8, find the magnitude and direction of the ball's velocity immediately after impact.

7. A ball is projected horizontally from a point at a height of 0.8 m above a smooth plane. The height and length of its first bounce are 0.6 m and 0.4 m respectively. Find the coefficient of restitution and the height and length of the second bounce.

8. A ball is projected from a point above a smooth horizontal plane with speed 0.2 m s^{-1}. The ball first hits the floor at a point whose horizontal displacement from the point of projection is 0.4 m and the length of its first bounce is 0.6 m. Find the coefficient of restitution and the height of the first bounce.

9. A small smooth ball is dropped vertically downwards to strike a smooth fixed plane inclined at an angle a to the horizontal. The ball rebounds horizontally. Given that the coefficient of restitution is 0.6, find the angle α.

10. A small smooth sphere is dropped from a height h on to a smooth plane inclined at an angle of 15° to the horizontal. The ball strikes the plane at a point A on the plane and bounces off. Given that the coefficient of restitution is 0.8, find the horizontal displacement of the ball from A when it is next level with A.

5.8   Both bodies free to move

It is convenient to consider separately the two categories: **direct collisions** where, for example, spheres are moving along the line of centres when they collide; and **oblique collisions** when this is not the case.

It is also convenient to assume that all the colliding bodies are smooth. This means that there is no impulse along the colliding surfaces, so that momentum is unchanged in that direction for each body and therefore the velocity perpendicular to the line of centres for each sphere remains constant.

When both bodies can move, Newton's experimental law takes a slightly more general form in that it is the relative velocity component after collision in a normal direction that is equal to $-e \times$ relative velocity component before collision in the same direction. This condition is often stated as

> velocity of separation $= -e \times$ velocity of approach

In the diagram, two bodies which collide are moving with velocity components in the direction of their common normal of u_1 and u_2 before collision, and the corresponding components after collision are v_1 and v_2. Then Newton's experimental law gives

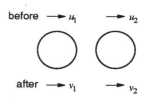

$$v_2 - v_1 = -e(u_2 - u_1)$$

In applying the above equation it is very important to pick a reference direction and calculate all the components in that direction. If you do this systematically you will avoid one of the biggest sources of error.

Direct collisions

In direct collisions the motion is all in one line and only two conditions have to be applied, namely

(1) Newton's experimental law,

(2) conservation of linear momentum.

These give two equations. Practically all direct collision problems are of the type where two velocity components are given and the other two have to be found, and there are sufficient equations to do this.

Example

A small smooth sphere of mass 0.1 kg moving with a speed of 20 m s^{-1} on a horizontal plane catches up and collides with a smooth sphere of the same radius, but of mass 0.9 kg and moving with a speed of 5 m s^{-1}. The coefficient of restitution is $\frac{1}{3}$. Find the speeds of the spheres immediately after collision and determine the loss in kinetic energy.

Solution

The most important step is to draw diagrams as shown opposite, to illustrate the motion before and after collision and to mark in a reference direction. There is no real point in trying to guess the directions of motion after collision and it is best to take all unknowns in the reference direction, since it avoids problems with signs.

In the diagram the spheres after collision have velocities v_1 m s^{-1} and v_2 m s^{-1} to the right.

The component of the linear momentum, in N s, to the right before collision is

$$0.9 \times 5 + 0.1 \times 20 = 6.5$$

and after collision it is

$$0.1v_1 + 0.9v_2$$

Conservation of linear momentum gives

$$6.5 = 0.1v_1 + 0.9v_2$$

Newton's experimental law gives

$$v_2 - v_1 = -\frac{1}{3}(5 - 20) = 5$$

Solving these gives

$$v_1 = 2, \; v_2 = 7$$

The kinetic energy before collision is

$$\frac{1}{2}\left(0.1 \times 20^2 + 0.9 \times 5^2\right) = 31.25 \text{ J}$$

the kinetic energy after collision is

$$\frac{1}{2}\left(0.1 \times 2^2 + 0.9 \times 7^2\right) = 22.25 \text{ J}$$

There is therefore a loss of kinetic energy in this collision of 9 J.

Example

Two small smooth spheres of equal radius but of mass 0.3 kg and 0.1 kg are moving directly towards each other with speeds of 4 m s^{-1} and 6 m s^{-1} respectively. The coefficient of restitution is 0.5. Find their speeds after collision.

Solution

A diagram similar to that in the previous example is used.

The component of the linear momentum, in N s, to the right before collision is

$$0.3 \times 4 - 0.1 \times 6 = 0.6$$

and after collision it is

$$0.3v_1 + 0.1v_2$$

Conservation of linear momentum gives

$$0.3 \times 4 - 0.1 \times 6 = 0.6 = 0.3v_1 + 0.1v_2$$

Newton's experimental law gives

$$v_2 - v_1 = -0.5(-6 - 4) = 5$$

Solving gives

$$v_1 = 0.25, \ v_2 = 5.25$$

Energy change

In the first example you found that there was an energy loss of 9 J. It turns out that for $e < 1$ there will be, as for collision with a rigid surface, an energy loss. You can now prove this by determining a general formula for energy change. In practice it is actually better to carry out any calculation of energy change directly rather than to try to remember a relatively complicated formula.

Look at a generalisation of the situation in the previous example, of two bodies with velocity components u_1 and u_2 before collision and v_1 and v_2 after collision. Assume that the corresponding masses are m_1 and m_2. The kinetic energies before and after collision are

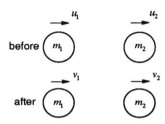

$$\frac{1}{2}\left(m_1 u_1^2 + m_2 u_2^2\right) \ \text{ and } \ \frac{1}{2}\left(m_1 v_1^2 + m_2 v_2^2\right)$$

You can prove by expanding out both sides that

$$\left(m_1 + m_2\right)\left(m_1 u_1^2 + m_2 u_2^2\right) = \left(m_1 u_1 + m_2 u_2\right)^2 + m_1 m_2 \left(u_1 - u_2\right)^2$$

for all u_1, u_2, m_1 and m_2. The same is therefore true for u_1, u_2 replaced by v_1, v_2.

That is

$$\left(m_1 + m_2\right)\left(m_1 v_1^2 + m_2 v_2^2\right) = \left(m_1 v_1 + m_2 v_2\right)^2 + m_1 m_2 \left(v_1 - v_2\right)^2$$

In the first equation, the left hand side is $2\left(m_1 + m_2\right)$ times the kinetic energy before collision and in the second equation the left hand side is $2\left(m_1 + m_2\right)$ times the kinetic energy after collision.

The first term on the right hand sides of both equations is the linear momentum squared and, as this is unchanged by the collision, you will get, on subtracting the equations,

$$2\left(m_1 + m_2\right) \text{ (kinetic energy before } - \text{ kinetic energy after)}$$
$$= m_1 m_2 \left(\left(u_1 - u_2\right)^2 - \left(v_1 - v_2\right)^2\right)$$

Using Newton's experimental law gives

$$v_1 - v_2 = -e(u_1 - u_2)$$

so that

kinetic energy before – kinetic energy after

$$= \frac{m_1 m_2}{2(m_1 + m_2)}\left((1 - e^2)(u_1 - u_2)^2\right)$$

This formula shows that energy is lost for $e < 1$.

Check that this formula gives the same result for kinetic energy change as obtained directly in the last example.

Exercise 5F

In Questions 1 to 3, a smooth sphere of mass m_1 kg moving with speed u_1 m s^{-1} overtakes and collides directly with a smooth sphere of mass m_2 kg moving with speed u_2 m s^{-1} in the same direction. The velocity components after impact and measured in the original direction of motion are denoted by v_1 m s^{-1} and v_2 m s^{-1}, respectively.

1. $m_1 = 3, m_2 = 1, u_1 = 6, u_2 = 1, e = 0.4$
    Find v_1 and v_2.

2. $m_1 = 2, m_2 = 3, u_1 = 6, u_2 = 2, v_1 = 3$
    Find e and v_2.

3. $m_2 = 10, u_1 = 9, u_2 = 2, v_1 = 2, v_2 = 5$
    Find e and m_1.

In Questions 4 to 6, a smooth sphere of mass m_1 kg moving with speed u_1 m s^{-1} collides directly with a smooth sphere of mass m_2 kg moving with speed u_2 m s^{-1} in the opposite direction. The velocity components after impact and measured in the direction of motion of the first sphere are denoted by v_1 m s^{-1} and v_2 m s^{-1}, respectively.

4. $m_1 = 4, m_2 = 1, u_1 = 3, u_2 = 1, e = 0.5$
    Find v_1 and v_2.

5. $m_1 = 4, u_1 = 3, u_2 = 5, v_1 = 2, e = 0.2$
    Find m_2 and v_2.

6. $m_2 = 12, u_1 = 10, u_2 = 2, v_1 = 2, v_2 = 4$
    Find e and m_1.

7. A smooth sphere of mass 3 kg collides directly with a smooth sphere of mass 5 kg which is at rest. Find the condition to be satisfied by e in order that the spheres move in opposite directions after collision.

8. An 18 tonne railway wagon moving at a speed of 0.4 m s^{-1} to the right collides with a 34 tonne wagon at rest. Immediately after the impact the second wagon moves off with speed 0.2 m s^{-1} to the right. Find the coefficient of restitution.

*9. A small smooth sphere of mass 0.2 kg dropped from a height of 16 cm on to a smooth rigid plate fixed on to a horizontal plane, first bounces to a height of 9 cm. The plate is then released from the plane and a foam rubber mat placed under it. The ball when dropped again, now first rises to a height of 4 cm. Find the coefficient of restitution and, assuming the same coefficient of restitution when the plate is on the mat, find the mass of the plate.

10. Identical cars A, B and C are in a straight line with their brakes off. Car A is pushed towards the others so that it hits car B with speed 2 m s^{-1}. Given that the coefficient of restitution between any two cars is 0.75, find the speeds of the cars after all collisions have finished.

5.9   Oblique collisions

Oblique collisions are those when, for example, balls are not all moving along the line of the centres.

The diagram shows two balls about to collide. Newton's experimental law only holds along the common perpendicular at contact and it is useful to take, as reference directions, this line and one perpendicular to it, the common normal. For two spheres, the common normal is the line of centres. The balls are moving at angles θ and ϕ to the line of centres with speeds V and U and have masses m and m' respectively.

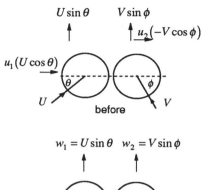

The first thing to do is to find the components of velocity along and perpendicular to the line of centres. The ones parallel are $U\cos\theta$ and $-V\cos\phi$; these are denoted by u_1 and u_2 and the corresponding ones after collision by v_1 and v_2. The initial components of velocity perpendicular to the line of centres are

$$U\sin\theta \quad \text{and} \quad V\sin\phi$$

and are denoted by w_1 and w_2.

Assuming that the balls are smooth means that there is no impulse perpendicular to the line of centres and therefore the linear momentum of each, and equivalently the velocity, is unchanged in this direction. This is illustrated in the diagram and it is good practice to show, in your diagram, that the velocities perpendicular to the line of centres are unchanged.

The problem, perpendicular to the line of centres, is now completed and the problem, along the line of centres, is exactly as for direct collisions.

The simplest type of problems are those where the components along and perpendicular to the line of centres are given but, in many practical problems, it is speeds and directions that are given and it is necessary to do some resolving before starting.

Example

A small smooth sphere of mass 0.4 kg is moving on a horizontal plane with velocity $(4\mathbf{i}+4\mathbf{j})$ m s^{-1} when it collides with a sphere of equal radius but of mass 0.1 kg and moving with velocity $(\mathbf{i}+3\mathbf{j})$ m s^{-1}. Given that the line of centres at collision is parallel to $\mathbf{i}$ and that the coefficient of restitution is 0.6, find the velocities immediately after collision.

Solution

The velocity components parallel to $\mathbf{j}$ are unchanged; this is shown in the diagram. The velocity components parallel to $\mathbf{i}$ after collision are denoted by

$$v_1 \text{ m s}^{-1} \text{ and } v_2 \text{ m s}^{-1}$$

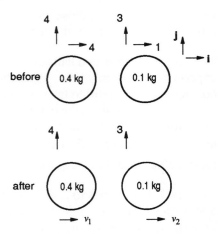

Conservation of linear momentum parallel to $\mathbf{i}$ gives

$$4v_1 + v_2 = 17$$

Newton's experimental law gives

$$v_2 - v_1 = 1.8$$

Solving these gives $v_1 = 3.04$, $v_2 = 4.84$

Now put together the velocity in vector form with the $\mathbf{j}$ components unchanged, so that the velocities after collision are

$$(3.04\mathbf{i} + 4\mathbf{j}) \text{ m s}^{-1} \text{ and } (4.84\mathbf{i} + 3\mathbf{j}) \text{ m s}^{-1}$$

Example

A small smooth sphere of mass 0.5 kg and moving with a speed of 7 m s^{-1}, collides obliquely with a similar stationary sphere of mass 0.1 kg which is at rest. Immediately before collision the direction of motion of the moving sphere makes an angle of 20° with the line of centres at collision, and $e = 0.5$.

Find the angle through which the direction of motion of the sphere is turned by the collision.

Solution

The velocity components perpendicular to the line of centres are unchanged and, in particular, the stationary sphere will move along the line of centres. This is shown in the diagram. The velocity components parallel to the line of centres after collision are denoted by v_1 m s^{-1} and v_2 m s^{-1}. The initial velocity component parallel to the line of centres is $5\cos 20°$ m s^{-1} and the conservation of linear momentum gives

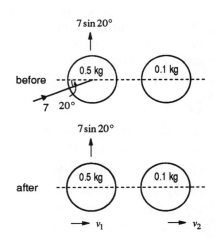

$$5v_1 + v_2 = 35\cos 20°$$

Newton's experimental law gives

$$v_2 - v_1 = 3.5\cos 20°$$

Solving these gives

$$v_1 = \frac{31.5\cos 20°}{6}$$

The velocity component perpendicular to the line of centres is $7\sin 20°$ m s^{-1} and therefore the tangent of the angle between the direction of motion and the line of centres is given by

$$\frac{42\tan 20°}{31.5} = \frac{4\tan 20°}{3}$$

This makes the new angle $25.9°$ and the deflection is $5.9°$.

Occasionally, in collision problems of this type, it is required to find the original direction of motion so that a particular deflection is obtained, e.g. a maximum deflection. In such cases it is necessary to find the solution when the angle between the direction of motion and the line of centres has a general value θ. The angle ϕ between the line of centres and the direction after collision will be of the form $c\tan\theta$ (as it is above) and use of the formula

$$\tan(\phi - \theta) = \frac{\tan\phi - \tan\theta}{1 + \tan\theta\tan\phi}$$

will give the deflection in terms of $\tan\theta$.

Exercise 5G

1. A small smooth sphere of mass 0.2 kg is moving on a horizontal plane with velocity $(6\mathbf{i}+5\mathbf{j})$ m s^{-1} when it collides with a sphere of equal radius but of mass 0.3 kg and moving with velocity $(2\mathbf{i}+7\mathbf{j})$ m s^{-1}. Given that the line of centres at collision is parallel to $\mathbf{i}$ and that the coefficient of restitution is 0.25, find the velocities immediately after collision.

2. A smooth snooker ball collides directly with an identical one. Show that, if the balls were perfectly elastic, they would move in perpendicular directions after collision.

3. A small smooth sphere of mass 0.9 kg and moving with speed of 4 m s^{-1} collides obliquely with a similar sphere of mass 0.3 kg and which is at rest. The direction of motion makes an angle of $25°$ with the line of centres at collision and $e = 0.75$.

   Find the angle through which the direction of motion of the sphere is turned by the collision.

4. A small smooth sphere moving with speed v on a smooth horizontal plane collides with an identical stationary sphere. The first sphere is moving, at the instant of impact, at an angle θ to the line of centres.

   Find the value of θ such that, immediately after impact, the component of the velocity of the second sphere perpendicular to the original direction of motion of the first is a maximum. Find this maximum value.

5. For the spheres in Question 4 and taking $e = \frac{1}{3}$, find, as the angle θ varies, the maximum angle through which the path of the first sphere can be turned.

6. A perfectly elastic smooth sphere of mass $2m$ moving on a horizontal plane collides with a similar stationary sphere but of mass m. Find, as the direction of motion of the moving sphere is varied, the maximum angle through which the path of that sphere can be deflected.

7. A small smooth ball of mass 0.5 kg falls on to a smooth plane, of mass 2 kg and inclined at an angle α to the horizontal and bounces horizontally. Given that the inclined plane can move freely horizontally and that the coefficient of restitution is 0.6, find α.

8.

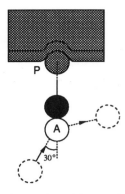

The diagram shows the white cue ball, A, about to strike the stationary black ball so that it enters the pocket P. Both balls have the same mass and diameter; the coefficient of restitution is 0.9. The angle between the cue ball and the line of centres at impact is 30°. Find the angle between the line of centres and the direction of motion of the cue ball immediately after impact.

9.

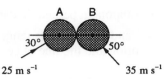

The diagram shows two identical smooth spheres colliding obliquely. The coefficient of restitution for collision between the spheres is 0.7. Find the speed of sphere A immediately after collision and the angle between its direction of motion and the line of centres.

10.

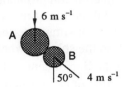

The diagram shows a ball of mass 2 kg falling vertically with a speed of 6 m s^{-1} when it is hit by a ball of mass 1 kg travelling along the line of centres at collision with a speed of 4 m s^{-1}. Given that the line of centres makes an angle of 50° with the vertical and that the coefficient of restitution is 0.6, find, assuming both balls are smooth, the speed of the heavier ball immediately after collision.

*5.10 Three-dimensional vector problems

Problems may be solved using an entirely vector approach. The key point to remember is that the velocities only change along the line of centres, so the first step is to find the components of the velocities along the line of centres. If the velocity is denoted by **v** and the **unit vector** along the line of centres is **n**, then that part of the velocity perpendicular to the line of centres is

$$\mathbf{v} - (\mathbf{v}.\mathbf{n})\mathbf{n}$$

This does not change for either sphere. The quantities (**v**.**n**) are the components parallel to **n** and the values after collision can be found as the solution to a direct collision problem. Having done this, the terms (**v**.**n**) **n** have to be added to the velocity component perpendicular to the line of centres, in order to complete the solution.

Example

A smooth sphere of mass 0.9 kg moving with velocity $(14\mathbf{i} + 12\mathbf{j} + 7\mathbf{k})$ m s^{-1} collides with a similar sphere of mass 0.2 kg and moving with velocity $(-7\mathbf{i} - 4\mathbf{j} - 9\mathbf{k})$ m s^{-1}. The line of centres is parallel to the vector $(2\mathbf{i} + \mathbf{j} + 2\mathbf{k})$ and the coefficient of restitution is 0.1. Find the velocities immediately after collision.

Solution

The first step is to work out the unit vector along the line of centres. This is

$$\mathbf{n} = \frac{(2\mathbf{i} + \mathbf{j} + 2\mathbf{k})}{3}$$

and the components of the initial velocities along it are 18 m s^{-1} and -12 m s^{-1}. Therefore the problem along the line of centres is that of the direct collision of two spheres moving directly towards each other with speeds of 18 m s^{-1} and 12 m s^{-1} respectively. This is shown in the diagram where v_1 m s^{-1} and v_2 m s^{-1} denote the velocity components parallel to the line of centres after collision.

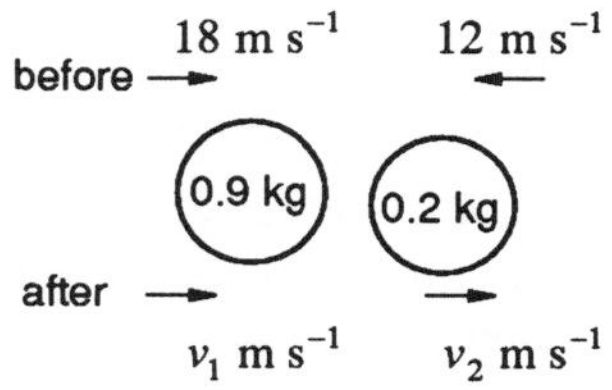

Conservation of linear momentum gives

$$9v_1 + 2v_2 = 138$$

Newton's experimental law gives

$$v_2 - v_1 = 3$$

Solving these gives

$$v_1 = 12, \; v_2 = 15$$

In order to complete the solution you will need to find the component of velocity perpendicular to the line of centres. To do this, subtract $18\mathbf{n}$ and $-12\mathbf{n}$, i.e. $6(2\mathbf{i} + \mathbf{j} + 2\mathbf{k})$ and $-4(2\mathbf{i} + \mathbf{j} + 2\mathbf{k})$ respectively from the original velocities.

This gives

$$2\mathbf{i} + 6\mathbf{j} - 5\mathbf{k} \;\; \text{and} \;\; \mathbf{i} - \mathbf{k}.$$

Now add $v_1\mathbf{n}$ and $v_2\mathbf{n}$ to these, giving the velocities immediately after collision as $(10\mathbf{i} + 10\mathbf{j} + 3\mathbf{k})$ m s^{-1} and $(11\mathbf{i} + 5\mathbf{j} + 9\mathbf{k})$ m s^{-1}.

5.11 Miscellaneous Exercises

1. Two uniform smooth spheres, A of mass 0.03 kg and B of mass 0.1 kg, have equal radii and are moving directly towards each other with speeds of 7 m s^{-1} and 4 m s^{-1} respectively. The spheres collide directly and B is reduced to rest by the impact. State the magnitude of the impulse experienced by B. Find the speed of A after impact, the coefficient of restitution between the spheres and the loss of kinetic energy due to the impact. (AEB)

2. A particle of mass 0.2 kg is moving with velocity $(5\mathbf{i} + 7\mathbf{j})$ m s^{-1} when an impulse $\mathbf{J}$ is applied to it so that its velocity becomes $(8\mathbf{i} - 3\mathbf{j})$ m s^{-1}. Find $\mathbf{J}$ and the kinetic energy of the particle immediately after the impulse has been applied. (AEB)

3. Two small uniform smooth spheres A and B of equal size and of mass m and $4m$ respectively are moving directly towards each other with speeds $2u$ and $6u$ respectively. The coefficient of restitution between the spheres is $\frac{1}{2}$. Find the speed of B immediately after the spheres collide. (AEB)

4. A particle P of mass 0.5 kg moves on a smooth horizontal table with constant velocity $(11\mathbf{i} + 8\mathbf{j})$ m s^{-1}, where $\mathbf{i}$ and $\mathbf{j}$ are perpendicular unit vectors in the plane of the table. An impulse is then applied to the particle so that its velocity becomes $(15\mathbf{i} + 10\mathbf{j})$ m s^{-1}. Find this impulse in the form $a\mathbf{i} + b\mathbf{j}$ and show that the kinetic energy generated by the impulse is the scalar product of the impulse and one half the sum of the velocities of P before and after the impulse is applied. (AEB)

5. A particle P of mass 0.25 kg moves on a smooth horizontal table with constant velocity $(17\mathbf{i} + 6\mathbf{j})$ m s^{-1}, where $\mathbf{i}$ and $\mathbf{j}$ are perpendicular constant unit vectors in the plane of the table. An impulse is then applied to the particle so that its velocity becomes $(29\mathbf{i} + 22\mathbf{j})$ m s^{-1}. Find this impulse in the form $a\mathbf{i} + b\mathbf{j}$.

   Determine a unit vector $\mathbf{n}$ such that the component of the velocity of P along $\mathbf{n}$ is unchanged by the impulse. Obtain the magnitude of this component. (AEB)

6. A small smooth sphere A of mass $3m$ collides directly with a small smooth sphere B of mass m which is moving in the opposite direction. The speed of B immediately before collision is $2u$ and immediately after collision its direction of motion is reversed and its speed reduced to u.

The coefficient of restitution for collision between the spheres is $\frac{1}{4}$. Find the speed of A immediately before collision and the magnitude of the impulse on B.

(AEB)

7. State the laws which determine the velocities of two uniform smooth spheres after impact.

A and B are two uniform smooth spheres with the same radius and with masses m and λm respectively. The spheres collide. Immediately before the impact the velocity of A makes an angle θ with the line of centres of the spheres and B is at rest. After the impact the velocity of A makes an angle of $(\theta + \phi)$ with the line of centres. Given that the coefficient of restitution between the spheres is e, show that

$$\tan(\theta + \phi) = \frac{(1 + \lambda)}{(1 - \lambda e)} \tan \theta$$

Hence, or otherwise, deduce that the final velocity of A is at right angles to its initial velocity when

$$\tan^2 \theta = \frac{e\lambda - 1}{\lambda + 1} \qquad \text{(AEB)}$$

8. The figure shows a horizontal rectangular billiard table ABCD with pockets at A, B C and D. A small uniform smooth billiard ball P is stationary at a point on the table whose distances from AD, BC and AB are $9a$, $16a$ and $12a$ respectively, where a is a constant . A second identical billiard ball Q is travelling with speed u on the table in a direction parallel to DA when it strikes ball P obliquely.

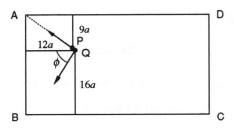

As a result of the collision ball P falls into the pocket at A and the direction of motion of ball Q is deflected through an angle ϕ. Given that P and Q are of equal mass and that the coefficient of restitution between the balls is e, show that

$$\tan \phi = \frac{6(e + 1)}{17 - 8e}$$

Given that ball Q falls into the pocket at B, find

(a) the coefficient of restitution between the balls,

(b) the angle between the directions of motion of P and Q immediately after the impact.

(AEB)

9. A small smooth uniform sphere A of mass m is at rest on a smooth horizontal table. A second smooth uniform sphere B, of the same radius, but of mass pm, moving with speed V, collides with A. At the instant of collision B is moving at an angle θ to the line of centres. The coefficient of restitution between the spheres is e. Find the components, along and perpendicular to the line of centres, of the velocities of the spheres immediately after impact.

Find also, in terms of e, the values of p such that the angle between the directions of motion of A and B after impact is

(a) $\tan^{-1}(2\tan\theta)$

(b) a right angle.

In the latter case find, in terms of m, V, e and θ the kinetic energy lost. (AEB)

10. The points B and C lie on a smooth rectangular table with $BC = a$. The line BC is perpendicular to an edge of the table with C being nearer to an edge than B. Small smooth uniform spheres P and Q, of equal radius but of mass m and $2m$ respectively, are placed at B and C respectively as shown in the figure.

The spheres remain at rest until a third smooth uniform sphere R, of equal radius but of mass $4m$, moving with speed $3u$ collides directly with P so that the latter moves along BC with speed $4u$. Find, in terms of u, the speed of R immediately after collision and the coefficient of restitution between the spheres R and P.

Given that the coefficient of restitution between spheres P and Q is $\frac{1}{8}$, find the speed of P immediately after colliding with Q.

Given also that sphere P drops off the table before colliding for a second time with R, find the maximum distance that the point C can be from the edge of the table.

(AEB)

11. Three small smooth spheres A, B and C, of equal radii and masses m, $2m$, and $3m$ respectively, are placed at rest with their centres in a straight line, l, on a smooth horizontal table with B between A and C. The sphere A is now projected along l towards B with speed $5u$. Given that, after the collision between A and B, B moves towards C with speed $3u$, find

(a) the magnitude and direction of the velocity of A after impact,

(b) the coefficient of restitution between A and B,

(c) the loss in kinetic energy due to the collision between A and B.

The sphere B now moves to collide with C and, as a result, C receives an impulse of magnitude $4mu$. Find the velocities of B and C after their collision and the coefficient of restitution between them. (AEB)

12. Two particles A and B, of masses m and M respectively, are connected by a light inextensible string of length $3a$. Initially A is held at rest alongside a small smooth pulley which is fixed at a height $2a$ above a horizontal table. The string is slack and passes over the pulley, which is vertically above the particle B on the table. The particle A is now released. Show that when B is jerked into motion both particles begin to move with speed u, where

$$u = \frac{m\sqrt{2ga}}{(M+m)}$$

[You should assume that the taut strings on each side of the pulley are vertical and that the length of string in contact with the pulley is negligible.]

Find, in terms of m, M and g, the tension in the string whilst both particles are moving.

Determine the value of $\dfrac{M}{m}$, which is such that when A is first instantaneously at rest, it has just reached the table.

For this value of $\dfrac{M}{m}$, briefly describe the next stage of the motion of the system up to the instant at which one of the particles next comes to instantaneous rest. (AEB)

13. A smooth uniform sphere A moving with speed u on a smooth horizontal plane collides with an identical sphere B at rest on the plane. The angle between the direction of motion of sphere A and the line of centres drawn from A to B is α immediately before collision, and $\theta + \alpha$ immediately after collision.

Given that the coefficient of restitution between the spheres is $\frac{1}{4}$ show that

$$\cot\theta = \frac{3}{5t} + \frac{8t}{5}$$

where $t = \tan\alpha$.

Find the maximum value of θ as α varies.

(AEB)

14. The figure shows a particle A of mass $10m$ on a smooth plane inclined at an angle θ to the horizontal, where $\sin\theta = 0.6$. The particle is attached to one end of a light inelastic string which passes over a smooth pulley P at the highest point of the plane. A particle B of mass $10m$ is attached to the other end of the string. Initially the system is held at rest with the string parallel to a line of greatest slope of the plane but not in contact with the plane and BP vertical, with B being at a distance d above an inelastic horizontal floor.

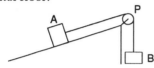

The system is released from rest so that B starts to fall. Find the acceleration of B and the tension in the string.

Determine,

(a) the further distance that A moves up the plane after B has struck the floor (you may assume that A does not reach the pulley),

(b) the time that B remains in contact with the floor,

(c) the speed with which B is jerked off the floor. (AEB)

15. Three particles A, B, C of mass m, $2m$ and $4m$ respectively are joined, with the strings taut, by two light inextensible strings AB and BC. The particles are initially at rest in a straight line on a smooth horizontal plane. An impulse of magnitude J is then applied to A in the sense from B to A. Find the initial speed of A.

The particles are then rearranged as shown in the figure and placed at rest on the smooth horizontal plane with the strings taut and with the angle between BC and AB produced equal to 60°.

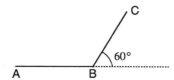

An impulse of magnitude J is again applied to A in the sense from B to A. Show that the initial speed of A is five times that of C and find the initial speed of A in terms of J and m. (Hint: the component of the initial velocity of B in the direction CB has to be equal to the speed of C.)

Find also, in terms of J, the magnitude of the impulse in AB. (AEB)

16.

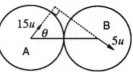

The figure shows the positions of two uniform smooth spheres A and B at the instant they collide. The spheres are of the same radius but of mass m and $2m$ respectively. Immediately before collision, A and B have speeds $15u$ and $5u$ in perpendicular directions, as shown in the figure. The line of centres makes an angle θ with the direction of motion of A, where

$\sin\theta = \dfrac{4}{5}$. Given that the coefficient of

restitution between the spheres is $\dfrac{1}{5}$

(a) show that the speed of B immediately after collision is $3u\sqrt{5}$, and find

(b) the impulse on B,

(c) the kinetic energy lost in the collision.

(AEB)

17. Two small identical uniform perfectly elastic smooth spheres A and B are moving directly towards each other with speeds u and v respectively. Show that after collision the direction of motion of both spheres is reversed and that the speeds of A and B, immediately after collision, are v and u respectively.

Sphere A is projected vertically upwards with speed 29.4 m s^{-1} from a point O and some time later sphere B is also projected vertically upwards from O with the same speed. Given that the spheres collide when they are both moving with speed 4.9 m s^{-1} and that the acceleration due to gravity is 9.8 m s^{-2}, find the time T taken for sphere B to reach the point of collision and the time that elapsed between the projection of the two spheres.

Given that O is on a perfectly elastic horizontal plane, determine the velocities of the spheres at a time t, $(t > T)$, after their first collision and before their second collision. Hence find the time that elapses before the spheres next collide.

(AEB)

18. A uniform smooth sphere A moves along a
horizontal plane and collides with an identical
stationary sphere B. The direction of motion of
A is such that it makes an angle $\frac{\pi}{6}$ with the line
of centres drawn from A to B immediately
before impact. Given that the direction of
motion of A makes an angle α with this line
immediately after impact, show that

$$\tan\alpha = \frac{2}{\sqrt{3}(1-e)}$$

where e is the coefficient of restitution between
the spheres.

Find the angle through which sphere A is
deflected when $e = \frac{1}{3}$ and show that in this case
one third of the original kinetic energy is lost in
the impact. (AEB)

19. Two uniform smooth spheres A and B have equal
radii but are of masses m and $4m$ respectively.
They are at rest on a smooth horizontal floor
with their line of centres perpendicular to a
smooth vertical wall and with A lying between B
and the wall.

A is projected away from the wall along the line
of centres towards B with speed u. The
coefficient of restitution between the spheres is
e. Find the speed of B after the impact and find
the condition that e has to satisfy in order that A
moves towards the wall after impact with B.

Given also that the coefficient of restitution
between A and the wall is e', find, in terms of e,
the range of values of e' such that there will be a
second collision between A and B.

Find the values of e and e' such that, after the
first collision, B has speed $\frac{7u}{20}$ and, after the
collision with the wall, A has speed $\frac{2u}{5}$.

Determine, in this case, the kinetic energy of the
system immediately before the second impact of
the spheres. (AEB)

20. Three identical spheres A, B and C lie on a
smooth horizontal table with their centres in a
straight line and with B between A and C. Given
that A is projected towards B with speed u, show
that, after impact, B moves with speed

$\frac{1}{2}u(1+e)$, where e is the coefficient of
restitution between each of the spheres.

When C first moves, it is found to have speed
$\frac{9u}{16}$. Find e.

In this case show that when C begins to move,
$\frac{75}{128}$ of the initial kinetic energy has been lost.
(AEB)

21. A particle is projected from a point O with speed
v at an angle α to the horizontal so as to hit a
smooth vertical wall which is perpendicular to
the plane of projection. The perpendicular
distance from O to the wall is a. The particle
strikes the wall at a point P and then returns to
O. Show that the time that elapses between the
particle leaving O and returning to O is

$$\frac{2v\sin\alpha}{g}$$

By considering the time taken for the horizontal
motion, show that

$$ev^2\sin 2\alpha = ga(1+e),$$

where e is the coefficient of restitution.

Show also that, immediately before impact at P,
the tangent of the angle between the horizontal
and the path of the particle is

$$\frac{(1-e)}{(1+e)}\tan\alpha$$

Given that the direction of motion of the particle
is turned through a right angle by the impact,
express $\tan\alpha$ in terms of e. (AEB)

22. PQRS is a horizontal smooth rectangular billiard
table with $PQ = 2a$ and $QR = a$. The smooth
edges of the table are vertical and have gaps at
the corners, P, Q, R and S. Balls entering the
gaps are collected in pockets.

A ball is on the table and just outside the pocket
at P. The ball is projected with speed u along the
table at an angle α to PQ. After collision with
the edge RS the direction of motion of the ball
makes an angle β with RS. Show that

$$\tan\beta = e\tan\alpha,$$

where e is the coefficient of restitution between
the ball and an edge of the table. Given that the
ball now rolls straight into the pocket at Q, show
that

$$\alpha = \tan^{-1}\left(\frac{1+e}{2e}\right)$$

Find a similar expression for the angle γ,
between PQ and the direction of motion of the
ball, at which the ball must be projected with
speed u from P if it is to collide with the edge RS
and then the edge PQ before rolling into the
pocket at R. Show that the time taken to reach R
in this case is $\frac{2a}{u\cos\gamma}$. (AEB)

23. Three small smooth uniform spheres A, B and C of equal radius, but of masses $9m$, $6m$ and $4m$ respectively, are at rest in a straight line on a smooth horizontal table with B between A and C. The coefficient of restitution for a collision between any pair of the spheres is $\frac{2}{3}$. Sphere A is projected with speed u so as to collide directly with sphere B.

    (a) Show that, immediately after the first collision, B moves with speed u.

    (b) Find the impulse of B on A.

    (c) Find the loss of kinetic energy in the collision between A and B.

    (d) Hence find the difference between the total kinetic energy of the spheres immediately before A first collides with B and immediately after B has first collided with C.

    (AEB)

24. A small smooth sphere A, of mass $2m$, moving on a smooth horizontal plane collides with a stationary sphere B of equal radius, but of mass m. The coefficient of restitution for collision between the spheres is e. Immediately before collision the sphere A is moving at an angle α to the line of centres. Express, in terms of e and $\tan \alpha$ the tangent of the angle through which the direction of motion of A is turned.

    Given that the direction of motion of A is turned through an angle $\tan^{-1} \frac{1}{\sqrt{15}}$ show that

    $$3\tan^2 \alpha - \sqrt{15}\,(1 + e)\tan \alpha + (2 - e) = 0$$

    Hence find the least value of e, and the corresponding value of $\tan \alpha$, such that this is possible.

    Taking $e = 1$ find the value of $\tan \alpha$ which gives the greatest possible value to the angle through which the direction of motion of A is turned.

    (AEB)

25. (a) A small smooth sphere moving on a smooth horizontal floor collides with a smooth vertical wall and rebounds off it. The velocity of the sphere before collision is $(7\mathbf{i} + 3\mathbf{j})$ m s^{-1} where $\mathbf{i}$ and $\mathbf{j}$ are perpendicular horizontal unit vectors. Given that the velocity after collision is

    $$\left(\frac{9\mathbf{i}}{2} - \frac{13\mathbf{j}}{4} \right) \text{m s}^{-1}$$

    find a vector perpendicular to the wall and also the coefficient of restitution.

    (b) A light inextensible string of length $2a$ passes through a light smooth fixed ring on a smooth horizontal table and particles of mass m are attached to each end. Initially the particles are at rest with the string straight and with the ring at its midpoint. One of the particles is then projected with speed u perpendicular to the string. Use the principles of conservation of angular momentum and of energy to find the speed of the other particle just as it reaches the ring.

    (AEB)

26. (a) Two identical smooth spheres A and B lie at rest on a smooth horizontal table.

    Sphere A is projected with speed u to strike B directly. The coefficient of restitution between the spheres is $\frac{2}{5}$. Find the speed of A immediately after the collision.

    (b) Show that, for any pair of small spheres of mass m and moving with constant velocities in a straight line, the sum of their kinetic energies can be written as

    $$\frac{l^2}{4m} + \frac{1}{4}\,mw^2,$$

    where l denotes their total linear momentum and w their relative velocity. Hence, given that the spheres are smooth and that the coefficient of restitution for collisions between them is e, express the kinetic energy loss in a single collision between the spheres in terms of e, m and their relative velocity w immediately before collision.

    (AEB)

27. The figure shows a horizontal rectangular table PQRS, which has vertical planes along its edges.

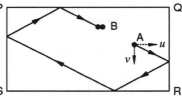

    A uniform smooth sphere A is projected towards QR with velocity components (u, v) parallel to the directions PQ and QR respectively, as shown. Given that A follows the path shown in the figure and that the coefficient of restitution, e, with each vertical edge of the table is the same, find its velocity components parallel to PQ and QR immediately prior to its impact with sphere B. If A now has $\frac{16}{81}$ of its initial kinetic energy left, show that $e = \frac{2}{3}$.

Sphere A, which is of mass m, now collides with a stationary uniform smooth sphere B, of equal radius but of mass $2m$. Given that the line of centres at the instant of impact is parallel to PQ and that, after impact, sphere A moves parallel to QR, find the coefficient of restitution between the spheres. If a further $\frac{4}{81}$ of the original kinetic energy is lost in the impact between the spheres, show that $u = v$. (AEB)

28. (a) A smooth uniform sphere S moves along a horizontal table and obliquely strikes an identical stationary sphere. Show that the ratio of the velocity component of sphere S along the line of centres before impact to that after impact is $\frac{2}{(1-e)}$, where e is the coefficient of restitution. For what value of e will the angle between the directions of motion of the two spheres after impact be a maximum?

    (b) Two identical smooth uniform spheres A and B rest side by side and just touching each other on a horizontal table. A third identical sphere C, travelling with speed u, moves towards A and B along the common tangent to A and B drawn through their point of contact. Show that after impact the speeds of A and B are given by

    $$\frac{\sqrt{3}}{5}(1+e)u,$$

    where e is the coefficient of restitution between the spheres, and find the speed of C. Given that one half of the original kinetic energy is lost in the collision, find e. (AEB)

29. A uniform smooth sphere A, of mass m, lies on a smooth horizontal table between a second uniform smooth sphere B, of equal size but of mass λm, $(\lambda > 0)$, and a fixed vertical plane. The line joining the centres of the spheres is normal to the plane. Between both the spheres and between a sphere and the plane the coefficient of restitution is $\frac{3}{5}$. Sphere A is projected along the table with speed u towards sphere B. Show that the direction of motion of A is reversed in the collision provided that $\lambda > \frac{5}{3}$. Also show that in this case sphere A, after rebounding from the vertical plane, will collide again with sphere B provided that $\lambda > \frac{55}{9}$.

    Given that $\lambda = 15$ show that sphere A is reduced to rest after its second collision with B and find the final velocity of B. (AEB)

30. A particle R of mass $2m$ is free to move on a smooth plane inclined at $30°$ to the horizontal. A light inextensible string, one end of which is attached to R, passes up the plane and over a small smooth light pulley P and has a particle S of mass $7m$ attached to its other end so that S can move freely in a vertical line. Initially the particles are held at rest with the string taut, with the part PR lying along a line of greatest slope of the plane and the part PS hanging vertically. Given that the system is released from rest write down the equations of motion of R and S and hence, or otherwise, find the tension in the string and the magnitude of the common acceleration of the particles.

    After S has dropped a distance h it strikes a horizontal inelastic floor so that it is brought to rest. Assuming that R does not reach P find

    (a) the further distance that R moves up the plane,

    (b) the speed with which S is first jerked off the floor. (AEB)

31. Two small smooth spheres A and B of equal radii but of masses m and $4m$ respectively are moving towards each other on a smooth horizontal table and collide directly. The speeds of A and B before collision are $2u$ and $4u$ respectively. After collision the direction of motion of A is reversed and it moves with speed $3u$. Find the speed of B after collision and also the coefficient of restitution between A and B.

    After collision, sphere A moves with constant speed $3u$ until it catches up and collides directly with a third sphere C which is identical to A and moving in the same direction as A with speed u. Given that the kinetic energy lost in this second collision is $\frac{1}{2}mu^2$ find the speed of A immediately after this collision.

    [The coefficient of restitution between spheres A and B is not the same as that between spheres A and C.] (AEB)

32. Two identical smooth uniform spheres are moving on a smooth table with the same speed u in opposite directions and their centres travelling along parallel lines l_1 and l_2. The coefficient of restitution for collisions between the spheres is e. Given that the spheres collide when the acute angle between the line of centres and the directions of motion is α, find the velocities of the spheres after collision.

    Given also that the spheres are of radius a and that, after collision, their directions of motion are perpendicular to the original directions, show that $\tan^2 \alpha = e$.

Also find

(a) in terms of a and e, the perpendicular distance between the lines l_1 and l_2,

(b) in terms of e, the fraction of the kinetic energy lost in the collision.   (AEB)

33. A uniform smooth sphere A collides with an identical stationary sphere B such that the angle between the velocity of A and the line joining the centre of the spheres at the instant of collision is α immediately before the collision and β immediately afterwards. Prove that

$$\cot\beta = \frac{1}{2}\left(1 - e\right)\cot\alpha$$

where e is the coefficient of restitution.

Show that the maximum deflection that can be produced in the direction of motion of A occurs

when $\tan\alpha = \sqrt{\dfrac{1-e}{2}}$.   (AEB)

34. (a) Two particles A and B of masses $3m$ and $5m$ respectively are placed on a smooth horizontal table. The particle A is projected along the table with speed u directly towards B, which is at rest. After impact A continues to move in the same direction but with speed

$\dfrac{u}{6}$. Find

(i)   the speed of B after impact,

(ii) the coefficient of restitution between A and B,

(iii) the loss in kinetic energy due to the collision.

(b) The same particles A and B are now connected by a light inextensible string and are placed side by side on the smooth horizontal table. The particle A is projected horizontally, directly away from B, with speed v.

Calculate

(i)   the resulting common speed of the two particles after the string has tightened,

(ii) the magnitude of the impulse in the string when the string tightens,

(iii) the loss in kinetic energy due to the tightening of the string.

35. A smooth uniform sphere P of mass m, moves along a horizontal plane with speed u and strikes an identical smooth uniform sphere Q, which is at rest.

The directions of motion of P before and after impact make angles $\dfrac{\pi}{3}$ and θ respectively with the line of centres drawn from P to Q at impact.

Show that $\tan\theta = \dfrac{2\sqrt{3}}{1-e}$, where e is the coefficient of restitution, and find, in terms of u and e, the speed of Q after impact. Show that the greatest possible speed of Q after impact is $\dfrac{u}{2}$ occurring when $\theta = \dfrac{\pi}{2}$. Further show that in this case the speed of P is $\dfrac{\sqrt{3}u}{2}$ and that this is the least speed P can have after impact.

When $e = \dfrac{2}{3}$, find the kinetic energy lost by the spheres in the impact.   (AEB)

36. A small smooth ball P of mass 0.02 kg is projected directly upwards from a point O. Before P returns to O a second small smooth ball Q of equal radius, but of mass 0.01 kg, is projected directly upwards from O with the same initial speed as that given to P. The balls collide 5 s after P has been projected and the coefficient of restitution for collision between them is $\dfrac{3}{5}$. Immediately after collision P is moving upwards with a speed of 1 m s^{-1} whilst Q is moving downwards with a speed of 17 m s^{-1}. Find

(a) the velocities of the balls immediately before impact,

(b) the impulse imparted to P by the collision,

(c) the initial speed of projection,

(d) the time interval between the projection of P and the projection of Q,

(e) the height above O at which the balls collide.

[Take g to be 10 m s^{-2}.]   (AEB)

37. Two identical small smooth spheres A and B are at rest on a smooth horizontal table which has a smooth plane vertical rim at one end. The centres of the spheres are in a line perpendicular to the rim of the table with B nearer to the rim than A. The coefficient of restitution between A and B is $\dfrac{1}{2}$ and that between B and the rim is e, $\left(0 < e < 1\right)$. A is projected directly towards B with speed u.

Show that the speed of B after impact is $\dfrac{3u}{4}$ and find the speed of A.

Sphere B then strikes the rim and rebounds to hit A again. Find the speeds of A and B after this impact and deduce that B will then be moving towards the rim whatever the value of e whilst A will be moving towards the rim provided that

$e < \dfrac{1}{9}$.   (AEB)

6 PLANAR MOTION

Objectives

After studying this chapter you should

- be able to solve problems of cars braking on circular curves;
- be able to investigate the motion of a particle moving in a vertical circle;
- be able to solve simple problems on the motion of satellites and spacecraft.

6.0 Introduction

Chapter 7 of the *Mechanics* text was on Circular Motion and it was assumed in all the models that the speed was **constant** in the motions considered. You may have realised when you carried out Activity 2 (rolling a marble round inside a cake tin) that this assumption would not always be valid since the marble eventually slowed down and its speed certainly did not stay the same! If you had carried out the same activity with a small coin, the coin would have slowed down much more quickly than the marble.

Why?

If a marble was rolled round the inside of a cake tin turned on its edge it would, at best, stop at a point and then move down and oscillate, so clearly the speed does not stay constant. It therefore appears that, in order to discuss problems like the marble rolling in a cake tin (it is actually a model of a 'Loop the Loop' ride) the model has to be refined to allow the possibility of the speed varying.

It is also mentioned in *Mechanics* Chapter 7 that the path of the moon round the sun is approximately circular. This model will also be refined and simple problems of planetary motion will be solved. In order to achieve this it is necessary to introduce a new system of coordinates (polar coordinates) and work out expressions for velocity and acceleration in these coordinates. Having obtained these expressions a large range of problems for planetary and satellite motion can be solved.

6.1 Circular motion with variable speed

The x and y-coordinates of a particle P moving on a circle of radius r are $r\cos\theta$ and $r\sin\theta$ respectively (see diagram) where θ is the angle between the radius and the x-axis. This means that the position vector of the particle can be written as

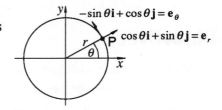

$$\mathbf{r} = x\mathbf{i} + y\mathbf{j} = r(\cos\theta\,\mathbf{i} + \sin\theta\,\mathbf{j})$$

where $\mathbf{i}$ and $\mathbf{j}$ are unit vectors parallel to the x and y-axes respectively.

The velocity $\mathbf{v}$ is found by differentiating the position vector with respect to time (remembering that r is constant) i.e.

$$\mathbf{v} = \frac{d\mathbf{r}}{dt}$$

$$= \frac{d}{dt}\left(r(\cos\theta\,\mathbf{i} + \sin\,\mathbf{j})\right)$$

$$= r\left(\frac{d}{dt}(\cos\theta)\mathbf{i} + \frac{d}{dt}(\sin\theta)\mathbf{j}\right)$$

$$= r\left(-\sin\theta\,\frac{d\theta}{dt}\mathbf{i} + \cos\theta\,\frac{d\theta}{dt}\mathbf{j}\right)$$

$$= r\frac{d\theta}{dt}(-\sin\theta\,\mathbf{i} + \cos\theta\,\mathbf{j})$$

Differentiating the velocity gives the acceleration $\mathbf{a}$, so that

$$\mathbf{a} = \frac{d\mathbf{v}}{dt}$$

$$= \frac{d}{dt}\left(r\frac{d\theta}{dt}(-\sin\theta\,\mathbf{i} + \cos\theta\,\mathbf{j})\right)$$

$$= r\frac{d^2\theta}{dt^2}(-\sin\theta\,\mathbf{i} + \cos\theta\,\mathbf{j}) - r\left(\frac{d\theta}{dt}\right)^2(\cos\theta\,\mathbf{i} + \sin\theta\,\mathbf{j})$$

The vector $-\sin\theta\mathbf{i}+\cos\theta\mathbf{j}$ is of unit length since $\sin^2\theta+\cos^2\theta=1$ and, as the diagram shows, it is parallel to the tangent at P and is in the sense of θ increasing. This unit vector will be denoted by $\mathbf{e}_\theta$ and the direction of $\mathbf{e}_\theta$ is referred to as the **transverse** direction.

Thus
$$\mathbf{e}_\theta=-\sin\theta\mathbf{i}+\cos\theta\mathbf{j}$$

The vector $\cos\theta\mathbf{i}+\sin\theta\mathbf{j}$ is the unit vector along the radius from O and this is denoted by $\mathbf{e}_r$. The direction of $\mathbf{e}_r$ is called the **radial** direction.

Thus
$$\mathbf{e}_r=\cos\theta\mathbf{i}+\sin\theta\mathbf{j}$$

Therefore

$$\mathbf{v}=r\frac{d\theta}{dt}\mathbf{e}_\theta$$

$$\mathbf{a}=-r\left(\frac{d\theta}{dt}\right)^2\mathbf{e}_r+r\frac{d^2\theta}{dt^2}\mathbf{e}_\theta$$

and writing $\dot{\theta}=\dfrac{d\theta}{dt}$, $\ddot{\theta}=\dfrac{d^2\theta}{dt^2}$ gives the results

$$\mathbf{v}=r\dot{\theta}\mathbf{e}_\theta$$

$$\mathbf{a}=-r\dot{\theta}^2\mathbf{e}_r+r\ddot{\theta}\mathbf{e}_\theta$$

In the *Mechanics* text $\dot{\theta}$ was defined as the **angular velocity** even though it was not a vector, but a direction was associated with it using the corkscrew rule. The definition of the angular velocity $\underset{\sim}{\omega}$ more precisely is

$$\underset{\sim}{\omega}=\dot{\theta}\mathbf{k}$$

where the unit vector $\mathbf{k}$ is perpendicular to the plane and such that $\mathbf{k}=\mathbf{i}\times\mathbf{j}$.

Note also that the position vector $\mathbf{r}$ can be written as

$$\mathbf{r}=r\mathbf{e}_r$$

and that

$$\underset{\sim}{\omega}\times\mathbf{r} = \left(\dot{\theta}\mathbf{k}\right)\times\left(r\mathbf{e}_r\right)$$

$$= r\dot{\theta}\left(\mathbf{k}\times\mathbf{e}_r\right)$$

$$= r\dot{\theta}\mathbf{e}_\theta$$

$$= \mathbf{v}$$

Why does $\mathbf{k}\times\mathbf{e}_r = \mathbf{e}_\theta$? What does $\mathbf{k}\times\mathbf{e}_\theta$ equal?

The result can be restated as

$$\boxed{\mathbf{v} = \underset{\sim}{\omega}\times\mathbf{r}}$$

and this is useful for 3-dimensional situations

You have met the equation for velocity before and it simply states that for any circular motion the velocity is perpendicular to the radius and of magnitude $\left|r\dot{\theta}\right|$. The first term in the equation for acceleration

$$\mathbf{a} = -r\dot{\theta}^2\mathbf{e}_r + r\ddot{\theta}\mathbf{e}_\theta$$

should also be familiar to you as it is the acceleration along the radius vector, directed towards the centre and of magnitude $r\dot{\theta}^2$. The second term is new and is the result of not restricting the speed to be constant. It shows that there will also be an acceleration perpendicular to the radius and of magnitude $\left|r\ddot{\theta}\right|$.

You already know that the radial component of the acceleration can be written in a different form, using $v = \left|r\dot{\theta}\right|$, as $\dfrac{v^2}{r}$.

The transverse component of acceleration can also be written in two other forms, which are useful in particular problems. The component of velocity, v, in the transverse direction is $r\dot{\theta}$ and, as

$r\ddot{\theta} = \dfrac{d\left(r\dot{\theta}\right)}{dt}$, since r is a constant, the transverse acceleration is

given by $\dfrac{dv}{dt}$ or $\dot{v}$.

Why is $r\dot{\theta}^2$ the same as $\dfrac{v^2}{r}$?

Also, the arc length, s, along a circle of radius r is given by

$$s = r\theta$$

and so

$$\frac{dv}{dt} = \frac{dv}{ds}\frac{ds}{dt}$$

and

$$= r\dot{\theta}\frac{dv}{ds}$$

$$= v\frac{dv}{ds}$$

Hence the transverse acceleration can also be written as $v\dfrac{dv}{ds}$.

To summarise, in circular motion the velocity is in the transverse direction and equal in magnitude to $\left|r\dot{\theta}\right|$. The velocity can be written as

$$\mathbf{v} = \underset{\sim}{\omega} \times \mathbf{r}, \quad \text{where} \quad \underset{\sim}{\omega} = \dot{\theta}\mathbf{k}$$

In circular motion, in general, there are two components of acceleration,

$$r\dot{\theta} = \frac{v^2}{r}$$

directed radially inwards and

$$r\ddot{\theta}^2 = \dot{v} = v\frac{dv}{ds}$$

in the transverse direction.

Example

A particle moves in a circular path of 0.4 m radius. Find the magnitude of the acceleration of the particle

(a) if its speed is constant at 0.6 m s^{-1} and

(b) if its speed is 0.6 m s^{-1} but is increasing at the rate of 1.2 m s^{-2}.

Solution

In (a) the speed is constant so the acceleration is radial and equal

to $\dfrac{v^2}{r} = \dfrac{(0.6)^2}{0.4}$ m s$^{-2} = 0.9$ m s^{-2}.

In (b) the speed is increasing at a rate of 1.2 m s^{-2} and therefore there is a transverse acceleration of this magnitude .

The magnitude of the total acceleration is therefore

$$\sqrt{1.2^2 + 0.9^2} \text{ m s}^{-2} = 1.5 \text{m s}^{-2}$$

Example

The speed of a car travelling on a horizontal circular track of radius 60 m decreases at the constant rate of 0.6 m s^{-2}. The speed of the car as it passes point A is 16 m s^{-1}. Find the magnitude of the total acceleration of the car as it passes point B which is 120 m along the road from A.

Solution

In this case the velocity v m s^{-1} at time t seconds is such that

$$\frac{dv}{dt} = v\frac{dv}{ds} = -0.6$$

Integrating with respect to s, from point $A(s = 0)$ to $B(s = 120)$

$$\int_0^{120} v\frac{dv}{ds}\, ds = \int_0^{120} (-0.6)ds$$

$$\Rightarrow \quad \int_{16}^{v} v\, dv = -0.6 \times 120 \qquad (v \text{ is the speed at } B)$$

$$\Rightarrow \quad \frac{1}{2}v^2 - \frac{1}{2} \times 16^2 = -72$$

$$\Rightarrow \quad v^2 = 112$$

$$\Rightarrow \quad v \approx 10.58 \text{ m s}^{-1}$$

The acceleration components at B are given by

radial: $\quad \dfrac{v^2}{r} = \dfrac{(10.58)^2}{60} \approx 1.87 \text{ m s}^{-2}$

transverse: $\quad \dot{v} = -0.6 \text{ m s}^{-2}$

Thus the total acceleration is given by

$$\sqrt{1.87^2 + (-0.6)^2} \text{ m s}^{-2} = 1.96 \text{m s}^{-2}$$

Exercise 6A

1. A car travels on a horizontal circular track of radius 150 m. The car's speed increases at a constant rate of 0.5 m s^{-2}. Find the total acceleration of the car after it has travelled a distance of 150 m from the point where its speed was 15 m s^{-1}.

2. A car is travelling on a horizontal road which is an arc of a circle of radius 400 m. The car is travelling at a speed of 30 m s^{-1} when the brakes are applied so that the speed decreases at a rate of 1 m s^{-2}. Find the total acceleration of the car
   (a) immediately after the brakes have been applied,
   (b) 5 seconds later.

3. A motorist is travelling on a circular track of radius 600 m and, when travelling at 35 m s^{-1} applies his brakes so that, ten seconds later, the car is moving with speed 25 m s^{-1}.

Assuming that the brakes produce a constant rate of decrease of speed, find the total acceleration of the car immediately after the brakes have been applied.

4. A car is travelling round a level road, which is an arc of a circle of radius 180 m. The speed of the car increases at the constant rate of 1.5 m s^{-2} and the magnitude of the total acceleration of the car at point A is 2.5 m s^{-2}. Find the speed of the car at this point.

5. A heavy lorry starts off on a curve of 250 m radius and its speed increases at a constant rate of 0.6 m s^{-2}. Find the distance that the lorry will travel before its total acceleration reaches 0.8 m s^{-2}.

6.2 Dynamical problems

The above results show that taking the speed of a particle describing circular motion to be constant is equivalent to assuming no transverse acceleration. Newton's law of motion states that the component of force in any direction is proportional to the acceleration in that direction and therefore assuming the speed to be constant assumes that there are no transverse forces acting (i.e. along the path).

In the case of the marble rolling around the inside of a cake tin, its motion is opposed by air resistance so it slows down. When a coin slides round the cake tin there will be energy loss due to friction as well as air resistance, whereas in rolling there is no energy loss due to friction so the rolling goes on longer than the sliding. In the case of the cake tin on its side there is a transverse component due to gravity and this also reduces the speed.

In the next few examples the acceleration formulae will be used to tackle problems of motion under various forces.

Example

A satellite is moving, with constant speed, in a circle of radius 6500 km about the centre of the earth. The earth is assumed to be a sphere of radius 6371 km and the acceleration due to gravity is proportional to the inverse square of the distance from the centre of the earth. Assuming that g is 9.81 m s^{-2} on the earth's surface, find the speed of the satellite.

Solution

The inverse square law can be written as

$$g = \frac{k}{r^2}$$

where r is the distance from the earth's surface.

Using the data

$$9.81 = \frac{k}{\left(6.371 \times 10^6\right)^2}$$

$$\Rightarrow \quad k = 9.81 \times (6.371)^2 \times 10^{12}$$

$$\Rightarrow \quad k = 3.982 \times 10^{14}$$

The radial equation of motion for the satellite is given by

$$mg = mf$$

where g is the gravitational force on the satellite, f is the radial acceleration and m is the mass of the satellite.

Hence

$$\frac{k}{R^2} = \frac{v^2}{R}$$

where $R = 6500 \times 10^3$ m is the satellite's distance from the centre of the earth.

Thus

$$v^2 = \frac{k}{R}$$

$$= \frac{3.982 \times 10^{14}}{6.500 \times 10^3}$$

$$\Rightarrow \quad v = 7.827 \text{ km s}^{-1} \left(\approx 28177 \text{ km h}^{-1} \right) \times \mathbf{e}_r = \mathbf{e}_\theta$$

Example

The diagram shows a light inextensible string AB of length a lying on a rough horizontal plane with the end A fixed to a point on the plane. A particle of mass m is attached to B. The string is taut when the particle is projected in a direction perpendicular to AB.

The coefficient of friction between the particle and the table is μ and the force of friction is assumed to directly oppose the motion of the particle. The particle just describes a semicircle before coming to rest. Find its initial speed and the initial tension in the string.

Solution

The only forces acting are the tension in the string, the vertical reaction of the plane and the force of friction.

Resolving vertically gives $R = mg$ and therefore the force of friction is μmg.

The tension in the string at any instant will be denoted by T and the particle speed by v.

The equations of motion along and perpendicular to the radius are

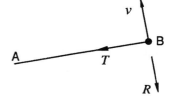

$$m\frac{v^2}{a} = T, \quad m\frac{dv}{dt} = -\mu mg$$

The second equation can be rewritten as

$$mv\frac{dv}{ds} = -\mu mg$$

where s is the arc length along the path.

Integrating,

$$v^2 = c - 2\mu g s$$

where c is a constant.

Denoting the initial velocity by V gives $c = V^2$, so

$$v^2 = V^2 - 2\mu g s$$

The particle comes to rest when $s = a\pi$ so $V = \sqrt{2ag\mu\pi}$.

Substituting in the equation for T gives $T = 2mg\mu\pi$.

Exercise 6B

1. A particle of mass m can slide on a horizontal circular wire of radius a and the only force acting along the direction of motion is a force of constant magnitude 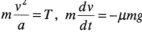 $m = \dfrac{V^2}{a}$ and opposing the motion.

    The particle is projected along the wire with speed $5V$. Find the distance that it travels before coming to rest.

2. Assume now that the force acting on the particle in the previous question is replaced by one resisting the motion and equal in magnitude to mkv, where k is a constant and v is the speed of the particle. Find the speed of the particle at time t after being projected with speed V.

3. A particle is threaded on a rough horizontal wire formed into a circle of radius a and is projected with angular speed Ω along the wire. The coefficient of friction between the particle and the wire is μ. Assuming that the vertical reaction of the wire may be neglected (i.e. the motion takes place in a gravity-free environment) find the total distance travelled by the bead in time t.

4. A particle, free to move on a horizontal table, is attached by a string of length a to a fixed point of the table. The particle is projected, with the string taut, with speed u perpendicular to the string. After turning through one radian the string strikes a fixed peg at a distance b from A and subsequently the particle starts to describe a circle about the peg. Given that the coefficient of friction is μ, find the total time that the particle is in motion.

5. A car of mass 1200 kg is driven at 10 m s^{-1} in a tight loop round a horizontal circle of radius 80 m. The tyres are limited to a total horizontal friction force of 10.6 kN. The driver then applies the brakes. What is the maximum possible deceleration?

6. A particle is threaded on a rough horizontal wire loop of radius a, the coefficient of friction between the wire and the bead being μ. The particle is projected with speed v along the wire. Determine the distance the particle travels along the wire before coming to rest.

[Hint: The components of reaction vertically and radially have to be taken into account to work out the friction force.]

[You will also need to use

$$\int \frac{dx}{\sqrt{x^2 + a^2}} = \operatorname{arcsinh}\left(\frac{x}{a}\right)]$$

7. The tyres on a car can each support a maximum friction force parallel to the road surface of 2500 N. The car is of mass 1250 kg and is travelling at a speed of 25 m s^{-1} on a horizontal track of radius 80 m when the brakes are applied. Assuming that the brakes are applied to the four wheels find the minimum stopping distance.

[You will need to use the result

$$\int \frac{dx}{\sqrt{a^2 - x^2}} = \arcsin\left(\frac{x}{a}\right)]$$

8. A small coin is placed on a rough circular disc at a distance a from its centre, the coefficient of friction between the coin and the disc being μ. Initially the disc is at rest and it is set in motion so that it moves with a constant angular acceleration α about the vertical axis through its centre. Find the total time during which the disc rotates.

9. Two particles A and B of masses m and $3m$ are on a rough horizontal table and joined by a light inextensible string. The coefficient of friction between either particle and the table is μ. Show that if particle A is projected perpendicular to the string, which is initially taut, and particle B does not move in the subsequent motion, then the string cannot have turned through more than $\frac{3}{2}$ radians.

6.3   Motion in a vertical circle

The acceleration formulae are particularly useful for problems involving motion in a vertical circle and the general theory of such problems will now be given.

There are four slightly different types of problem involving motion in a vertical circle: a particle can be whirled at the end of a string, a particle can move on the inside or outside of a smooth vertical cylinder; or be threaded on a loop of wire; or attached to the end of a light rod (the last two are essentially the same type). The problems are mathematically the same and the main difference is in the interpretation of the results.

The basic issues are best seen by considering the motion of a particle threaded on a smooth vertical circular loop of wire.

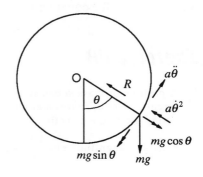

The diagram shows a vertical circular wire of centre O and radius a on which a bead P of mass m is threaded. The angle between OP and the downward vertical is denoted by θ. The wire is assumed to be smooth so that the only force that it exerts on P is radial and of magnitude R and this is shown in the diagram acting radially inwards. The only other force acting on P is the force of gravity vertically downwards which has a component $mg\cos\theta$ acting outwards and a component $mg\sin\theta$ acting tangentially in the direction of decreasing θ. The components of the acceleration of P radially inwards and tangentially are $a\dot\theta^2$ and $a\ddot\theta$.

Hence the equations of motion are

radial: $\qquad R - mg\cos\theta = ma\dot\theta^2$
tangential: $ma\ddot\theta = -mg\sin\theta$

The second equation is a differential equation relating θ with t, and the first step is to integrate this equation.

Multiplying the equation by $\dot\theta$ gives

$$ma\ddot\theta\,\dot\theta = -mg\sin\theta\,\dot\theta$$

$$\Rightarrow \quad \frac{1}{2}ma\frac{d}{dt}\left(\dot\theta^2\right) = mg\frac{d}{dt}(\cos\theta)$$

This follows since

$$\frac{d}{dt}\left(\dot\theta^2\right) = 2\dot\theta\ddot\theta \quad\text{and}\quad \frac{d}{dt}(\cos\theta) = -\sin\theta\,\dot\theta$$

The differential equation can now be integrated with respect to t to give

$$\frac{1}{2}ma\dot\theta^2 = mg\cos\theta + K \qquad (K\text{ constant})$$

If P has a speed u (i.e. $\dot\theta = \dfrac{u}{a}$) at its lowest point A (when $\theta = 0$), the constant can be found by substituting into this expression, giving

$$\frac{1}{2}ma\left(\frac{u^2}{a^2}\right) = mg + K$$

$$\Rightarrow \quad K = \frac{1}{2}m\frac{u^2}{a} - mg$$

$$\Rightarrow \quad \frac{1}{2}ma\dot{\theta}^2 = mg\cos\theta + \frac{1}{2}m\frac{u^2}{a} - mg$$

$$\Rightarrow \quad \boxed{a^2\dot{\theta}^2 = u^2 + 2ag(\cos\theta - 1)}$$

(This is essentially the equation of conservation of energy.)

The value of $\dot{\theta}$ can now be substituted into the equation for R giving

$$R = \frac{mu^2}{a} + mg(3\cos\theta - 2)$$

The basic problem has now been solved and it now remains to interpret it. Before doing this it is worth looking at energy consevation since it is so useful in many problems.

Energy conservation

You know from your earlier work that change in kinetic energy is equal to work done. You also know that the work done by the force of gravity is – (change in potential energy). If it is assumed that the forces acting are gravity and others then

change in kinetic energy
$\qquad$ = – change in potential energy + work done by other forces

or $\quad$ | change in total energy = work done by other forces |

In the case of the bead threaded on the wire the only other force acting is the reaction. The wire is smooth so the reaction is always perpendicular to the direction of motion and is therefore zero. Therefore the total energy is conserved.

The work done by the tension in an inextensible string is also zero and energy is again conserved.

If a problem is further complicated by the particle being attached to a point by an elastic string, then the work done by the tension in the string has to be included. Again you know, from earlier work in Mechanics, that this is – (the change in elastic energy) and so energy conservation holds, provided the elastic energy is included.

Applying conservation of energy directly to the problem of the bead threaded on a wire given above,

$$\frac{1}{2}mv^2 - mga\cos\theta = \text{constant}$$

Activity 1

Show that the energy conservation equation and the previous boxed equation are identical.

Whenever energy is conserved, using energy conservation avoids having to integrate the transverse equation directly.

Interpretation of results

The basic results for the bead on a circular wire are

$$a^2\dot{\theta}^2 = u^2 + 2ag(\cos\theta - 1)$$

and

$$R = \frac{mu^2}{a} + mg(3\cos\theta - 2)$$

If $\theta = \pi$ is substituted into the equation for $\dot{\theta}^2$ this gives its value at the highest point as $u^2 - 4ag$.

What happens if $u^2 < 4ag$?

If $u^2 < 4ag$ this expression will be negative, meaning that the particle will not reach the highest point and will just oscillate on either side of the vertical through the centre. To make further progress it is best to look at the different types of problems.

Particle on string or on inside of cylinder

For a particle on a string or on the inside of a cylinder the reaction R is inwards and so the expression for R must always be positive. For $\theta = \pi$,

$$R = u^2 - 5ag$$

If $u^2 < 5ag$ the particle will drop off the cylinder, or the string will become slack, and the particle will move as a projectile until it comes into contact with the surface of the cylinder again, or until the string becomes taut again.

Particle on outside of cylinder

In this case the normal reaction will be radially outward. To see what happens it is easier to use different initial conditions so that the speed of the particle at the top is U where $U^2 < ga$.

Substituting $v = U$ when $\theta = \pi$ into the energy conservation equation to find the constant gives

$$a^2\dot{\theta}^2 = U^2 + 2ag(\cos\theta + 1)$$

It also makes things clearer to denote the outward reaction of the cylinder by T, this means replacing R by $-T$ in the radial equation of motion. Using the above form of $a^2\dot{\theta}^2 = u^2$ in the equation for R gives

$$-T = \frac{mU^2}{a} + mg(\cos\theta + 2)$$

Substituting $\theta = \pi$ in this equation for T gives

$$T = mg - \frac{mU^2}{a}$$

and the restriction on U means that this is positive.

What happens if $U^2 > ga$?

For $\theta = \dfrac{\pi}{2}$, T will be negative so the particle will fall off before getting to the level of the centre of the cylinder. The actual value of θ at which this happens is found by substituting $T = 0$ to give

$$\cos\theta = -\frac{U^2}{3ga} - \frac{2}{3}$$

The cosine will be negative since θ, as defined, is measured from the downward vertical.

Activity 2

Take a round cake tin, rest it on its side, dust the outside edge with talcum powder and release a marble gently to roll down it. Use the marks on the powder to find the angle it has turned through before coming off. Since you are starting the marble virtually from rest the value of U should be zero and this gives the angle turned through as roughly $70°$.

Are you anywhere near this?

It is better to use a marble rather than a small coin since it rolls rather than slides and does not lose energy. The other effect of using a marble is that its kinetic energy due to rolling is greater than $\dfrac{1}{2}v^2$ and to get some idea of this you can replace v^2 by $\dfrac{7}{5}v^2$ in the equation of energy .

Activity 3

Replace v^2 by $\dfrac{7}{5}v^2$ in the energy equation to find a new expression for the reaction and see whether this gives better agreement.

The next two examples illustrate the method of solving problems of this type.

Example

A child of mass 35 kg sits on a swing and swings freely through an angle of 60° on either side of the vertical. The ropes of the swing are 2.5 m long. Modelling the motion as that of a particle of mass 35 kg attached to an inextensible rope of length 2.5 m find the speed of the child when the rope is vertical and also the tension in the rope at that instant. (Take $g = 9.8\,\text{m s}^{-2}$)

Solution

The diagram shows the motion when the rope is at an angle θ to the vertical with the tension in the rope being denoted by T and acting inwards.

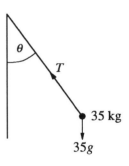

The radial equation of motion is

$$T - 35 \times 9.8 \cos\theta = 35\dfrac{v^2}{2.5}$$

The equation of conservation of energy gives

$$\dfrac{1}{2} \times 35v^2 - 35 \times 9.8 \times 2.5\cos\theta = K \quad (K \text{ constant})$$

The swing stops at 60° on either side of the vertical so $v = 0$ for $\theta = 60°$, giving

$$K = -35 \times 9.8 \times 2.5\cos 60°$$

$$\approx -428.75$$

Substituting $\theta = 0$ in the equation now gives

$$\frac{1}{2} \times 35v^2 = -428.75 + 35 \times 9.8 \times 2.5 \times 1$$

$$v \approx 4.94 \text{ m s}^{-1}$$

Substituting this speed into the radial equation of motion for $\theta = 0$ gives

$$T = 35 \times 9.8 \times 1 + 35\left(\frac{4.94^2}{2.5}\right) \approx 686 \text{N}$$

Example

A particle can move on the smooth outer surface of a fixed cylinder of radius a. The particle is released from rest at a point at a height of $\dfrac{9a}{10}$ above the centre of the cylinder. Find the height above the centre of the cylinder at which the particle leaves it.

Solution

The diagram shows the situation after the particle has been released with θ denoting the angle between the upward vertical and the radius to the particle. The reaction of the cylinder will be radially outwards and will be denoted by R.

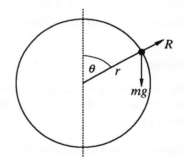

The radial equation of motion is

$$mg \cos \theta - R = ma\dot{\theta}^2$$

and the energy equation is

$$\frac{1}{2} ma^2 \dot{\theta}^2 + mga \cos \theta = K \quad (K \text{ constant})$$

In this case $\dot{\theta} = 0$ when $\cos \theta = \dfrac{9}{10}$ and this gives

$$K = \frac{9mga}{10}$$

and so $\qquad 5a^2\dot{\theta}^2 + 10ga \cos \theta = 9ga$

Substituting for $\dot{\theta}^2$ in the radial equation gives

$$5R = 15mg \cos \theta - 9mg$$

R vanishes when $\cos\theta = \dfrac{3}{5}$ so the particle leaves the cylinder at

this point which is at a height $\dfrac{3a}{5}$ above the centre.

Exercise 6C

In numerical exercises take $g = 9.8 \text{ m s}^{-2}$.

Questions 1 and 2 refer to a particle, describing complete vertical circles, attached to one end of a light inextensible string of length a.

1. Given that the speed at the highest point is $8ga$ find the speed at the lowest point.

2. Given that $a = 0.5$ m and that the greatest and least tensions are in the ratio 3 to 1, find the greatest speed of the particle.

3. An aeroplane is flown at a constant speed of 175 m s^{-1} in a vertical circle of radius 1000 m. Find the force exerted by the seat on the pilot, of mass 80 kg, at the lowest and highest points.

4. A man swings a bucket full of water in a vertical plane in a circle of radius 0.5 m. What is the smallest velocity that the bucket should have at the top of the circle if no water is to be spilt?

5. The diagram below shows a vertical section of a skateboard rink. The section consists of two quadrants of a circle of radius 4 m joined by a straight horizontal part. A skateboarder moves in a vertical plane and the speeds corresponding to $\theta = 0°$, $60°$ and $90°$ are 8 m s^{-1}, 5.5 m s^{-1} and zero respectively. Modelling the skateboarder as a particle of mass 65 kg, find the normal force exerted by the surface at the points B and C corresponding to $\theta = 0$ and $60°$. Find also the work done against friction and air resistance in moving from A to B and from B to C.

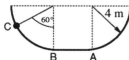

6. The diagram below illustrates a model of a fairground ride with the two circular arcs ABC and DEF joined by a straight track CD. The radius of the arc ABC is 35 m whilst that of DEF is 25 m. The point B is directly below the centre of the arc ABC and the point E is directly above the centre of the arc DEF. The cars of the ride have a speed of 20 m s^{-1} at B and 15 m s^{-1} at E. Find the normal reaction at B and E on a passenger of mass 70 kg.

7. The diagram shows the rotating drum of a spin dryer. The radius of the drum is 0.3 m. Find the angular velocity of the drum so that a small article of clothing drops off the drum when $\theta = 40°$. You may assume that the surface of the drum is such as to prevent slipping before loss of contact.

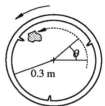

8. A bead of mass m is threaded on a smooth circular loop of wire of radius a and which is fixed in a vertical plane. The bead is released from rest at the end of a horizontal diameter. Find the reaction of the wire when the bead has turned through an angle θ.

9. A particle is released from rest at a height $\dfrac{a}{2}$ above the centre of a smooth sphere of radius a. Find the height above the centre at which the particle leaves the sphere.

10. A particle of mass m is free to slide on a circular wire hoop of radius a in a vertical plane. The wire is such that, once the particle is set in motion, it experiences a constant force of magnitude $2mg$ opposing its motion. The particle is projected from the lowest point of the wire and it comes to instantaneous rest opposite the centre of the wire. Find the speed of projection.

11.

The diagram above shows a track in the form of an arc of a circle of radius r on which a small rocket-propelled vehicle of mass m can travel under the action of a constant thrust F.

Given that the vehicle sets off from rest at A find its speed at B and also the reaction of the track at B. The track may be assumed to be smooth and any mass loss due to the rocket may be ignored.

6.4   Polar coordinates

A problem is often simplified by changing to a coordinate system which takes advantage of the symmetry of the problem. In problems of **planetary motion** the coordinate system which is best suited is the **plane polar system** (r, θ). In this system the variable r is the distance from a fixed point O (the origin or pole) and θ is the angle between OP and a fixed direction which is taken to be the direction of the unit vector **i**.

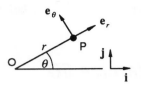

Therefore the position vector **r** of P is given by

$$\boxed{\mathbf{r} = r(\cos\theta\,\mathbf{i} + \sin\theta\,\mathbf{j})}$$

This is exactly the same form as used for motion in a circle, in Section 6.1, although here the variable r is no longer constant. In finding the acceleration formulae for circular motion the unit vectors $\mathbf{e}_r$, $\mathbf{e}_\theta$ defined by

$$\boxed{\mathbf{e}_r = \cos\theta\,\mathbf{i} + \sin\theta\,\mathbf{j}, \quad \mathbf{e}_\theta = -\sin\theta\,\mathbf{i} + \cos\theta\,\mathbf{j}}$$

were introduced and these are also useful in simplifying the calculation of the acceleration and velocity components in polar coordinates.

Differentiating both the above vectors with respect to t gives

$$\dot{\mathbf{e}}_r = \dot{\theta}(-\sin\theta\,\mathbf{i} + \cos\theta\,\mathbf{j}) = \dot{\theta}\,\mathbf{e}_\theta$$

$$\dot{\mathbf{e}}_\theta = -\dot{\theta}(\cos\theta\,\mathbf{i} + \sin\theta\,\mathbf{j}) = -\dot{\theta}\,\mathbf{e}_r$$

The position vector **r** can be written as

$$\mathbf{r} = r\mathbf{e}_r$$

and differentiating this with respect to t gives the velocity **v**, i.e

$$\mathbf{v} = \frac{d}{dt}(r\,\mathbf{e}_r) = \dot{r}\,\mathbf{e}_r + r\dot{\mathbf{e}}_r$$

i.e.
$$\boxed{\mathbf{v} = \dot{r}\,\mathbf{e}_r + r\dot{\theta}\,\mathbf{e}_\theta}$$

There are therefore two components of velocity, $\dot{r}$ radially and $r\dot{\theta}$ transversely.

What happens if $r = a$ **constant?**

Differentiating **v** again gives the acceleration **a** as

$$\mathbf{a} = \frac{d\mathbf{v}}{dt} = \frac{d}{dt}(\dot{r}\mathbf{e}_r) + \frac{d}{dt}(r\dot{\theta}\mathbf{e}_\theta)$$

$$= \ddot{r}\mathbf{e}_r + \dot{r}\dot{\mathbf{e}}_r + \dot{r}\dot{\theta}\mathbf{e}_\theta + r\ddot{\theta}\mathbf{e}_\theta + r\dot{\theta}\dot{\mathbf{e}}_\theta$$

Substituting $\dot{\mathbf{e}}_r = \dot{\theta}\mathbf{e}_\theta$, and $\dot{\mathbf{e}}_\theta = -\dot{\theta}\mathbf{e}_r$ and gathering up the coefficients of $\mathbf{e}_r$ and $\mathbf{e}_\theta$ gives

$$\boxed{\mathbf{a} = \left(\ddot{r} - r\dot{\theta}^2\right)\mathbf{e}_r + \left(2\dot{r}\dot{\theta} + r\ddot{\theta}\right)\mathbf{e}_\theta}$$

The radial component of acceleration is therefore $\ddot{r} - \ddot{r}\dot{\theta}^2$ and the transverse component is $2\dot{r}\dot{\theta} + r\ddot{\theta}$. Many problems are simplified by noting that the latter can be written as

$$\frac{1}{r}\frac{d}{dt}\left(r^2\dot{\theta}\right)$$

since $\dfrac{1}{r}\dfrac{d}{dt}\left(r^2\dot{\theta}\right) = 2\dot{r}\dot{\theta} + r\ddot{\theta}$

Activity 4

Confirm that putting $r =$ constant in the acceleration vector results in the formula found earlier in Section 6.1

To summarise, in polar coordinates

(a)   the radial and transverse components of velocity are
$\dot{r}$ and $r\dot{\theta}$

(b)   the radial and transverse components of acceleration are
$$\ddot{r} - r\dot{\theta}^2 \text{ and } \frac{1}{r}\frac{d}{dt}\left(r^2\dot{\theta}\right) = 2\dot{r}\dot{\theta} + r\ddot{\theta}.$$

Example

The polar coordinates of a particle at time t seconds are $r = \dfrac{t^3}{3}$ and $\theta = 72\cos\left(\dfrac{t\pi}{6}\right)$, where r is in metres, θ is in radians. Find the velocity and acceleration of the particle for $t = 3$.

Solution

$$\dot{r} = t^2, \ \ddot{r} = 2t, \ \dot{\theta} = -12\pi \sin\left(\frac{t\pi}{6}\right), \ \ddot{\theta} = -2\pi^2 \cos\left(\frac{t\pi}{6}\right)$$

and for $t = 3$ these become

$$\dot{r} = 9, \ \ddot{r} = 6, \ \dot{\theta} = -12\pi, \ \ddot{\theta} = 0 \text{ and also } r = 9$$

The radial and transverse components of velocity are 9 m s^{-1} and -108π m s^{-1} and the corresponding components of acceleration are $6 - 1296\pi^2$ and $-216\pi^2$.

Example

A rocket is fired vertically from a point on the ground and continues to move vertically. It is tracked, as shown in the diagram, by radar at a horizontal distance a from the launch point.

Find the speed of the rocket in terms of a, θ and $\dot{\theta}$.

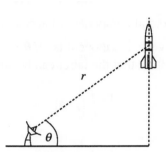

Solution

Since the rocket moves vertically $a = r \cos\theta$ and differentiating this with respect to t gives

$$\dot{r} \cos\theta - r \sin\theta \ \dot{\theta} = 0$$

Therefore the radial component of velocity is

$$\dot{r} = a \tan\theta \sec\theta \ \dot{\theta}$$

and the transverse component of velocity is

$$r\ddot{\theta} = a \sec\theta \ \dot{\theta}h\left(\frac{x}{a}\right)$$

$$v^2 = \dot{r}^2 + \left(r\ddot{\theta}\right)^2$$

$$= a^2 \tan^2\theta \sec^2\theta \ \dot{\theta}^2 + a^2 \sec^2\theta \ \dot{\theta}^2$$

$$= a^2 \sec^2\theta\left(\tan^2\theta + 1\right)\dot{\theta}^2$$

$$= a^2 \sec^4\theta \ \dot{\theta}^2$$

Hence the speed is given by

$$v = a \sec^2\theta \ \dot{\theta}$$

Exercise 6D

1. The polar coordinates of a particle are given by $r = 2a\cos\theta$ and $\theta = \omega t$, where a and ω are constants. Find the speed and magnitude of the acceleration of the particle at any time.

2. The polar coordinates of a particle are given by $r = 2a(1 + \cos 2\pi t)$ and $\theta = 2\pi t$. Find the radial and transverse components of the velocity and acceleration of the particle for

   (a) $t = 0.25$,   (b) $t = 0.5$

3.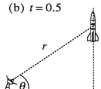

   The diagram above shows a rocket fired vertically and tracked by the radar. When θ reaches $30°$, $r = 7$ km, and $\dot\theta = 0.025$ rad s^{-1}. Find the magnitude of the velocity of the rocket at this time.

4. A bead moves on a rotating wire so that at time t seconds its polar coordinates (measured in metres and radians respectively) are

   $$r = 0.9 + 0.15t^2 \quad \text{and} \quad \theta = 0.12t^2.$$

   Find the radial and transverse components of the velocity and acceleration of the bead after the wire has rotated through $\dfrac{\pi}{3}$ from the position $\theta = 0$.

5. If r and θ in the previous question are $t^2 + t^3$ and $4t + t^3$ find the speed and magnitude of the acceleration of the bead for $t = 1$.

6. A particle describes the elliptic path defined by $r = \dfrac{5}{1 + 0.5\cos\pi t}$, $\theta = \pi t$. Distance is measured in metres, angle in radians and time in seconds. Find the speed and magnitude of the acceleration of the particle for $t = 1$.

7. A disc is made to rotate with constant angular speed ω and a small insect walks along a radius with constant speed u relative to the disc. Find the magnitude of the acceleration of the insect when it is at a distance r from the axis of rotation.

8. A particle describes the curve $r(\theta + 4) = 5$ in such a way that the transverse acceleration is always constant. Show that r will always be of the form $a + bt$.

9. A particle describes the curve $r = \dfrac{1}{a + \cos\theta}$, where a is a constant, so that $r^2\dot\theta = h$, where h is a constant. Show that $\dot r = h\sin\theta$ and find the acceleration of the particle in terms of a, h and r.

6.5   Application of polar coordinates

Polar coordinates are particularly useful for solving problems involving the motion of a particle acted on by forces which are directed towards a fixed point. They are also useful for some types of relative velocity problems where motion is directed towards a fixed point. The following are typical general examples involving the use of polar coordinates.

Example

A boat which is rowed with constant speed v relative to the water is rowed across a river which flows with constant speed v. The rower, throughout the journey, aims at a point O on the opposite bank directly opposite his start point. Given that the river is of width a find the path of the boat referred to polar coordinates with origin at O.

Solution

The position at any time is shown in the diagram. The rower's actual velocity will be the vector sum of the velocity v directed towards O and the velocity of the river parallel to the banks. The radial velocity is $v\cos\theta - v$ and the transverse velocity is $-v\sin\theta$. Therefore, using the velocity components in polar coordinates,

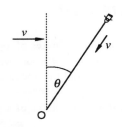

radial: $\qquad \dot{r} = v\cos\theta - v$

transverse: $\quad r\dot{\theta} = -v\sin\theta$

Dividing these equations gives

$$\frac{1}{r}\frac{dr}{d\theta} = -\frac{\cos\theta - 1}{\sin\theta}$$

the right hand side can be simplified to $-\tan\dfrac{\theta}{2}$ and both sides can

then be integrated to give $r = A\sec^2\dfrac{\theta}{2}$.

When $\theta = \dfrac{\pi}{2}$, $r = a$ so $A = \dfrac{a}{2}$ and $r = \dfrac{a}{2}\sec^2\dfrac{\theta}{2}$.

Why does $\dfrac{1}{r}\dfrac{dr}{d\theta} = \dfrac{\dot{r}}{r\dot{\theta}}$**?**

Example

A smooth straight cylindrical tube is made to rotate in a horizontal plane about a vertical axis through a point O of itself with constant angular speed ω. At time $t = 0$ a particle of mass m is projected along the tube towards O, from a point at a distance a from O, with speed ωa relative to the tube. Find the distance of the particle from O at time t and the horizontal component of the reaction of the tube at this time.

Solution

This problem is effectively a disguised 'polar coordinate' problem with $\dot{\theta} = \omega$. Since the tube is smooth there is no force along it and therefore the radial acceleration is zero. Substituting $\dot{\theta} = \omega$ into the expression for radial acceleration gives

$$\ddot{r} - r\omega^2 = 0$$

This is a linear second order differential equation and from Chapter 3 the general solution is given by

$$r = Ae^{-\omega t} + Be^{\omega t}$$

where A and B are constants.

Check that r is in fact a solution of the differential equation.

The initial conditions are, at $t = 0$

$$r = a \text{ and } \dot{r} = -a\omega$$

Hence $\qquad a = A + B, \ -a\omega = -\omega(A - B)$

and $\qquad A = a, B = 0$

$$r = ae^{-\omega t}$$

The only horizontal force exerted by the tube is perpendicular to the sides, i.e. in the transverse direction and this is equal to mass times the transverse acceleration, i.e.

$$m \frac{1}{r} \frac{d}{dt}\left(r^2 \dot{\theta}\right) = m \frac{1}{r} \frac{d}{dt}\left(r^2 \omega\right)$$

$$= 2ma\omega r \dot{r}$$

$$= -2ma\omega^2 e^{-\omega t}$$

Example

A light elastic string of natural length a and modulus of elasticity $3mg$, carries a particle of mass $2m$ at one end. The other end is attached to a fixed point O on a smooth table, and initially the particle is at rest on the table with the string straight and of length $2a$. It is then set in motion with initial speed $4\sqrt{ga}$ perpendicular to the string. Show that the particle's radial speed will be zero when the spring is of length $4a$.

Solution

This problem is of the type to be solved by using polar coordinates and the general position is shown in the diagram.

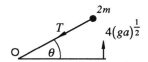

The first step in solving the problem is to write down the radial and transverse equations of motion. These are

radial: $\qquad 2m\left(\ddot{r} - r\dot{\theta}^2\right) = -T$

transverse: $\qquad 2m \frac{1}{r} \frac{d}{dt}\left(r^2 \dot{\theta}\right) = 0$ (no transverse force)

where T denotes the tension in the string and

$$T = \frac{3mg}{a}(r - a)$$

The second equation is easy to solve and gives

$$r^2\dot\theta = \text{constant} = h$$

(This condition occurs in all problems with central force, i.e. zero transverse acceleration, and its significance will be examined more carefully in discussing planetary orbits.) Now $r^2\dot\theta = r\left(r\dot\theta\right)$, which is the product of the velocity component perpendicular to the string and the distance from O. These are given initially so

$$h = 2a\left(4\sqrt{ga}\right) = 8a\sqrt{ga}$$

The next step is to integrate the radial equation, but it is actually easier in problems like this (where there is no friction and the only horizontal force acting on the particle is the tension in an elastic string) to use the conservation of energy. This gives

$$m\left(\dot r^2 + r^2\dot\theta^2\right) + \frac{3mg}{2a}(r-a)^2 = K \quad (K \text{ constant})$$

The factor multiplying m is the square of the speed of the particle and the other term is the elastic energy. The initial conditions give the constant, K as $\dfrac{3mga}{2}$ and substituting for $\dot\theta$ in terms of r, using

$$r^2\dot\theta = 8a\sqrt{ga}$$

gives $\qquad m\left(\dot r^2 + \dfrac{64a^3g}{r^2}\right) + \dfrac{3mg}{2a}(r-a)^2 = \dfrac{35mga}{2}$

Substituting $r = 4a$ shows that $\dot r = 0$ as required.

The question could, instead of requiring the condition for $\dot r = 0$, have asked for proof that r always varied between $2a$ and $4a$. This is a slightly harder demand but it can be answered as follows.

The equation above can be rearranged as

$$\dot r^2 = -\frac{g\left(3r^4 - 6ar^3 - 32a^2r^2 + 128a^4\right)}{2ar^2}$$

You know that the left hand side vanishes for $r = 2a$ and $4a$ so that it has factors $(r-2a)$ and $(4a-r)$. Therefore multiplying these, it has the factor $-\left(r^2 - 6ar + 8a^2\right)$. Dividing this into the right hand side gives the other factor as $3r^2 + 12ar + 16$. The equation

$$3r^2 + 12ar + 16 = 0$$

has complex roots so it is never zero and, by substituting a value of r, you can see that it is always positive. Therefore r lies between the required limits.

Activity 5

Try and get the equation for $\dot{r}^2$ above directly from the radial equation of motion; you need to carry out the following steps.

1. Substitute for T in terms of r, using Hooke's law, and $\dot{\theta}$ in terms of r, using $r^2\dot{\theta} = 8a\sqrt{ga}$.

2. Use the identity $\ddot{r} = \dot{r}\dfrac{d\dot{r}}{dr}$ (which you can prove using the chain rule) and integrate the equation with respect to r. You should obtain the equation .

Exercise 6E

1. A man swims across a river 100 m wide and he always heads for a tree directly opposite his starting point. He swims at a rate of 3 m s^{-1} in still water. Find the polar equation of his path referred to polar coordinates with origin at the tree so that his starting point is $r = 100$ m, $\theta = 0$, for the three cases when the river flows with a speed of

    (i) 1 m s^{-1} (ii) 3 m s^{-1} (iii) 4 m s^{-1}.

2. A pilot always keeps the nose of her plane directed towards a radar beacon which is initially 200 km away. A wind is blowing from the south at speed of 20 km h^{-1} and her speed relative to the wind is 300 km h^{-1}. Find the polar equation of her path relative to polar coordinates at the beacon and such that the initial point of the plane is $r = 200$ km, $\theta = 0$.

3. A smooth rod is rotated in a horizontal plane about a vertical axis through one end A. A smooth ring that can slide on the rod is projected from A with speed V relative to the rod. Find its distance from A at any subsequent time t.

4. A particle of mass m is attached to one end of a light elastic string of modulus mg and natural length a. The other end of the string is attached to a fixed point O on a smooth horizontal table. The particle is placed on the table and the string stretched to a length $3a$ when the particle is projected perpendicular to the string with speed v. In the subsequent motion the maximum length of the string is $5a$. Find v^2.

5. A particle P is fastened to one end of a string which passes through a small hole in a smooth horizontal table and supports a particle Q of equal mass which hangs beneath the table. P is held in contact with the table at a distance a from the hole and projected horizontally with velocity $\sqrt{\dfrac{ag}{3}}$ at right angles to that portion of the string resting on the table. Show that when the length of the string on the table is $\dfrac{a}{2}$, P is again moving at right angles to the portion of string on the table.

6. Assume that in question 5 the particle Q is replaced by one whose mass is three times that of P. Find the speed of Q when it has descended a distance $\dfrac{a}{2}$.

7. A particle of mass m on a smooth plane is attached to a fixed point O of the plane by a light spring of natural length a and modulus $2mg$. The particle is projected perpendicular to the spring with speed $3\sqrt{ga}$ with the spring at its natural length. Show that the distance r of the particle from O satisfies $a \le r \le 3a$.

8. Find for the motion in question 5 the tension in the string when the distance of P from the hole, O, is r and the mass of P is m.

9. Show that if the spring in Question 7 is replaced by one of modulus $20mg$ then the maximum length of the spring in the subsequent motion is $\dfrac{3a}{2}$.

10. A light elastic spring of natural length a and modulus mg carries a particle of mass m at one end. The other end is attached to a fixed point O on a smooth table and the particle is initially at rest on the table with the spring at its natural length. It is then projected with speed $\sqrt{ga}$ at an angle of 30° to the spring produced.

    Prove that the maximum length r of the spring in the subsequent motion satisfies the equation
    $$4r^4 - 8ar^3 + a^4 = 0.$$

11. A smooth hollow tube is made to rotate with constant angular speed ω about a horizontal axis through a point O of itself. A particle is released from relative rest at O at time $t = 0$ when the tube is horizontal. Find the distance of the particle from O at a subsequent time t.

6.6   Motion under central forces

A **central force** is one acting towards a fixed point O. It can be shown that the motion of a particle under the action of such a force will always be in the plane containing the initial velocity and the line from O to the initial point. There is initially no force acting perpendicular to this plane, the initial velocity perpendicular to the plane is zero and therefore there will be no tendency for motion perpendicular to the plane.

Polar coordinates are the most suitable ones for dealing with central force problems.

The only force acting is radial and it will also be assumed that its magnitude depends only on r and that the force is directed towards the origin. The radial force component F_r can be written as $-f(r)$. The radial and transverse equations of motion for a particle of mass m are

radial: $$m\left(\ddot{r} - r\dot{\theta}^2\right) = -f(r)$$

transverse: $$m\frac{1}{r}\frac{d}{dt}\left(r^2\dot{\theta}\right) = 0$$

The transverse equation gives

$$\boxed{mr^2\dot{\theta} = \text{constant}}$$

This, as was mentioned above, is a fundamental result for central force theory and it is necessary to look at it more carefully. (The factor m has been included since it makes the explanation slightly simpler.)

Considering the vector with radial and transverse components, $m\dot{r}$ and $mr\dot{\theta}$, as a force, it can be seen from the diagram that $mr^2\dot{\theta}$ can be regarded as the moment of this 'force' about O. The vector is, in fact, the momentum and so $mr^2\dot{\theta}$ is the **moment of the momentum**, or angular momentum, about O.

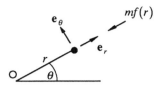

You know the from the vector definition of moment in Chapter 2 that the moment of momentum about O is $\mathbf{r} \times m\dot{\mathbf{r}}$ and using

$$\mathbf{r} = r\mathbf{e}_r \text{ and } \dot{\mathbf{r}} = \dot{r}\mathbf{e}_r + r\dot{\theta}\mathbf{e}_\theta$$

gives the angular momentum as $mr^2\dot{\theta}\mathbf{k}$, where $\mathbf{k}$ is a unit vector perpendicular to the plane of the polar coordinates. Therefore, exactly as for the moment of a force, angular momentum is a vector perpendicular to the plane of motion. It can therefore be treated in the same way as a scalar with a sign determined by the corkscrew rule.

To summarise, for a central force the angular momentum about the origin is conserved, in particular

$$\boxed{r^2\dot{\theta} = \text{constant}}$$

and the motion is always planar.

Having found as much information as possible from the transverse equation of motion the next step is to integrate the radial equation. This can be done directly (see Activity 6) but it is much simpler to use **conservation of energy**.

The work-energy principle states that the change in kinetic energy is the work done by the forces acting.

For the force $f(r)$ acting radially inwards the work done in moving from $r = a$ to $r = b$ along the radius is

$$\int_a^b f(s)ds$$

Therefore

$$\text{kinetic energy change } = \int_a^b f(s)ds$$

The integral can be written as

$$\int_X^b f(s)ds - \int_X^a f(s)ds$$

where X is some standard position and therefore

$$(\text{KE})_{r=b} + \int_X^b f(s)ds = (\text{KE})_{r=a} + \int_X^a f(s)ds$$

This is the equation of **conservation of energy** if $\int_X^r f(s)ds$ is defined as the **potential energy** at a general point. This is exactly the same kind of definition as you used to define the elastic energy of a spring. In central force problems X is usually taken as infinity, since most practically occurring central forces tend to zero as r becomes infinite and taking X as infinite avoids having an arbitrary constant in the potential energy. Therefore applying the conservation of energy to the motion of a particle gives

$$\frac{1}{2}m\left(\dot{r}^2 + r^2\dot{\theta}\right) + \int_\infty^r f(s)ds = \text{constant}$$

An alternative method of arriving at this equation is to use the idea that work done is equal to minus the change in potential energy.

In the above calculation work done was calculated by assuming that motion from point to point was along the radius vector whereas, in fact, the path from one point to another will not normally be in a straight line. It is however possible to show that the work done in travelling from (a, θ_1) to (b, θ_2) is just the work done in going from $r = a$ to $r = b$ for any constant value of θ. This requires more mathematical knowledge than you have and an alternative vector proof is given at the end of the chapter. You can also obtain the equation directly from integrating the radial equation of motion (See Activity below).

Activity 6

Carry out the following steps

(1) Replace $\dot{\theta}$, using $r^2\dot{\theta} = h$, in the radial equation.

(2) Use the identity $\ddot{r} = \dot{r}\dfrac{d\dot{r}}{dr}$ and integrate the equation with respect to r.

(3) Replace h by $\dot{r}^2\dot{\theta}$ in the resulting equation and you should get the conservation of energy equation above.

This general theory will now be applied to planetary motion.

Planetary motion

The theory of planetary motion is based on the model of gravitational attraction postulated by Newton and described in section 1.3 of the *Mechanics* text.

Before Newton postulated his theory of gravitation Kepler had formulated three laws on the basis of empirical observation.

Kepler's laws

1. The planets move in elliptic orbits round the sun as focus.
2. The position vector relative to the sun sweeps out equal areas in equal times.
3. The ratio of the square of the orbital period to the cube of the mean distance from the sun is the same for all planets. (The mean distance is the mean of the maximum and minimum distances)

Newton's model had therefore, if at all possible, to be consistent with Kepler's laws.

Newton's model assumed

(1) the sun is fixed;

(2) the planets and the sun can be treated as points;

(3) the force of the sun (mass M) on a planet of mass m is an attractive force directed along the line joining them and of

magnitude $\dfrac{GMm}{d^2}$, where d is the distance between them

and G is the universal constant of gravitation.

(The values currently used are $G = 6.673 \times 10^{-11} \mathrm{m}^3 \, \mathrm{kg}^{-1} \, \mathrm{s}^{-2}$,

$M = 5.976 \times 10^{25}$ kg so that the product GM is $3.988 \times 10^{14} \, \mathrm{m}^3 \, \mathrm{s}^{-2}$)

These assumptions will now be examined to see whether they lead to a model consistent with Kepler's laws.

Since the force acts along the line joining a planet to the sun (i.e. is a central force) is, from the work above, you know that

$$r^2 \dot{\theta} = \text{constant}$$

Referring to the diagram and assuming $\delta\theta$ to be the change in θ in time δt you can see that the element of area swept out in time

δt is $\dfrac{1}{2} r^2 \delta\theta$, so that the rate of sweep of area is $\dfrac{1}{2} r^2 \dot{\theta}$. The

constancy of angular momentum is therefore equivalent to saying that the rate of sweep of area is constant. This is effectively Kepler's second law.

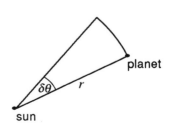

It is possible to make some progress with the third law by considering the special case of **circular orbits** described at constant speed. In this case the acceleration $r\dot{\theta}^2$ towards the centre is equal to

$$\frac{GM}{r^2} \text{ so that } \dot{\theta}^2 = \frac{GM}{r^3}$$

Denoting the period by T it follows that the area swept out in the period is

$$\frac{1}{2} r^2 \dot{\theta} T$$

and this is also equal to the area of the circle of radius r. Hence

$$\frac{1}{2} r^2 \dot{\theta} T = \pi r^2$$

$$\Rightarrow \quad T = \frac{2\pi}{\dot{\theta}}$$

and using the expression found above for $\dot{\theta}^2$ gives

$$\boxed{T^2 = \frac{4\pi^2 r^3}{GM}}$$

For a circle the mean distance is r so that $\dfrac{T^2}{r^3}$ is constant, which is consistent with Kepler's third law. At the end of the chapter it will be shown that the law is valid for all closed orbits but that there has to be a slight correction to allow for the motion of the sun.

Further progress needs the use of the conservation ofenergy equation and for a central force of the form $f = \dfrac{GMm}{r^2}$ this becomes

$$\frac{m}{2}\left(\dot{r}^2 + r^2\dot{\theta}^2\right) - \frac{GMm}{r} = \text{constant.}$$

This equation can be rewritten, substituting for $\dot{\theta}$ using $r^2\dot{\theta} = h$, as

$$\dot{r}^2 + \frac{h^2}{r^2} - \frac{2GM}{r} = \text{constant}$$

Denoting the constant by k (k is therefore twice the energy per unit mass) and GM by μ the equation can be rearranged to give $\dot{r}^2$ in terms of r so that

$$\dot{r}^2 = \frac{kr^2 + 2\mu r - h^2}{r^2}$$

This is a differential equation which can be solved by separation of variables to give r in terms of t, and to find out the form of the path it is necessary to do this. However, you can obtain a reasonable amount of information without much calculation.

First though some simple properties of the quadratic equation are needed.

Activity 7

For the quadratic equation

$$ax^2 + bx + c = 0$$

show that its roots α and β satisfy

$$\alpha + \beta = -\frac{b}{a} \quad \text{and} \quad \alpha\beta = \frac{c}{a}$$

In the quadratic $kr^2 + 2\mu r - h^2 = 0$, which occurs on the right hand side, the sum of the roots is $\dfrac{-2\mu}{k}$ and the product of the roots is $\dfrac{-h^2}{k}$ so, for $k < 0$, the roots are both positive and the graph will be as in the diagram with roots at r_1 and r_2 .

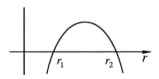

For $r = r_1$ and $r = r_2$, $\dot{r}$ will be zero so the path will be perpendicular to the radius vector. Also since $\dot{r}^2$ has to be positive then $r_1 \le r \le r_2$.

Since $r^2\dot{\theta} = h$ you can see that $\dot{\theta}$ never changes sign and therefore the path must have $r_1 \le r \le r_2$ and θ continuously increasing or decreasing, so a possible path is shown by the diagram opposite.

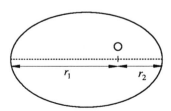

The positions of maximum and minimum distance are referred to as the **perigee** and the **apogee** respectively.

For $k > 0$ there will only be one positive root since the product of the roots is negative. Then the graph of the quadratic is as shown in the diagram.

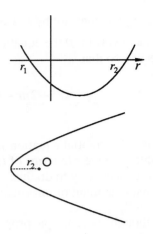

Again using the fact that $\dot{\theta}$ never changes sign you see that the path will be roughly as shown opposite with $r \geq r_2$.

The above shows that the path will either be closed or go to infinity, depending on the sign of k, which is twice the energy per unit mass. Substituting $k = 0$ in the quadratic shows that it will have only one positive root so that its path will be roughly similar to that for $k > 0$.

Therefore if a particle has speed v at a distance r from O then it will have a closed path for $v^2 - \dfrac{2\mu}{r} < 0$ and its path will go to infinity otherwise. Therefore if a particle is projected from any point at a distance r with speed v then in order for it to escape to infinity its speed must satisfy

$$\boxed{v \geq \sqrt{\dfrac{2\mu}{r}}}$$

This latter quantity is known as the **escape velocity**.

These results can now be used to give some support to Kepler's first law. You may not have met the **ellipse** before – it is a closed curve of the type shown for $k > 0$. You need more precise evidence before establishing that Kepler's first law does hold and this follows in the next section. It will be shown that all closed orbits are ellipses and, to avoid confusion, it seems reasonable to make this assumption from now on. The ellipse is the curve defined by the equation

$$\frac{x^2}{a^2} + \frac{y^2}{b^2} = 1$$

for real a and b.

Activity 8

Use the equation for an ellipse and a graphic calculator to plot ellipses for various values of a and b and see whether they are of the general shape found for $k > 0$.

The other curves found are not ellipses but they are other examples of curves known as conics (they occur when a cone is sliced in various ways). It turns out that for $k > 0$ the curves are **hyperbolae**, these are curves defined by

$$\frac{x^2}{a^2} - \frac{y^2}{b^2} = 1$$

for real a and b.

Activity 9

Use the equation for a hyperbola and a graphic calculator to plot hyperbolae for various values of a and b and see whether they are of the general shape found for $k > 0$.

(You will notice that there will be two separate curves.)

The curves found for $k = 0$ turn out to be parabolae. These have an equation of the form

$$\boxed{y^2 = 4ax}$$

and you have probably come across them before.

Activity 10

Use a graphic calculator to plot parabolae for various values of a and find the precise way in which they vary from hyperbolae.

It is possible to obtain information about the motion of particles (satellites, space shuttles, etc) by using the equation of conservation of energy and the conservation of angular momentum, and this is illustrated in the following examples. The perigee and apogee are particularly important because they are the points from which a spacecraft or shuttle can be most easily moved from one circular orbit to another.

The diagram shows a craft on a circular path being given a boost in speed at A so that it describes an elliptic path with apogee at B. It is then given a further boost so that it will then follow the circular path through B.

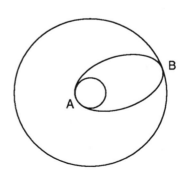

Some of the numbers occurring in planetary calculations are rather awkward and therefore, in some of the Examples and Exercises, artificial problems with simple numbers are used so that you can first understand the basic ideas without too much arithmetic or algebra. These simpler problems can be created from real ones by changing units, and therefore no units are used in these problems.

Example

The period of Callisto, one of Jupiter's moons, is 16 days 18 hours and 28 minutes and the radius of its orbit (assumed circular) is 1.884×10^6 km. Estimate the mass of Jupiter.

Solution

If the angular speed of the satellite at a distance R from the centre of Jupiter is ω then the formula for acceleration in a circle gives

$$\omega^2 R = \frac{GM}{R^2}$$

where M now denotes the mass of Jupiter .

The period T is given by $T = \frac{2\pi}{\omega}$ and therefore

$$M = \frac{R^3}{G}\left(\frac{2\pi}{T}\right)^2$$

This is the result obtained before when looking at Kepler's laws.

The mass is found by substituting values in the above formula and it is important to convert all the quantities to the correct units. In this case

$$T = 1441680\text{s}, \ G = 6.673 \times 10^{-11}\text{m}^3 \text{ kg}^{-1}\text{s}^{-2}, \ R = 1.884 \times 10^9\text{m}$$

and these give $M = 1.903 \times 10^{27}\text{kg}$

Example

A spacecraft returning from a mission has a speed of 7000 m s^{-1} at a distance of 7500 km from the earth's centre. Find its speed at a distance of 7000 km from the earth's centre. Assume that $\mu = 3.988 \times 10^{14}\text{m}^3 \text{ s}^{-2} (= GM)$.

Solution

You are given speed and distance at one instant and this gives the energy. This problem can then be solved by using the equation of conservation of energy.

If v_1 and r_1 are values of speed and distance at one instant and v_2 and r_2 are the corresponding values at a different time then, by using the energy equation,

$$v_1^2 - \frac{2\mu}{r_1} = v_2^2 - \frac{2\mu}{r_2}$$

In this case $v_1 = 7000\,\text{m s}^{-1}$, $r_1 = 7500 \times 10^3\,\text{m}$, $r_2 = 7000 \times 10^3\,\text{m}$. Substituting these values and the numerical value of μ gives $v_2 = 7523\,\text{m s}^{-1}$.

Example

A particle is acted on by a force directed to a point O such that its acceleration towards O is $\frac{6}{r^2}$, where r is the distance from O. It is projected from a point at a distance 1 from O with speed 2 perpendicular to the radius vector from O. Find its distance from O when it is next moving perpendicular to the radius vector from O.

Solution

The initial condition shows that the angular momentum (per unit mass) is 2 and the energy conservation equation gives, using the initial values,

$$v^2 - \frac{12}{r} = -8$$

The velocity will be perpendicular to the radius vector when the radial velocity is zero and at these points

$$vr = \text{angular momentum per unit mass} = 2$$

Therefore substituting in the equation above gives

$$\frac{4}{r^2} - \frac{12}{r} = -8$$

This is a particular case of the quadratic examined earlier. You can solve it using the formula but it is much easier to use the fact that you know one solution ($r = 1$) and that the product of the roots, for a quadratic in $\dfrac{1}{r}$, is 2 so that $r = \dfrac{1}{2}$ is the second solution.

Substituting in $vr = 2$ gives $v = 4$.

Exercise 6F

Questions 1 to 5 refer to the motion of a particle under the action of a central force producing an acceleration $\dfrac{\mu}{r^2}$ for various values of μ.

1. In this question $\mu = 8$. A particle has speed 3 when at a distance 4 from O. Find its speed when at a distance 5 from O.

2. In this question $\mu = 54$. A particle is projected from a point at a distance 3 from O with speed 6 so that, as shown in the diagram below, the perpendicular distance from O to the vector defining the initial velocity is 2. Find the smallest distance between the particle and O and its speed in this position.

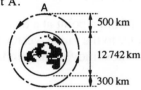

3. In this question $\mu = 8$. A particle is projected from a point at a distance 4 from O with speed 1 with the velocity of projection being perpendicular to the radius vector from O. Find the distance of the particle from O when it is again moving perpendicular to the radius vector from O.

4. In this question $\mu = 4$. The smallest and greatest distances from O of a particle travelling in an elliptic path are 2 and 6. Find, for the position when the particle is at its furthest distance from O, the increase in speed that it would have to be given at this point in order for it to move in a circular path of radius 6.

5. In this question $\mu = 21$. A particle is describing a circle of unit radius and it is desired to move it to a path of radius 6, as shown in the diagram, by first increasing its speed at A and then further increasing its speed at B. Find the increases in speed required at the two points.

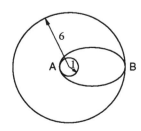

6. The period of another of Jupiter's satellites, Io, is 1 day, 18 hours and 28 minutes. The radius of its circular orbit is 421 307 km. Use these facts to find another estimate of the mass of Jupiter.

In questions 7 to 10 GM is to be taken equal to $3.988 \times 10^{14} \, \text{m}^3 \, \text{s}^{-2}$ and the radius of the earth as 6371 km.

7. A spacecraft has a speed of 22 000 km h^{-1} at a distance of 7200 km from the earth's centre. Find its speed at a distance of 6800 km from the earth's centre.

8. The diagram below shows an elliptic orbit of a spacecraft with apogee altitude of 500 km and perigee altitude of 300 km. Find the speed of the particle at A.

   A

   500 km

   12 742 km

   300 km

9. A satellite is launched at a distance of 7000 km from the centre of the earth so that it is initially moving perpendicular to the radius vector with speed 10 000 m s^{-1}.

   Find its maximum distance from the centre of the earth.

10. A satellite describing a circle of radius 6800 km around the centre of the earth is to be moved into a circular orbit of radius 36 000 km as in question 5. Find the two increases in velocity required to achieve this.

11. A satellite is moving perpendicular to the radius vector with speed $\dfrac{1}{2}\sqrt{\dfrac{GM}{a}}$ at a distance a from the centre of the earth. Find its distance from the earth's centre when it is next moving perpendicular to the radius vector.

12. A satellite describing a circular orbit of radius a is to be transferred, as in question 5, to a circular orbit of radius $5a$. Find the increases in speed necessary to achieve this.

6.7   Equation of orbit

In order to make further progress it is necessary to work out the orbit of a particle and this, in turn, means solving the radial equation

$$m\left(\ddot{r} - r\dot{\theta}^2\right) = -f(r)$$

to find r in terms of t. This turns out to be quite a challenge though it is straightforward to get r in terms of θ. To do this it is necessary to change variable from r to θ and using the chain rule

$$\frac{d}{dt} = \dot{\theta}\frac{d}{d\theta}$$

It also turns out to be helpful to change variables from r to $u = \dfrac{1}{r}$ so that

$$\dot{r} = \frac{d}{dt}\left(\frac{1}{u}\right)$$

$$= -\frac{1}{u^2}\frac{du}{dt}$$

$$= -\frac{\dot{\theta}}{u^2}\frac{du}{d\theta}$$

Since

$$\frac{\dot{\theta}}{u^2} = r^2\dot{\theta} = h,$$

then
$$\dot{r} = -h\frac{du}{d\theta}$$

Differentiating again with respect to t gives

$$\ddot{r} = -h\dot{\theta}\frac{d^2 u}{d\theta^2}$$

Substituting this expression into the radial equation of motion when $f(r) = \dfrac{GMm}{r^2}$ and substituting for $\dot{\theta}$, using $r^2\dot{\theta} = h$, and then replacing r by $\dfrac{1}{u}$ gives

$$\frac{h}{r^2}\frac{d^2u}{d\theta^2}+r\frac{h^2}{r^4}=\frac{GM}{r^2}$$

$$\Rightarrow \quad \boxed{\frac{d^2u}{d\theta^2}+u=\frac{GM}{h^2}}$$

This is a type of equation that you met in Chapter 4; a particular integral is $\dfrac{GM}{h^2}$ and the complementary function is $A\cos(\theta-\alpha)$, where A and α are arbitrary constants.

The solution for r is therefore

$$\boxed{\frac{1}{r}=\frac{GM}{h^2}+A\cos(\theta-\alpha)}$$

The problem of finding a particular orbit then becomes that of finding the above arbitrary constants from initial conditions and this is very similar to solving problems of simple harmonic motion. In order to relate the result to other areas of Mathematics it is helpful to rearrange the equation as

$$\frac{1}{r}=l+e\cos(\theta-\alpha)$$

where l is $\dfrac{h^2}{GM}$ and e is another arbitrary constant.

The above form is the standard form for the equation of a **conic** in polar coordinates. There are, as mentioned earlier, three types of conics, namely ellipses, parabolae and hyperbolae, and these correspond to $e<1$, $e=1$ and $e>1$ respectively. You are unlikely to know any of the geometric properties of the conics and it will be sufficient if you can just visualise the general shapes of these curves. To do this take $\alpha=0$ for simplicity and consider the curve

$$\boxed{\frac{l}{r}=1+e\cos\theta}$$

For $e<1$ the minimum value of r occurs for $\theta=0$ and the maximum for $\theta=\pi$, and r increases from its minimum value at $\theta=0$ to its maximum value at $\theta=\pi$ and then decreases back to its minimum value as θ increases to 2π. The path will therefore be as in the diagram ($e=0$ corresponds to a circle).

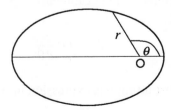

The minimum and maximum values of r are $\dfrac{1}{1+e}$ and $\dfrac{1}{1-e}$ and the line joining them is called the major axis of the ellipse. The length of this is usually denoted by a so that $a = \dfrac{1}{1-e^2}$. The other parameter b in the equation $\dfrac{x^2}{a^2} + \dfrac{y^2}{b^2} = 1$ is given by

$$b^2 = a^2\left(1-e^2\right).$$

Activity 11

Use a graphic calculator to plot

$$\frac{l}{r} = 1 + e\cos\theta$$

for various values of $e < 1$ and various values of l. If your graphic calculator cannot give plots in polar coordinates then use the expressions above for a and b in the cartesian equation of the ellipse.

The origin for the cartesian equation is not the same as that for the polar equation. In the latter case the origin is at a point called the **focus** of the ellipse; there are two of these, on the major axis and at a distance ae from the origin used in the cartesian equation.

For $e \geq 1$ the minimum value of r still occurs at $\theta = 0$ and as θ increases, r increases but you will see that for $\cos\theta = -\dfrac{1}{e}$,

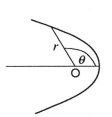

r becomes infinite and it is not defined for $\theta > -\arccos\left(\dfrac{1}{e}\right)$. The curve is therefore as in the diagram with the curve tending to be tangent to the two lines with $\cos\theta = -\dfrac{1}{e}$; these are the asymptotes of the curve which is a hyperbola. The major axis is the line joining the origin to the nearest point and the values of a and b for substitution in the cartesian equation

$$\frac{x^2}{a^2} - \frac{y^2}{b^2} = 1$$

are $$l = \frac{a}{e^2-1}, \quad b^2 = a^2\left(e^2-1\right)$$

Activity 12

Use a graphic calculator to plot $\dfrac{l}{r} = 1 + e\cos\theta$ for various values

of $e > 1$ and various values of l.

If your graphic calculator cannot give plots in polar coordinates then use the expressions above for a and b in the cartesian equation of the hyperbola.

The origin of the polar equation is again at the focus of the hyperbola, which is at a distance of ae from the origin in cartesian coordinates.

The case $e = 1$ is similar to the previous one in that the curve goes to infinity but r is defined for all θ, i.e. there are no asymptotes.

The curve is now a parabola, its cartesian form is $y^2 = 4ax$ and the origin of the polar system is at the focus of the parabola which is at a distance a from the origin of cartesian coordinates. (Replacing θ by $\theta - \alpha$ means that the major axis is now at an angle α to the line $\theta = 0$).

The above analysis is not necessary in finding the polar equations of the orbits though it may help you to interpret your results. The only fact that is worth remembering, rather than have to derive it from first principles, is that $l = \dfrac{h^2}{GM}$.

If you have difficulty in remembering it you can work it out very quickly from the results for a circular orbit as follows. For a circular orbit moving in a circle of radius a with speed v, the radial equation of motion is

$$\frac{GM}{a^2} = \frac{v^2}{a}$$

Also $h = va$ so eliminating v gives $a = \dfrac{h^2}{GM}$. For a circular orbit

$e = 0$, so $l = r$ and therefore $l = \dfrac{h^2}{GM}$.

To summarise, the starting point in determining the equation of a path is

$$\boxed{\frac{l}{r} = 1 + e\cos\theta(\theta - \alpha), \text{ with } l = \frac{h^2}{GM}}$$

The initial conditions are then used to find h, e and α.

Example

A particle initially at a distance $2a$ from the centre of force O is projected perpendicular to the radius vector with speed $\frac{1}{3}\sqrt{\frac{GM}{a}}$. Find the equation of the subsequent orbit.

Solution

The initial position is as shown in the diagram and $\theta = 0$ will be taken to be the initial line. The key step is working out h; this is ,

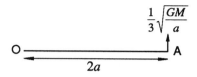

from the diagram, $\frac{2}{3}\sqrt{GMa}$ so that $l = \frac{4a}{9}$. The equation of the orbit is therefore

$$\frac{4a}{9r} = 1 + e\cos(\theta - \alpha)$$

Initially $r = 2a$, $\theta = 0$ and $\dot{r} = 0$ and therefore

$$\frac{2}{9} = 1 + e\cos\alpha$$

and from differentiating the orbit equation with respect to t,

$$-\frac{4a\dot{r}}{9r^2} = -e\sin(\theta - \alpha)\dot{\theta}$$

giving $\qquad 0 = \dot{\theta}e\sin\alpha$

Therefore, so that e is positive, $\alpha = \pi$ and $e = \frac{7}{9}$.

The equation of the orbit is therefore

$$\boxed{\frac{4a}{9r} = 1 - \frac{7}{9}\cos\theta}$$

The only significance of the minus sign is that $\theta = 0$ is the furthest point from O so that the orbit will be as shown in the diagram.

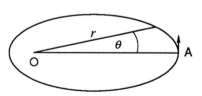

Example

A particle initially at the point A at a distance a from the centre of force O is projected with speed $\sqrt{\frac{GM}{2a}}$ at an angle of $\frac{\pi}{4}$ to OA produced. Find the equation of the subsequent orbit.

Solution

The initial position is as shown in the diagram and $\theta = 0$ will be taken to be the initial line. You will see from the diagram that

$h = \frac{1}{2}\sqrt{GMa}$ so that $l = \frac{a}{4}$. The equation of the orbit is therefore

$$\frac{a}{4r} = 1 + e\cos(\theta - \alpha)$$

Initially $r = a$ and $\dot{r} = \frac{1}{2}\sqrt{\frac{GM}{a}}$ and therefore

$$\frac{1}{4} = 1 + e\cos\alpha$$

$$\Rightarrow \quad e\cos\alpha = \frac{3}{4}$$

Differentiating the polar equation with respect to t gives

$$-\frac{\dot{r}}{r^2} = e\dot{\theta}\sin(\theta - \alpha)$$

and substituting for $\dot{r}$, r, θ and $\dot{\theta}$ gives $e\sin\alpha = -\frac{1}{4}$.

Squaring and adding these equations gives $e = \sqrt{\frac{5}{8}}$ and dividing

the equations, gives $\tan\alpha = \frac{1}{3}$. Since both $\sin\alpha$ and $\cos\alpha$ are

negative this gives $\alpha = \pi + \beta$, where β is the acute angle such that

$\tan\beta = \frac{1}{3}$.

The equation of the path is therefore

$$\frac{a}{4r} = 1 - \sqrt{\frac{5}{8}}\cos(\theta - \beta)$$

and this is shown in the diagram.

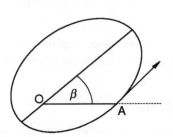

Exercise 6G

All the questions refer to motion under the attractive central force $\dfrac{GM}{r^2}$ where r is the distance from the centre O.

1. Find the subsequent orbit of a particle projected, when at a distance a from O, perpendicular to the radius vector with

   (i) speed $\dfrac{1}{4}\sqrt{\dfrac{GM}{a}}$,

   (ii) speed $2\sqrt{\dfrac{GM}{a}}$.

2. A spacecraft is describing a circle of radius c with constant speed v when its speed is suddenly reduced to $\dfrac{v}{2}$. Find the subsequent orbit.

3. Find the subsequent orbit of a particle projected from a point at a distance a from O with velocity components $\sqrt{\dfrac{GM}{a}}$ radially outwards and $2\sqrt{\dfrac{GM}{a}}$ perpendicular to the radius vector.

4. A particle is projected with speed $\sqrt{\dfrac{GM}{a}}$ from a point A at distance a from O at an acute angle β to AO. Find its subsequent orbit.

5. A satellite describing a circle of radius a is struck by a meteor shower which gives it a radial velocity outwards of $\sqrt{\dfrac{GM}{3a}}$ without changing its transverse velocity component. Find its subsequent orbit.

*6.8 Proofs and derivations

The following analysis is added for completeness. The first result has already been assumed but here is the formal proof using vectors.

Proof that paths under a central force are all in a plane

The equation of motion under a central force will be of the form

$$m\ddot{\mathbf{r}} = p\mathbf{r}$$

Taking the vector product of this with $\mathbf{r}$ gives

$$\mathbf{r} \times \ddot{\mathbf{r}} = 0$$

You can show that, for any vectors $\mathbf{a}$ and $\mathbf{b}$,

$$\frac{d}{dt}(\mathbf{a} \times \mathbf{b}) = \mathbf{a} \times \frac{d\mathbf{b}}{dt} + \mathbf{b} \times \frac{d\mathbf{a}}{dt}$$

so $$\frac{d}{dt}(\mathbf{r} \times \dot{\mathbf{r}}) = \mathbf{r} \times \ddot{\mathbf{r}} + \dot{\mathbf{r}} \times \dot{\mathbf{r}}$$

The second term in this equation is zero therefore, integrating the equation,

$$\mathbf{r} \times \dot{\mathbf{r}} = \text{constant} = \mathbf{h} \quad \text{(say)}$$

This is merely showing again that angular momentum is conserved. Taking the scalar product of **h** with **r** and using the fact that **r** is perpendicular to $\mathbf{r} \times \dot{\mathbf{r}}$ gives

$$\mathbf{h} \times \mathbf{r} = 0$$

This you should recognise as the equation of a **plane** through the origin.

Alternative derivation of the energy equation

The next result is an alternative form of the energy equation, derived this time using vectors.

For the inverse square law the equation of motion becomes

$$m\ddot{\mathbf{r}} = -\frac{GMm}{r^3}\mathbf{r}$$

The cube has to be inserted so as to keep the magnitude of the force as $\dfrac{GMm}{r^2}$.

Scalar multiplication of the equation by $\dot{\mathbf{r}}$ gives

$$m\dot{\mathbf{r}}.\ddot{\mathbf{r}} = -\frac{GMm}{r^3}\mathbf{r}.\dot{\mathbf{r}}$$

You can show that for any vectors **a** and **b**

$$\frac{d}{dt}(\mathbf{a}.\mathbf{b}) = \mathbf{a}.\frac{d\mathbf{b}}{dt} + \mathbf{b}.\frac{d\mathbf{a}}{dt}$$

so that

$$2\dot{\mathbf{r}}.\ddot{\mathbf{r}} = \frac{d}{dt}(\dot{\mathbf{r}}.\dot{\mathbf{r}}) \text{ and } 2\mathbf{r}.\dot{\mathbf{r}} = \frac{d}{dt}(\mathbf{r}.\mathbf{r})$$

Also $\mathbf{r}.\mathbf{r} = r^2$ and $\dot{\mathbf{r}}.\dot{\mathbf{r}} = \dot{r}^2$ and making these substitutions gives

$$\frac{1}{2}\frac{d\dot{r}^2}{dt} = -\frac{GM}{2r^3}\frac{dr^2}{dt} = -\frac{GM\dot{r}}{r^2} = \frac{d}{dt}\left(\frac{GM}{r}\right)$$

Integrating this gives

$$\frac{1}{2}\dot{r}^2 - \frac{GM}{r} = \text{constant}$$

Since $\dot{r}^2$ is the speed, this is the equation of conservation of energy.

One final result relates to planetary motion.

More about Kepler's third law

In looking at Kepler's third law for a circle, the area swept out in the period T was found as

$$\frac{1}{2}r^2\dot{\theta}T = \frac{1}{2}hT$$

This is equal to the total area swept out and for an ellipse the total area is known to be $\pi a^2\sqrt{1-e^2}$, so that

$$\frac{T^2}{4\pi^2} = \frac{a^4(1-e^2)}{h^2}$$

$$= \frac{la^3}{h^2}$$

Also $\frac{h^2}{l} = GM$ and therefore T^2 is proportional to a^3 for all ellipses. Since a is the mean of the greatest and least distances this confirms Kepler's third law.

There is also a slight correction necessary to Kepler's law to take into account that the sun moves. Letting the position vectors of the sun and a planet of mass m be denoted by $\mathbf{r}_1$ and $\mathbf{r}_2$ respectively, their equations of motion are

$$M\ddot{\mathbf{r}}_1 = \frac{GMm}{r^3}(\mathbf{r}_2 - \mathbf{r}_1)$$

$$m\ddot{\mathbf{r}}_2 = -\frac{GMm}{r^3}(\mathbf{r}_2 - \mathbf{r}_1)$$

where r is the distance between the planet and the sun and $r = |\mathbf{r}_2 - \mathbf{r}_1|$.

Dividing the first equation by M and the second by m and subtracting gives

$$\ddot{\mathbf{r}}_2 - \ddot{\mathbf{r}}_1 = -\frac{G(M+m)}{r^3}(\mathbf{r}_2 - \mathbf{r}_1)$$

or, in scalar terms

$$\ddot{r} = -\frac{G(M+m)}{r^2}$$

Therefore in the motion relative to the sun the quantity GM has to be replaced by $G(M+m)$ so that there will be a slight correction to the third law.

6.9 Miscellaneous Exercises

1. (a) The figure shows a circle, centre the origin O and radius a. P is a point which moves anti-clockwise around the circle such that its position vector $\mathbf{r}$, relative to O, is given by

$$\mathbf{r} = a\cos\theta\mathbf{i} + a\sin\theta\mathbf{j},$$

where θ is the angle which OP makes with the positive x-axis.

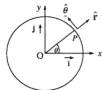

Find the unit vector $\hat{\mathbf{r}}$ in the direction of $\mathbf{r}$ and show that

$$\frac{d\hat{\mathbf{r}}}{dt} = \dot{\theta}\,\hat{\underset{\sim}{\theta}},$$

where $\hat{\underset{\sim}{\theta}} = -\sin\theta\mathbf{i} + \cos\theta\mathbf{j}$ is the unit vector which is tangential to the circle in the direction of increasing θ.

Show that $\dot{\mathbf{r}} = a\dot{\theta}\hat{\underset{\sim}{\theta}}$ and $\ddot{\mathbf{r}} = a\ddot{\theta}\hat{\underset{\sim}{\theta}} - a\dot{\theta}^2\hat{\mathbf{r}}$.

   (b) An inextensible string of length a has one end fixed to a point O and the other end attached to a particle P of mass m. P is held vertically above O with the string taut and projected horizontally with speed $\sqrt{2ga}$. Given that the string will break when the tension is $6mg$, find the angle which OP makes with the upward vertical when the string breaks. (AEB)

2. A particle P of mass m is attached to one end of a light inextensible string of length a, the other end of which is attached to a fixed point O. The particle is projected from its equilibrium position directly below O so that it starts to describe a vertical circle, centre O. Given that the string becomes slack at the point A, where OA is

inclined at an angle α to the upward vertical through O, and that P is then moving with speed V, express V in terms of a, g and α.

Show that the tension in the string when inclined at an angle θ ($> \alpha$) to the upward vertical is $3mg(\cos\alpha - \cos\theta)$.

Show that the height above O of the point where P is directly above its equilibrium position is

$$a\left(\frac{\sin^2\alpha\cos 2\alpha}{2\cos^3\alpha} + \cos\alpha\right) \qquad \text{(AEB)}$$

3. A particle P is suspended from a fixed point O by a light inextensible string of length l. Initially the particle is in equilibrium with OP vertical and it is then projected horizontally with speed u. Find the range of values of u for which the particle subsequently leaves its circular path.

Given that u lies in this range and that the particle leaves its circular path when OP makes an angle α with the upward vertical find, in terms of l and α, the maximum height above O attained by the particle. (AEB)

4. A particle of mass m is attached to a fixed point O by a light inextensible string of length a. It is held with the string taut and making an angle of 60° with the upward vertical through O and is then released from rest. At the instant when the string again becomes taut, find the impulse on the particle and show that the speed of the particle immediately afterwards is $\left(\frac{3ga}{2}\right)^{\frac{1}{2}}$.

When the particle is in its subsequent circular motion find the tension in the string when the string makes an angle θ with the downward vertical and find the value of θ when the string becomes slack. What is the speed of the particle when this happens? (AEB)

5. A particle P, of mass m, lies on a smooth horizontal table and is attached to one end of an extended light elastic string, of natural length a and modulus λ. The other end of the string is attached to a fixed point O on the table.

   The particle is held at rest at a point A on the table where $OA = 6a$. Write down an expression for the energy stored in the string. The particle is now projected from A with speed $\sqrt{\dfrac{3a\lambda}{m}}$ at right angles to OA. Show that the total initial energy is $14\lambda a$.

   At time t, when $OP = r$ and OP makes an angle θ with OA, show that conservation of angular momentum gives

   $$\left(\frac{d\theta}{dt}\right)^2 = \frac{108a^3\lambda}{mr^4}$$

   By considering conservation of energy, or otherwise, show that

   $$r^2\left(\frac{dr}{dt}\right)^2 + \frac{\lambda(r-6a)(r-2a)(r+3a)^2}{ma} = 0$$

   Deduce the region of the table in which the motion is confined. (AEB)

6. Two particles A and B, of masses $2m$ and $3m$ respectively, are connected by a light inextensible string of length πa. The string passes over a smooth circular cylinder, of radius a, which is fixed with its axis horizontal. Initially A and B are at opposite ends of a horizontal diameter of cross-section of the cylinder. The particles are released from rest, whereupon B falls vertically and A begins to move on the upper surface of the cylinder. Show that, after time t, when A has moved a distance $a\theta$ over the cylinder and has remained in contact with it,

   $$\frac{d^2\theta}{dt^2} = \frac{g(3 - 2\cos\theta)}{5a}$$

   Find, in terms of m, g and θ, the tension in the string and the reaction of the cylinder on A. Verify that the reaction of the cylinder on A vanishes when θ is approximately 1.5 radians. (AEB)

7. A particle P of mass m moves in a plane under the action of a force directed towards a fixed point O of the plane and of magnitude $\dfrac{mk}{r^3}$, where k is a positive constant and $r = OP$. The particle moves so that OP is continually decreasing and its velocity makes a constant angle $\dfrac{\pi}{4}$ with PO. Show that the angular

momentum of the particle about O is constant and, denoting this constant value by mh, show that

(a) $\dfrac{dr}{dt} = -r\dfrac{d\theta}{dt}$, where θ is the angle OP makes with a fixed line,

(b) $\dfrac{dr}{dt} = -\dfrac{h}{r}$,

(c) $\dfrac{d^2r}{dt^2} = -\dfrac{h^2}{r^3}$

By determining the radial component of acceleration, express h in terms of k.

Find, in terms of k and a, the time taken for r to decrease from $2a$ to a. (AEB)

8. A bowl, as shown in the diagram below, is formed by removing, from a fixed hollow sphere of radius a, that part of the sphere whch is at a height greater than $\dfrac{1}{2}a$ above the horizontal plane through its centre. The inner surface of the bowl is smooth. A particle is projectd horizontally from the lowest point on the inside of the bowl with speed u.

Find, in terms of g and a, the range of values of u so that

(a) the particle oscillates within the bowl without ever reaching a height a above the lowest point of the bowl,

(b) the particle flies out of the bowl, though remaining in contact with it until reaching the rim,

(c) the particle, having flown out of the bowl as in (b), eventually drops back into it.

(AEB)

9. A particle A is free to move on the smooth inner surface of a fixed spherical shell of internal radius a and centre O. Given that A passes through the lowest point of the spherical surface with speed u and that A leaves the surface when OA is inclined at an angle α to the horizontal, and A is above the horizontal through O, show that

$$u^2 = ga(1 + 3\sin\alpha)$$

Given also that A passes through O before next meeting the surface, show that $\sin^2\alpha = \dfrac{1}{3}$.

(AEB)

10. A light inextensible string of length a has one end attached to a fixed point O and the other end is attached to a particle of mass m.

   When the particle is hanging in equilibrium it is given a horizontal velocity of magnitude $2\sqrt{ga}$. Obtain an expression for the magnitude of the tension in the string when the particle is still on its circular path and the string has rotated through an angle θ.

   Deduce that the tension in the string vanishes when the particle is at a point at a height $\frac{2}{3}a$ above the level of O.

   Show that in the subsequent motion the particle passes through a point distant $\frac{9}{16}a$ directly above O.   (AEB)

11. A particle of mass m moves in a vertical circle on the smooth inner surface of a fixed hollow sphere of internal radius a and centre O. The plane of the motion passes through O. The particle is projected horizontally from the lowest point A of the surface with speed u, where $u^2 > 2ga$. Find , in terms of m, g, a, u and θ as appropriate, expressions for the speed and the reaction of the surface on the particle when it reaches the point B on the surface, where OB makes an angle θ with the upward vertical through O.

   Show that, if $u^2 < 5ga$, the particle leaves the surface when $\theta = \alpha$, where

   $$\cos\alpha = \frac{u^2 - 2ga}{3ga}$$

   Given that $u^2 = \frac{7}{2}ga$, determine α and prove that, in the subsequent motion, the particle meets the inner surface again at the point A.   (AEB)

12. A ferry boat F, which travels with constant speed $4u$ in still water, crosses a river which flows with constant speed $2u$ parallel to its banks. The boat crosses the river by always pointing its bows towards its point of destination O, which is directly opposite its starting point. Given that r is the distance OF and θ is the angle which OF makes with the direction of the velocity of the river show that, at time t after leaving the starting point

   $$\frac{dr}{dt} = 2u(\cos\theta - 2)$$

   and find a similar expression for $r\frac{d\theta}{dt}$.

Hence deduce that

$$\frac{dr}{d\theta} = \frac{r(2 - \cos\theta)}{\sin\theta}$$

Given that the starting point and the destination O are a distance a apart, find the equation of the path of the boat.

[You may assume that

$$\int \frac{d\theta}{\sin\theta} = \ln\left(\frac{\sin\theta}{1 + \cos\theta}\right) + \text{constant.}]$$ (AEB)

13. A particle P moves on the curve with equation $r = ae^{\theta\sqrt{3}}$, where a is a constant and r, θ are polar coordinates relative to a fixed pole O and an initial line OA. Show that at time t,

   $$\frac{dr}{dt} = \sqrt{3}\,r\frac{d\theta}{dt}$$

   and deduce that the angle between the velocity of P and the line OP is always equal to $\frac{\pi}{6}$.

   Given that the radial and transverse components of the acceleration of P are equal, show that

   $$\frac{d^2\theta}{dt^2} = 2\left(\frac{d\theta}{dt}\right)^2$$

   Verify that this equation is satisfied by

   $\frac{d\theta}{dt} = \frac{Ve^{2\theta}}{2a}$, where V is a constant.

   Deduce that V is the speed of P at the point where $r = a$.   (AEB)

14. A particle P moves on the circle with equation $r = 2a\sin\theta$, where (r, θ) are polar coordinates relative to a fixed origin O and an initial line OA. When P is at the point with coordinates (r, θ) it has speed $\lambda\,\text{cosec}^2\theta$, where λ is a constant. Prove that, at time t,

   $$\frac{d\theta}{dt} = \frac{\lambda}{2a\sin^2\theta} \quad \text{and} \quad \frac{dr}{dt} = \lambda\frac{\cos\theta}{\sin^2\theta}$$

   Show that the transverse component of the acceleration is zero.

   Hence find, in terms of a, λ and r, the magnitude of the acceleration of P.   (AEB)

15. A particle P moves so that at time t, its polar coordinates (r, θ), with respect to a fixed origin O, are such that

   $$r = \frac{a}{1 + 3\cos\theta}$$

   Given that P is nearest to O at the point A, find OA in terms of a.

Show that

$$\frac{dr}{dt} = \frac{3r^2}{a} \sin\theta \frac{d\theta}{dt}$$

and by differentiating this equation with respect to t show that, at A,

$$\frac{d^2r}{dt^2} = \frac{3}{16} a \left(\frac{d\theta}{dt}\right)^2$$

Given also that the acceleration of P towards O is of the form $\frac{k}{r^2}$, where k is a constant, express the speed at A in terms of k and a.　　(AEB)

16. At time t the position of a particle P moving on a smooth horizontal plane is defined by the polar coordinates r and θ. The particle describes the curve $r = ae^{3\theta}$, where a is a constant.

Show that

(a) the component of its radial acceleration in the sense of r increasing is

$$ae^{3\theta}\left(3\frac{d^2\theta}{dt^2} + 8\left(\frac{d\theta}{dt}\right)^2\right),$$

(b) the component of its transverse acceleration in the sense of θ increasing is

$$ae^{3\theta}\left(\frac{d^2\theta}{dt^2} + 6\left(\frac{d\theta}{dt}\right)^2\right)$$

Given that the motion is such that the above quantities are equal, find the relationship between $\frac{d^2\theta}{dt^2}$ and $\frac{d\theta}{dt}$ and show that it is satisfied by $\frac{d\theta}{dt} = Ce^{-\theta}$, where C is any constant.

Given that the speed of the particle is v when $\theta = 0$, find C in terms of v and a.　　(AEB)

17. A particle P, of mass m, is free to move in a plane. The position of P is defined by its polar coordinates (r, θ) relative to a fixed origin O and a fixed line through O. The particle is attracted towards O by a force of magnitude $\frac{ma^2V^2}{r^3}$, where a and V are constants. At time $t = 0$ the particle is projected from the point A $(3a, 0)$ with speed V perpendicular to OA in the sense of θ increasing. Show that in the subsequent motion

(a) $\dfrac{d\theta}{dt} = \dfrac{3aV}{r^2}$,

(b) $\dfrac{d^2r}{dt^2} = \dfrac{8a^2V^2}{r^3}$.

Find an expression for $\left(\frac{dr}{dt}\right)^2$ in terms of a, V, r and hence, or otherwise, show that

$$9\left(\frac{du}{d\theta}\right)^2 = 8\left(\frac{1}{9a^2} - u^2\right)$$

where $u = \frac{1}{r}$.　　(AEB)

18. A particle P moves in a plane so that at time t s its distance from a fixed point O in the plane is r m and the angle between OP and a fixed line in the plane is θ radians. The quantities r and θ satisfy the equations

$$r(2 + \cos\theta) = 4, \quad r^2\frac{d\theta}{dt} = 12.$$

Prove that

$$\frac{dr}{dt} = 3\sin\theta$$

Express the speed v ms^{-1} of P in terms of θ. Hence show that

$$v^2 - \frac{144}{r}$$

is a constant and find its numerical value.

Find the maximum and minimum values of v as θ varies from O to 2π.　　(AEB)

19. Show that the equation of planetary motion, using plane polar coordinates, r and θ, can be expressed in the form

$$\ddot{r} - r\dot{\theta}^2 = -\frac{\gamma m_s}{r^2}$$

$$\frac{d}{dt}\left(r^2\dot{\theta}\right) = 0$$

Here γ is the universal gravitational constant and m_s is the mass of the sun.

Also, by integrating the second equation and eliminating $\dot{\theta}$, show that

$$\ddot{r} - \frac{h^2}{r^3} = -\frac{\lambda m_s}{r^2}$$

where h is a constant.

Deduce that circular motion, $r = a$, is a possible solution provided that $a^3 = \frac{\gamma m_s}{\omega^2}$ where $\omega = \dot{\theta}$ is a constant.

Taking $\gamma m_s = 1.3 \times 10^{20}$ m^3 s^{-2}, and by calculating ω, the angular speed of the earth in radians per second, estimate the radius of the earth's orbit about the sun, assuming that it is circular.　　(AEB)

7 RIGID BODY MOTION

Objectives

After studying this chapter you should

- be able to find the centre of mass of a system of particles and rigid bodies;

- be able to take into account the size of a body in discussing its motion;

- be able to solve simple problems relating to the motion of a wheel on an axle and model the motion of a solid pendulum.

7.0   Introduction

The bodies which will be considered are assumed to be **rigid** in the sense that they cannot be deformed, i.e. they are not like a rubber ball, though for many purposes even such a ball can be treated as rigid.

The model that will be taken of a **rigid body** is a large assembly of particles rigidly connected together. In order to study the motion of such a body it is necessary to introduce two new concepts associated with a rigid body, namely **centre of mass** and **moment of inertia**; the centre of mass of a system of particles will be introduced first.

Consider the problem of the motion in a straight line of two particles P_1 and P_2 of mass m_1 and m_2 respectively, joined together in some way (by a string, rod or even an elastic spring). Though the main interest is in particles **rigidly** joined together, the idea of centre of mass is important for any system of interacting particles (joining the particles produces this interaction) and, assuming that the connection is not rigid, makes no difference to the basic result. The first step is to specify the positions of the particles by specifying the displacements of both particles at any time.

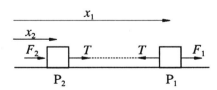

Define the coordinates of P_1 and P_2, relative to the same origin O, as x_1 and x_2 respectively, the positive sense being that shown in the diagram. The centre of mass of this system is defined as the point with coordinate

$$\bar{x} = \frac{m_1 x_1 + m_2 x_2}{m_1 + m_2}$$

Multiplying both sides of this equation by $(m_1 + m_2)g$ gives

$$(m_1 + m_2)g\bar{x} = m_1 g x_1 + m_2 g x_2$$

The left hand side of this equation is the moment about an axis through the origin of the total force of gravity on the two particles and acting at the centre of mass. The right hand side is the corresponding sum of the moments of the force of gravity (i.e. the weight) about the same axis. You may therefore recall from your earlier work on centre of gravity in Chapter 6 that this means that the centre of mass is the **centre of gravity**. (This is most often the case and this point will be returned to later.)

By Newton's third law, the force acting on P_1 due to P_2 will be equal and opposite to that acting on P_2 due to P_1. The latter force is denoted by T acting to the right. There may also be external forces (i.e. not due to interactions between the two particles) acting on the particles and these are denoted by F_1 and F_2 respectively, acting in the senses shown.

The equations of motion of P_1 and P_2 are

$$[P_1] \quad m_1 \ddot{x}_1 = -T + F_1$$

$$[P_2] \quad m_2 \ddot{x}_2 = T + F_2$$

Adding

$$m_1 \ddot{x}_1 + m_2 \ddot{x}_2 = F_1 + F_2$$

but from the definition of centre of mass above, after differentiating twice,

$$m_1 \ddot{x}_1 + m_2 \ddot{x}_2 = (m_1 + m_2)\ddot{\bar{x}}$$

giving

$$(m_1 + m_2)\ddot{\bar{x}} = F_1 + F_2$$

The right hand side is the total **external force** acting on the two particle system so that

$$\boxed{(m_1 + m_2)\ddot{\bar{x}} = \text{sum of external forces acting on } P_1 \text{ and } P_2}$$

Writing the total mass of the system as

$$M = m_1 + m_2$$

you can write this equation as

$$\boxed{M\ddot{\bar{x}} = \text{total force on system}}$$

This shows that the motion of the centre of mass is the same as that of a particle of total mass equal to that of the system, and acted on by a force equal to the total external force acting on the system of particles.

This means that a problem can be considerably simplified by looking at the two separate problems of

(i) the motion of the centre of mass,

(ii) the motion relative to it.

The motion of the centre of mass avoids the complication of internal forces.

7.1 Centre of mass of a system of particles

For a system of particles P_i of mass m_i, on a line, with coordinates x_i with respect to an origin on the line, the centre of mass is defined as the point with coordinate $\bar{x}$ where

$$\boxed{\bar{x} = \frac{\displaystyle\sum_{i=1}^{n} m_i x_i}{\displaystyle\sum_{i=1}^{n} m_i}}$$

Does this agree with the two particle definition for $n = 2$?

When the particles are not on a line and there are n particles P_i $(i = 1, 2, \ldots, n)$ with coordinates (x_i, y_i, z_i), then the centre of mass is the point with coordinates $(\bar{x}, \bar{y}, \bar{z})$, where

$$\boxed{\bar{x} = \frac{\displaystyle\sum_{i=1}^{n} m_i x_i}{\displaystyle\sum_{i=1}^{n} m_i} \;,\; \bar{y} = \frac{\displaystyle\sum_{i=1}^{n} m_i y_i}{\displaystyle\sum_{i=1}^{n} m_i} \;,\; \bar{z} = \frac{\displaystyle\sum_{i=1}^{n} m_i z_i}{\displaystyle\sum_{i=1}^{n} m_i}}$$

These equations look complicated but can be interpreted in a simple way using the idea of moments.

The denominator $(M = \displaystyle\sum_{i=1}^{n} m_i)$ is the total mass of all the particles; the products $m_i x_i$ are effectively moments, being products of mass (which is proportional to weight) and distances.

When all the particles lie in the $x - y$ plane, then

$$\bar{x} = \frac{\text{moments about } y\text{-axis}}{\text{total mass}}, \quad \bar{y} = \frac{\text{moments about } x\text{-axis}}{\text{total mass}}$$

Example

Find the coordinates of the centre of mass of particles of mass m, $2m$ and $3m$ respectively, which are positioned at the points with coordinates $(1, 2)$, $(5, 5)$ and $(3, -1)$ respectively.

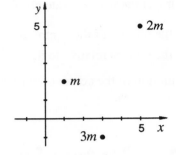

Solution

The situation is illustrated opposite.

Since the total mass is

$$m + 2m + 3m = 6m$$

from the definition of centre of mass,

$$6m\bar{x} = \text{moments about } y\text{-axis}$$

$$= m \times 1 + 2m \times 5 + 3m \times 3$$

$$= m + 10m + 9m$$

$$= 20m$$

Hence $\bar{x} = \dfrac{10}{3}$

Similarly

$$6m\bar{y} = \text{moments about } x\text{-axis}$$

$$= m \times 2 + 2m \times 5 + 3m \times (-1)$$

$$= 2m + 10m - 3m$$

$$= 9m$$

giving $\bar{y} = \dfrac{3}{2}$

Can the centre of mass of three particles ever lie outside the triangle formed by the three positions of the particles?

The equations defining centre of mass can be put in a more compact form by using vector notation with particle P_i being at the point with position vector $\mathbf{r}_i$. The position vector $\bar{\mathbf{r}}$ is now defined by

$$\bar{\mathbf{r}} = \frac{\displaystyle\sum_{i=1}^{n} m_i \mathbf{r}_i}{\displaystyle\sum_{i=1}^{n} m_i}$$

An alternative method of defining the centre of mass is to use it as the origin; this is illustrated by considering a system of two particles of mass m_1 and m_2 at the points with position vectors $\mathbf{r}_1$ and $\mathbf{r}_2$, respectively. The position vectors $\mathbf{R}_1$ and $\mathbf{R}_2$ of these particles relative to the centre of mass are

$$\mathbf{R}_1 = \mathbf{r}_1 - \bar{\mathbf{r}}$$

$$= \mathbf{r}_1 - \left(\frac{m_1 \mathbf{r}_1 + m_2 \mathbf{r}_2}{m_1 + m_2} \right)$$

$$= \frac{m_2 \mathbf{r}_1 - m_2 \mathbf{r}_2}{\left(m_1 + m_2 \right)}$$

Similarly,

$$\mathbf{R}_2 = \mathbf{r}_2 - \bar{\mathbf{r}}$$

$$= \mathbf{r}_2 - \left(\frac{m_1 \mathbf{r}_1 + m_2 \mathbf{r}_2}{m_1 + m_2} \right)$$

$$= \frac{m_1 \mathbf{r}_2 - m_1 \mathbf{r}_1}{\left(m_1 + m_2 \right)}$$

What can you say about $m_1 \mathbf{R}_1 + m_2 \mathbf{R}_2$?

Now

$$m_1 \mathbf{R}_1 + m_2 \mathbf{R}_2 = \frac{\left(m_1 m_2 \mathbf{r}_1 - m_1 m_2 \mathbf{r}_2 \right)}{\left(m_1 + m_2 \right)} + \frac{\left(m_2 m_1 \mathbf{r}_2 - m_2 m_1 \mathbf{r}_1 \right)}{\left(m_1 + m_2 \right)}$$

$$= 0$$

This result can be generalised.

Activity 1

Using a similar analysis, show that for three particles, using the notation above,

$$\sum_{i=1}^{3} m_i \mathbf{R}_i = 0$$

In fact, for n particles, the result

$$\boxed{\sum_{i=1}^{n} m_i \mathbf{R}_i = 0}$$

holds, where $\mathbf{R}_i$ is the positive vector relative to the centre of mass of particle P_i of mass m_i.

Example

Particles of mass m, $5m$ and $2m$ are placed at points with position vectors $2\mathbf{j}+4\mathbf{k}$, $2\mathbf{i}+2\mathbf{k}$ and $3\mathbf{i}+3\mathbf{j}+5\mathbf{k}$ respectively. Find the position vector of the centre of mass, and verify the result above.

Solution

By definition

$$(m+5m+2m)\bar{\mathbf{r}} = m(+2\mathbf{j}+4\mathbf{k}) + 5m(2\mathbf{i}+2\mathbf{k}) + 2m(3\mathbf{i}+3\mathbf{j}+5\mathbf{k})$$

$$= m(16\mathbf{i}+8\mathbf{j}+24\mathbf{k})$$

$$\Rightarrow \quad \bar{\mathbf{r}} = 2\mathbf{i}+\mathbf{j}+3\mathbf{k}$$

The position vectors of the particles, relative to the centre of mass, are

$$\mathbf{R}_1 = \mathbf{r}_1 - \bar{\mathbf{r}} = 2\mathbf{j}+4\mathbf{k} - (2\mathbf{i}+\mathbf{j}+3\mathbf{k})$$

$$= -2\mathbf{i}+\mathbf{j}+\mathbf{k}$$

$$\mathbf{R}_2 = \mathbf{r}_2 - \bar{\mathbf{r}} = 2\mathbf{i}+2\mathbf{k} - (2\mathbf{i}+\mathbf{j}+3\mathbf{k})$$

$$= 0\mathbf{i}-\mathbf{j}-\mathbf{k}$$

$$\mathbf{R}_3 = \mathbf{r}_3 - \bar{\mathbf{r}} = 3\mathbf{i}+3\mathbf{j}+5\mathbf{k} - (2\mathbf{i}+\mathbf{j}+3\mathbf{k})$$

$$= \mathbf{i}+2\mathbf{j}+2\mathbf{k}$$

Thus

$$\sum_{i=1}^{3} m_i \mathbf{R}_i = m(-2\mathbf{i}+\mathbf{j}+\mathbf{k})+5m(-\mathbf{j}-\mathbf{k})+2m(\mathbf{i}+2\mathbf{j}+2\mathbf{k})$$

$$= m\big((-2+2)\mathbf{i}+(1-5+4)\mathbf{j}+(1-5+4)\mathbf{k}\big)$$

$$= \mathbf{0}$$

which verifies the result.

Activity 2

Show that the centre of mass of three particles, each of mass m, at position vectors $\mathbf{a}$, $\mathbf{b}$ and $\mathbf{c}$ respectively, is given by

$$\mathbf{r} = \frac{1}{3}(\mathbf{a}+\mathbf{b}+\mathbf{c})$$

Generalise this result.

Exercise 7A

1. Find the position vector of the centre of mass of the particles of masses m, $2m$, $4m$ and $3m$ at the points with position vectors $\mathbf{r}_1$, $\mathbf{r}_2$, $\mathbf{r}_3$ and $\mathbf{r}_4$ respectively, when

    (a) $\mathbf{r}_1 = \mathbf{i}+\mathbf{k}$, $\mathbf{r}_2 = 3\mathbf{i}+4\mathbf{k}$, $\mathbf{r}_3 = -5\mathbf{i}+2\mathbf{j}-\mathbf{k}$
    and $\mathbf{r}_4 = \mathbf{i}+2\mathbf{j}+8\mathbf{k}$

    (b) $\mathbf{r}_1 = -\mathbf{i}+3\mathbf{j}-5\mathbf{k}$, $\mathbf{r}_2 = 3\mathbf{i}+7\mathbf{j}-9\mathbf{k}$,
    $\mathbf{r}_3 = -8\mathbf{i}+4\mathbf{j}-2\mathbf{k}$ and $\mathbf{r}_4 = -3\mathbf{i}+2\mathbf{j}+\mathbf{k}$

    (c) $\mathbf{r}_1 = \mathbf{0}$, $\mathbf{r}_2 = 3\mathbf{i}+2\mathbf{j}+\mathbf{k}$, $\mathbf{r}_3 = -5\mathbf{i}+2\mathbf{j}-\mathbf{k}$
    and $\mathbf{r}_4 = -\mathbf{i}+\mathbf{j}+3\mathbf{k}$

2. Particles of masses 6, 4, 3 and 7 kg are at the points position vectors $\mathbf{i}+2\mathbf{j}+3\mathbf{k}$, $4\mathbf{i}+6\mathbf{j}+2\mathbf{k}$, $3\mathbf{i}+7\mathbf{j}-5\mathbf{k}$ and $\mathbf{a}$ respectively. Find $\mathbf{a}$ if the mass of the system is at the point with position vector $2\mathbf{i}+4\mathbf{k}$.

3. Masses p, q and r are placed at the points with coordinates $(0, 0)$, $(10, 0)$ and $(0, 8)$. The centre of mass is at $(5, 3)$. Find the ratio $p : q : r$.

4. Particles of masses m, $2m$ and $3m$ are at points with position vectors $2\mathbf{i}+\mathbf{k}$, $2\mathbf{i}+3\mathbf{j}+\mathbf{k}$, $4\mathbf{i}+2\mathbf{j}+3\mathbf{k}$ respectively. Find the centre of mass of the system, and show that

    $$m\mathbf{R}_1 + 2m\mathbf{R}_2 + 3m\mathbf{R}_3$$

    is the zero vector when $\mathbf{R}_i$ is the position vector relative to the centre of mass of the ith particle.

5. Particles P_1 and P_2 have masses m and $2m$ and position vectors $\mathbf{r}_1$ and $\mathbf{r}_2$, where

    $$\mathbf{r}_1 = R(\mathbf{i}\cos\omega_1 t + \mathbf{j}\sin\omega_1 t)$$

    $$\mathbf{r}_2 = \frac{1}{2}R(\mathbf{i}\cos\omega_2 t + \mathbf{j}\sin\omega_2 t)$$

    R, ω_1 and ω_2 $(\omega_2 > \omega_1)$ are constants. What time elapses before the centre of mass coincides with the origin on the first occasion? Determine the position vector of P_1 at that instant, in the case when $\omega_2 = 3\omega_1$.

7.2   Calculation of the position of the centre of mass

In calculating the position of the centre of mass of a system it is often convenient to subdivide the system into clusters and treat each cluster as one particle. This will be illustrated for particles of mass m_1, m_2 and m_3 at the points with position vectors $\mathbf{r}_1$, $\mathbf{r}_2$ and $\mathbf{r}_3$, respectively.

The position vector $\bar{\mathbf{r}}$ of the centre of mass of this system is defined by

$$\bar{\mathbf{r}} = \frac{m_1\mathbf{r}_1 + m_2\mathbf{r}_2 + m_3\mathbf{r}_3}{m_1 + m_2 + m_3}$$

Writing $M = m_1 + m_2$,

$$\bar{\mathbf{r}} = \frac{\dfrac{M\left(m_1\mathbf{r}_1 + m_2\mathbf{r}_2\right)}{M} + m_3\mathbf{r}_3}{M + m_3}$$

Let $\qquad \bar{\mathbf{r}}* = \dfrac{m_1\mathbf{r}_1 + m_2\mathbf{r}_2}{M}$

so $\bar{\mathbf{r}}*$ is the position vector of the two particle system, P_1 and P_2. Then

$$\bar{\mathbf{r}} = \frac{M\bar{\mathbf{r}}* + m_3\mathbf{r}_3}{\left(M + m_3\right)}$$

showing that the position of the centre of mass of the three particle system is the same as that of the particle P_3 of mass m_3, together with a particle of mass $m_1 + m_2$ at the position of the centre of mass of the two particle system P_1 and P_2.

This can be shown to be true for any number of particles, giving the following result.

> In calculating the centre of mass of a system, any subgroup of the system can be replaced by one particle of total mass equal to that of the subgroup and located at the centre of mass of the subgroup.

Activity 3

Illustrate this concept by considering a four particle system and dividing this into subgroups of three particles and one particle.

Before looking again at the motion of the centre of mass it is necessary to see how to calculate the position of the centre of mass for rigid bodies.

Methods often rely on the result above concerning subdivision; the essential trick is to use the subdivision which makes the calculation relatively easy. There are two basic approaches, use of symmetry and use of integration.

Use of symmetry

If the coordinates of a particle P_i relative to the centre of mass are denoted by X_i, Y_i and Z_i then, by definition

$$\sum_{i=1}^{n} m_i X_i = 0 \, , \; \sum_{i=1}^{n} m_i Y_i = 0 \, , \; \sum_{i=1}^{n} m_i Z_i = 0$$

Therefore the centre of mass will lie in any plane of symmetry and, if there is more than one such plane it will lie in the intersection of planes of symmetry.

Therefore the centre of mass of a uniform rod or rectangle is at its geometric centre. The same is true for a uniform circular disc or wire.

Triangular lamina

A slightly more complicated problem is that of the centre of mass of a uniform triangular lamina as shown in the diagram.

The lamina is divided into thin strips parallel to BC. The centre of mass of the strip will be the same as that of a series of particles equal in mass to that of the strip and situated at the centre of mass of the strip. Each strip is uniform, so the centre of mass is at its centre and the centre of mass of the triangle is therefore on the line joining the centres of the strips, i.e. the line from A to the midpoint of BC. This is known as the **median**.

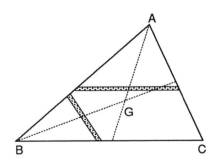

The triangle can also be divided into strips parallel to AC and, by the same argument, the centre of mass is on the line joining B to the midpoint of AC. Therefore the centre of mass is at the intersection of the medians through A and B.

In case you think there is an inconsistency here, it can be shown that all three medians intersect at a point and therefore the same result would have been obtained if strips had been chosen parallel to BC and AB. It can also be shown that the medians intersect at a point $\frac{2}{3}$ along the median from a vertex.

Use of integration

A wire in the form of a circular arc

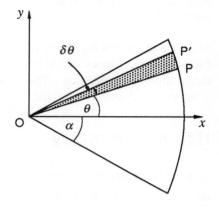

The diagram shows a wire bent in the shape of a circular arc of radius r which subtends an angle of 2α at the centre, O, of the circle, of which the arc is a part. The radius to the midpoint of the arc is taken as the x-axis, and the arc is divided into a number of elements, a typical one being the arc PP′ where OP makes an angle θ with the x-axis and OP′ makes an angle $\theta + \delta\theta$.

The mass of this element is $kr\delta\theta$, where k is the mass of the wire per unit length, and the x-coordinate of its centre of mass is approximately $r\cos\theta$. The actual value of θ corresponding to the centre of mass of the arc will be $\left(\theta + \frac{1}{2}\delta\theta\right)$, and therefore the x-coordinate will be

$$r\cos(\theta + \delta\theta) = r\cos\theta\cos\delta\theta - r\sin\theta\sin\delta\theta$$

$$\approx r\cos\theta - r\delta\theta\sin\theta \quad (\text{since } \sin\delta\theta \approx \delta\theta)$$

and the contribution of this element to the moment about the y-axis is

$$(kr\delta\theta)(r\cos\theta - r\delta\theta\sin\theta)$$

$$= kr^2\delta\theta\cos\theta - kr^2\sin\theta(\delta\theta)^2$$

Neglecting the $(\delta\theta)^2$ term gives

$$\left(kr^2\cos\theta\right)\delta\theta$$

Adding all the elements gives

$$M\bar{x} = \Sigma\left(kr^2\cos\theta\right)\delta\theta$$

and, in the limit, as $\delta\theta \to 0$,

$$M\bar{x} = \int_{-\alpha}^{\alpha} kr^2\cos\theta\, d\theta$$

What is the mass of the wire?

218

Hence

$$M\bar{x} = \left[kr^2 \sin\theta \right]_{-\alpha}^{\alpha}$$

$$= 2kr^2 \sin\alpha$$

Then

$$\bar{x} = \frac{2kr^2 \sin\alpha}{2kr\alpha}$$

since the total mass is $k \times \text{area} = k \times 2\alpha r$

So
$$\boxed{\bar{x} = \frac{r\sin\alpha}{\alpha}}$$

and, from symmetry, $\bar{y} = 0$

Find $\bar{x}$ when $\alpha = \dfrac{\pi}{2}$ and $\alpha = \pi$. Interpret the answers.

Right-angled triangular lamina

The diagram shows a triangle OAB, right-angled at A, with
$OA = h$ and $AB = a$. Axes are taken at O with the x-axis along
OA and the y-axis parallel to AB.

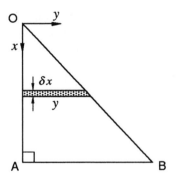

The lamina may be divided into a number of strips of width δx, a
typical strip being shown in the diagram. The mass of a strip is
$ky\delta x$, where k is the mass per unit area of the lamina, and the
distance of the centre of mass from the y-axis is x, correct to the
first order in δx, and so its contribution to the total moment

(i.e. $\displaystyle\sum_{i=1}^{n} m_i x_i$) is $kxy\delta x$ and in the limit, as the subdivision becomes

infinitely fine the sum becomes the integral, and hence
$$M\bar{x} = \int_0^h kxy\,dx$$

If angle AOB is denoted by θ, then

$$\tan\theta = \frac{y}{x}$$

and
$$\tan\theta = \frac{a}{h}$$

and therefore

$$\frac{y}{x} = \frac{a}{h} \quad \Rightarrow \quad y = \frac{ax}{h}$$

(This could also have been found using similar triangles.)

Substituting for y in terms of x gives

$$M\bar{x} = \int_0^h kxy\,dx$$

$$= \int_o^h kx\frac{ax}{h}dx$$

$$= \frac{1}{3}kah^2$$

The total mass is given by

$$M = k \times \text{area} = k \times \left(\frac{1}{2}ah\right) = \frac{1}{2}kah$$

Hence $\qquad \bar{x} = \dfrac{\dfrac{1}{3}kah^2}{\dfrac{1}{2}kah} = \dfrac{2}{3}h$

The simplest way of calculating the y-coordinate is to carry out the same kind of calculation with origin at B and taking the x-axis along BA. This means just replacing h by a, so that the perpendicular distance of the centre of mass from B is $\dfrac{2a}{3}$.

Therefore, reverting to the origin at O, the y-coordinate is $\dfrac{a}{3}$.

Does this result confirm that the centre of mass lies on the median?

Plane lamina with a curved boundary

The method used for the triangle can be extended to the area bounded by the curve $y = f(x)$, the lines $x = a, x = b$ and the x-axis as shown in the diagram opposite.

The area is divided into strips parallel to the y-axis as shown, and all that it is necessary to do in the integrals for the triangle is to replace y by $f(x)$, and the limits of integration by a and b, so

$$\bar{x} = \frac{\displaystyle\int_a^b xf(x)dx}{\displaystyle\int_a^b f(x)dx}$$

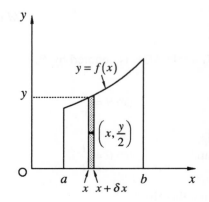

Note that the total mass is proportional to the area, which is the denominator.

The calculation of the y-coordinate is slightly different. The y-coordinate of the centre of mass of the strip is $\frac{1}{2}y$ and so the contribution of the strip to the moment about the x-axis

(i.e. $\sum\limits_{i=1}^{n} m_i y_i$) is

$$\int_a^b k \frac{1}{2} y^2 dx$$

Replacing y by $f(x)$ gives

$$\bar{y} = \frac{\frac{1}{2}\int_a^b f^2(x)dx}{\int_a^b f(x)dx}$$

Example

Find the coordinates of the uniform plane lamina bounded by the curve $y = 12x^2$, the lines $x = 1, x = 2$ and the x-axis.

Solution

In this case $f(x) = 12x^2$, $a = 1, b = 2$, and

$$\int_1^3 x f(x)dx = \int_1^3 12x^3 dx$$

$$= \left[3x^4\right]_1^3$$

$$= 240$$

and $$\int_1^3 f(x) = \int_1^3 12x^2 dx$$

$$= \left[4x^3\right]_1^3$$

$$= 104$$

Hence $$\bar{x} = \frac{240}{104} = \frac{30}{13}$$

Similarly

$$\int_a^b f^2(x)dx = \frac{34\,848}{5}$$

and therefore

$$\bar{y} = \frac{1}{2} \times \frac{34848}{5} \times \frac{1}{104} = \frac{2178}{65}$$

Sector of a circle

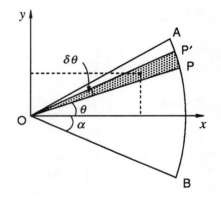

In the diagram, OAB represents a uniform lamina in the form of a sector of a circle, with the arc AB subtending an angle 2α at the centre O of the circle. Let k be the mass per unit area and Ox the axis of symmetry.

The elementary sector OPP′ has mass $\dfrac{kr^2 \delta\theta}{2}$, where k is the mass per unit area. Take the triangle OPP′ as an approximation to this sector. From the results for the triangle, the centre of mass has x-coordinate $\dfrac{2r \cos\theta}{3}$, correct to the first order in $\delta\theta$. Therefore the contribution to the moment about the y-axis

(i.e. $\displaystyle\sum_{i=1}^{n} m_i x_i$) is $k\dfrac{r^3}{3}\cos\theta\,\delta\theta$ and in the limit as the subdivision becomes infinitely small the sum becomes the integral, giving

$$\left(\int_{-\alpha}^{\alpha} \frac{kr^2}{2}\,d\theta \right)\bar{x} = \int_{-\alpha}^{\alpha} \frac{kr^3 \cos\theta}{3}\,d\theta$$

$$\Rightarrow \qquad kr^2 \alpha\bar{x} = \frac{kr^3}{3}[\sin\theta]_{-\alpha}^{\alpha}$$

$$\bar{x} = \frac{2r\sin\alpha}{3\alpha}$$

Volumes of revolution

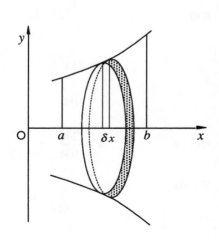

There are several commonly occurring bodies which are formed by revolving a curve about a line. The most obvious examples are the cone (formed by rotating a line segment) and a hemisphere, or any part of a sphere between two parallel plane sections (formed by rotating an arc of a circle about a diameter perpendicular to the planes forming the section).

The diagram shows a uniform **solid** of revolution, obtained by revolving the region bounded by the curve $y = f(x)$, the lines $x = a$ and $x = b$, and the x-axis, about the x-axis.

The **volume of revolution** can be divided into a number of disc-like elements, formed by revolving the arc of the curve between two points on the curve whose x-coordinates differ by δx.

If ρ is the density of the material, then the mass of the element is $\rho \pi y^2 \delta x$, and its contribution to the moment about the y-axis

(i.e. $\displaystyle\sum_{i=1}^{n} m_i x_i$) is $\rho \pi x y^2 \delta x$, correct to the first order in δx. In the limit the sum becomes the integral, giving

$$M \bar{x} = \rho \pi \int_a^b x y^2 \, dx \qquad (M = \text{total mass})$$

The total mass is found similarly as

$$M = \rho \pi \int_a^b y^2 \, dx$$

Therefore, dividing the total moment by the total mass,

$$\boxed{\bar{x} = \frac{\displaystyle\int_a^b x y^2 \, dx}{\displaystyle\int_a^b y^2 \, dx}}$$

By construction the centre of mass lies on the x-axis.

Hemisphere

A hemisphere of radius r is generated by the curve $x^2 + y^2 = r^2$ as shown in the diagram; so $a = 0$ and $b = r$ and

$$\int_a^b x y^2 \, dx = \int_0^r x \left(r^2 - x^2 \right) dx$$

$$= \frac{r^4}{4}$$

Also $\qquad \displaystyle\int_a^b y^2 \, dx = \int_0^r \left(r^2 - x^2 \right) dx$

$$= \frac{2 r^3}{3}$$

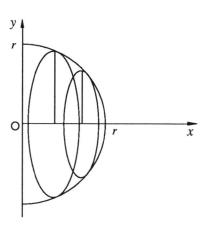

Dividing the moment by the mass shows that the centre of mass is on the perpendicular through the centre of the base and at a distance $\dfrac{3r}{8}$ from the base.

Cone

A cone is generated by rotating the line $y = x \tan \alpha$, $0 \le x \le h$, where h is the height of the cone about the x-axis (see diagram).

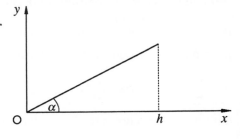

Thus

$$\int_a^b xy^2 dx = \int_0^h \tan^2 \alpha \, x^3 dx$$

$$= \frac{h^4 \tan^2 \alpha}{4}$$

Similarly

$$\int_a^b y^2 dx = \int_0^h \tan^2 \alpha \, x^2 dx$$

$$= \frac{h^3 \tan^2 \alpha}{3}$$

The centre of mass is therefore on the axis of the cone at a distance $\frac{3h}{4}$ from the vertex.

Hemispherical shell

This is a surface of revolution so a different approach has to be used.

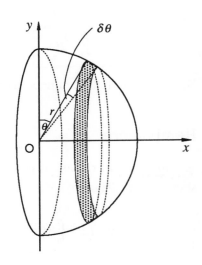

The surface of the hemisphere can be divided into a series of small rings, as shown the diagram, where a typical ring subtends an angle $\delta\theta$ at the centre of the base of the hemisphere. The centre of mass of the ring is at a perpendicular distance $r \sin\theta$ from the base of the hemisphere. The ring is of radius $r \cos\theta$ and therefore of mass $2\pi k r \cos\theta \, r \delta\theta$, where k is the mass per unit area. The contribution to the total moment about the y-axis, correct to the first order in $\delta\theta$, is $2\pi k r^3 \cos\theta \sin\theta \, \delta\theta$ and in the limit the total moment becomes

$$M\bar{x} = 2\pi \int_0^{\frac{\pi}{2}} kr^3 \cos\theta \sin\theta \, d\theta$$

Activity 4

Evaluate $\int_0^{\frac{\pi}{2}} \cos\theta \sin\theta \, d\theta$ and hence show that the centre of mass of a hemispherical shell is at a distance $\frac{r}{2}$ from its base on the x-axis.

In the examples above the bodies are all uniform (i.e. the mass per unit area or volume is constant), but integration can also be applied to problems where the density is not constant. This is illustrated in the following example.

Example

Find the position of the centre of mass of a rod of length a in which the mass per unit length varies directly as the distance from one end. (This could be a model of a tapered rod.)

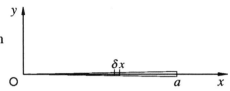

Solution

The origin of x is taken at one end of the rod, and the rod is subdivided into small elements, the typical element lying between x and $x + \delta x$. If k is the mass per unit length of this element, then the mass of the element is $k\delta x$ and its contribution, correct to the first order in δx, to the total moment, is $kx\delta x$. In this case, k is not constant but of the form px and making this substitution and, taking the limit as the subdivision becomes infinitely fine, gives

the total moment as $\displaystyle\int_0^a px^2 dx = \frac{pa^3}{3}$

Similarly the mass is

$$\int_0^a px\,dx = \frac{pa^2}{2}$$

Dividing these expressions gives the centre of mass to be at a distance of $\dfrac{2a}{3}$ from O.

Summary

It might be useful at this stage to summarise the positions of the centres of mass of some uniform bodies.

circular wire of angle 2α, radius r	$\dfrac{r\sin\alpha}{\alpha}$	from centre
circular sector of angle 2α, radius r	$\dfrac{2r\sin\alpha}{3\alpha}$	from centre
triangular lamina	$\dfrac{2}{3}$	along any median from a vertex
solid hemisphere, radius r	$\dfrac{3r}{8}$	from base along axis
solid cone, height h	$\dfrac{3h}{4}$	from vertex along axis
hemispherical shell, radius r	$\dfrac{r}{2}$	from base along axis

Exercise 7B

In Questions 1 to 4, find the centre of mass of the uniform solids formed by rotating through 4 right angles the area bounded by the given curves and lines.

1. $y = \dfrac{x^2}{a}$, $y = 0$, $x = 2a$, rotated about the x-axis.

2. $x = \dfrac{y^2}{a}$, $y = 0$, $x = 6a$, about the x-axis.

3. $y = \dfrac{x^4}{a^3}$, $x = 0$, $y = 16a$, about the y-axis.

4. $x^2 y = a^3$, $y = 0$, $x = a$, $x = 2a$, about the x-axis.

In Questions 5 to 7 find the centres of mass of the uniform laminae bounded by the given lines and curves.

5. $y^2 = 4ax$, $x = 9a$

6. $x = \dfrac{y^2}{a}$, $x = 6a$.

7. $y^2 = \dfrac{x^3}{a}$, $x = 5a$.

7.3   Composite bodies

Some bodies can be looked on as being made up of simpler bodies, the position of whose centres of mass are known. The centre of mass of the composite body can be found using the general principle that, for finding a centre of mass, any body can be represented by a particle at its centre of mass.

Example

A composite body is formed by joining, at the rim of their bases, a uniform cone of height h and base radius r, and a uniform hemisphere of base radius r. The bodies are made of the same material. Find the distance of the centre of mass of the composite body from the vertex of the cone.

Solution

The centre of mass of the composite body will lie on the common axis of symmetry. If the density is ρ, the masses of the cone and hemisphere are

$$\frac{1}{3}\rho\pi r^2 h \quad \text{and} \quad \frac{2}{3}\pi r^3 \rho$$

respectively.

The centres of mass of the cone and hemisphere are at a distance

$$\frac{3h}{4} \quad \text{and} \quad h + \frac{3r}{8}$$

respectively from the vertex of the cone. In problems involving composite bodies it is often useful to tabulate the results.

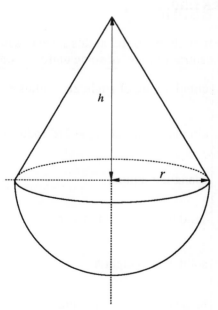

Part	Mass	Distance	Moment
cone	$\frac{1}{3}\rho\pi r^2 h$	$\frac{3h}{4}$	$\rho\frac{\pi r^2 h^2}{4}$
hemisphere	$\frac{2}{3}\pi r^3\rho$	$h+\frac{3r}{8}$	$\frac{2}{3}\pi r^3\rho\left(h+\frac{3r}{8}\right)$
whole body	$\frac{1}{3}\rho\pi r^2 h + \frac{2}{3}\pi r^3\rho$	$\bar{x}$	$\frac{1}{3}\rho\pi r^2(h+2r)\bar{x}$

The total moment of the whole body is equal to the sum of the moments of the parts.

Hence

$$\frac{1}{3}\rho\pi r^2(h+2r)\bar{x} = \rho\frac{\pi r^2 h^2}{4} + \frac{2}{3}\pi r^3\rho\left(h+\frac{3r}{8}\right)$$

i.e. $$\bar{x} = \frac{3h^2 + 3r^2 + 8rh}{4(h+2r)}$$

Remainders

There are some problems where part of a body has been removed and you are required to find the position of the centre of mass of the remainder. Problems like this can be solved by regarding the original body as the composite body, with the part remaining and the part cut out, as the constituent parts.

Example

A uniform square lamina of side $4a$ has a square of side $2a$ removed from one corner. Find the position of the centre of mass of the lamina so formed.

Solution

The configuration is as shown in the diagram. Let x denote the distance of the centre of mass from AB. If the density is ρ, then the masses of the large and small squares are $4\rho a^2$ and $16\rho a^2$ respectively and you can write these as m and $4m$ respectively. The distances of the centres of mass from AB are a and $2a$ respectively, giving the table below.

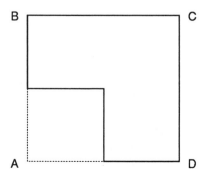

Part	Mass	Distance	Moment
large square	$4m$	$2a$	$8ma$
small square	m	a	ma
remainder	$3m$	$\bar{x}$	$3m\bar{x}$

The moment of the large square (the composite) is equal to the sum
of the other moments, i.e.

$$8ma = ma + 3m\bar{x}$$

$$\Rightarrow \qquad \bar{x} = \frac{7a}{3}$$

Exercise 7C

1. A composite body is formed by joining at their
    circular bases, a uniform solid right circular cone
    of height $3r$ and radius r, and a uniform solid
    hemisphere of radius r. The density of the
    material forming the hemisphere is three times
    that of the material forming the cone. Find the
    distance of the centre of gravity of the body from
    the vertex of the cone.

2. A uniform solid cone of height h and base radius
    r is joined at its base to a plane face of a uniform
    solid right circular cylinder, of the same
    material, with base radius r and height $4h$. Find
    the position of the centre of mass of the solid so
    formed.

3. A cylindrical can, made of thin material and
    open at the top, is of height $2a$ and the radius of
    the plane base is a. The curved surface and the
    base are made from different, but uniform
    materials, so that the mass of the curved surface
    is twice that of the base. Find the distance of the
    centre of mass of the empty can from the centre
    of the base.

4. A uniform solid cylinder of radius $4a$ and height
    $6a$ has a cylindrical hole of radius $2a$ and depth
    $3a$ bored centrally at one end. Find the position
    of the centre of mass of the remainder.

5. A spherical shell of external radius $5r$ and
    internal radius r is cut in half by a plane through
    its centre. Find the distance of the centre of
    mass of either half from the centre of the sphere.

*7.4 The centre of gravity

You have already met the idea of centre of gravity and, when the
centre of mass was introduced earlier, it seemed to be identical
with it.

The **centre of gravity** of a body or of a set of particles, is the point
through which the total weight of the body, or of the particles, may
be considered to act. If g, the acceleration due to gravity, is
assumed to be constant over the body or the particles in question,
then it can be shown that the centre of gravity will coincide with
the centre of mass. This is summarised as:

> The centres of gravity and mass for a rigid body or system of
> particles coincide when the acceleration due to gravity is
> assumed constant at all points of the system.

This result can be proved, although this is beyond what is expected
for your module assessment.

Denoting the acceleration due to gravity by the vector $\mathbf{g}$, the force
on a particle of mass m_i at the point with position vector $\mathbf{r}_i$ is $m_i\mathbf{g}$
The condition that the point with position vector $\bar{\mathbf{r}}$ is the centre of
gravity is that the sum of the moments about a point of the forces
acting on the individual particles is equal to the moment of the

total force acting at the centre of gravity.

If M is the total mass, then the total force is $M\mathbf{g}$, and the basic condition becomes

$$\bar{\mathbf{r}} \times M\mathbf{g} = \sum_{i=1}^{n} \mathbf{r}_i \times (m_i \mathbf{g})$$

This can be rearranged by taking the vector $\mathbf{g}$ outside the sum as

$$\left(M\bar{\mathbf{r}} - \sum_{i=1}^{n} \mathbf{r}_i m_i \right) \times \mathbf{g} = 0$$

A solution of this is

$$M\bar{\mathbf{r}} = \sum_{i=1}^{n} \mathbf{r}_i m_i$$

but any multiple of $\mathbf{g}$ could be added to it, so the most that can be said is that

$$M\bar{\mathbf{r}} = \sum_{i=1}^{n} \mathbf{r}_i m_i + c\mathbf{g}$$

where c is a constant.

Why can you add a term $c\mathbf{g}$?

This suggests that the definition of centre of gravity is inadequate and needs to be thought about more carefully. If you tried to find the centre of gravity of a closed tin can by trying to balance it on a point of its base, the most you would be able to do is to say that the centre of gravity lies on the axis. In order to be more precise, you would then have to try and balance the can at a point on its side, so as to give another line along which the centre of gravity acts. Effectively you would have had to reorientate the body. You can use the same process in the above, by assuming that the body is reorientated so that gravity acts in a direction $\mathbf{g}'$ perpendicular to $\mathbf{g}$, so that

$$M\bar{\mathbf{r}} = \sum_{i=1}^{n} \mathbf{r}_i m_i + c'\mathbf{g}'$$

The only way for both of these to be true is that the constants are zero so that

$$\boxed{M\bar{\mathbf{r}} = \sum_{i=1}^{n} \mathbf{r}_i m_i}$$

i.e. the centres of mass and gravity coincide.

7.5 Motion of the centre of mass of a system of particles

Having seen how to find centres of mass, the next step is to see whether the general definition used earlier can help to simplify the problem of the motion of a system of particles.

This will be considered first for three individual particles P_1, P_2 and P_3 of masses m_1, m_2 and m_3, with each particle being under the action only of external forces. It will be assumed that at time t these particles have position vectors $\mathbf{r}_1$, $\mathbf{r}_2$ and $\mathbf{r}_3$ respectively with respect to a fixed origin O, and that the forces acting on the particles are $\mathbf{P}_1$, $\mathbf{P}_2$ and $\mathbf{P}_3$ respectively (see diagram). Then

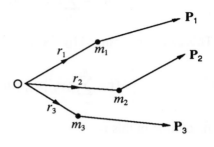

$$m_1\ddot{\mathbf{r}}_1 = \mathbf{P}_1, \quad m_2\ddot{\mathbf{r}}_2 = \mathbf{P}_2, \quad m_3\ddot{\mathbf{r}}_3 = \mathbf{P}_3$$

and adding them gives

$$m_1\ddot{\mathbf{r}}_1 + m_2\ddot{\mathbf{r}}_2 + m_3\ddot{\mathbf{r}}_3 = \mathbf{P}_1 + \mathbf{P}_2 + \mathbf{P}_3$$

Since the position vector $\bar{\mathbf{r}}$ of the centre of mass is defined by

$$\bar{\mathbf{r}} = \frac{m_1\mathbf{r}_1 + m_2\mathbf{r}_2 + m_3\mathbf{r}_3}{m_1 + m_2 + m_3}$$

the equation of motion can be written as

$$\boxed{M\ddot{\bar{\mathbf{r}}} = \mathbf{P}_1 + \mathbf{P}_2 + \mathbf{P}_3}$$

where $\quad M = m_1 + m_2 + m_3$

This equation states that the motion of the centre of mass is exactly the same as that of a particle of mass M (i.e. the total mass of the particles), under the action of a force equal to the vector sum of the forces acting on the particles. Though this has only been proved for three particles, it can also be proved for any number of particles.

The next step is to extend the calculation to cover a slightly more general case when it is assumed that there is an external force $\mathbf{F}_i$ on particle P_i and that there can be interactive forces on the particle, so that there is a force $\mathbf{R}_{ij}$ on the ith particle due to the jth and by Newton's third law $\mathbf{R}_{ij} = -\mathbf{R}_{ji}$.

The forces $\mathbf{P}_1, \mathbf{P}_2, \mathbf{P}_3$ above have therefore to be replaced by

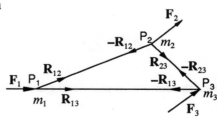

$$\mathbf{P}_1 = \mathbf{F}_1 + \mathbf{R}_{12} + \mathbf{R}_{13}$$

$$\mathbf{P}_2 = \mathbf{F}_2 + \mathbf{R}_{21} + \mathbf{R}_{23}$$

$$\mathbf{P}_3 = \mathbf{F}_3 + \mathbf{R}_{31} + \mathbf{R}_{32}$$

Newton's third law gives

$$\mathbf{R}_{21} = -\mathbf{R}_{12},\ \mathbf{R}_{31} = -\mathbf{R}_{13},\ \mathbf{R}_{32} = -\mathbf{R}_{23}$$

Hence

$$\mathbf{P}_1 = \mathbf{F}_1 + \mathbf{R}_{12} + \mathbf{R}_{13}$$

$$\mathbf{P}_2 = \mathbf{F}_2 - \mathbf{R}_{12} + \mathbf{R}_{23}$$

$$\mathbf{P}_3 = \mathbf{F}_3 - \mathbf{R}_{13} - \mathbf{R}_{23}$$

Adding these gives

$$\boxed{\mathbf{P}_1 + \mathbf{P}_2 + \mathbf{P}_3 = \mathbf{F}_1 + \mathbf{F}_2 + \mathbf{F}_3}$$

You now have a more general result about the motion of the centre of mass, namely that for three interacting particles, the motion of the centre of mass is exactly the same as that of a particle of mass M (i.e. the total mass of the particles) under the action of a force equal to the vector sum of the external forces acting on the particles.

Though this has only been shown for three particles, it can be shown to be true for any number.

This result can be used to solve problems involving connected particles like that for two particles on a string, where changing origin to the centre of mass produces a simple problem for the relative motion.

7.6   Rigid bodies

The above property of the centre of mass will now be used to solve the problem of the motion of a **rigid body**. To do this, it is necessary to construct a simple model of such a body.

A rigid body is taken to be an infinite assembly of particles with the distance between any two constituent particles remaining constant. The particles are taken to be bonded together and the bonding force on particle i due to particle j to be equal in magnitude and opposite in direction to that on particle j due to particle i.

These are the assumptions that were made about the system of interacting particles above and, from the result for interacting particles, it follows that the motion of the centre of mass of a rigid body is identical with that of a particle, of mass equal to that of the whole body, occupying the position of the centre of mass and acted on by the vector sum of all the external forces acting on the body.

This basic result enables a very wide range of problems involving rigid bodies to be solved. The simplest class is that where the body rotates about a fixed axis.

Rotation of a rigid body about a fixed axis

To start with, fairly simple motions of a rigid body rotating about a fixed axis, will be considered. Simple examples are a flywheel or the motion of a bicycle wheel when the bicycle is held fixed and one wheel moved off the ground and made to turn. The motion of the earth round its axis is also an example of a body turning about an axis, but in that case the axis is not fixed.

A door is a simple example of a rigid body moving about a fixed axis and you know that applying a force will change the angular speed. You also know that applying the same force, if you can measure it, at different distances from the hinge, has different effects; the greater the distance from the hinge the greater the effect. It is also impossible to open a door by exerting a force that passes through the line of the hinges! Any force, such as one at the edge and parallel to the door, whose line of action meets the axis, has no turning effect, and no angular acceleration results. It therefore appears that it is the **moment of the force** that produces a change in angular speed, i.e. produces an angular acceleration.

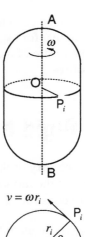

Suppose that the rigid body illustrated in the first diagram is rotating with angular speed ω about the fixed axis AB. The second diagram represents a plane section through P_i perpendicular to the axis and, since the distances between the particles are fixed, the path of the point P_i will be a circle in this plane, the centre O being on the axis AB. The speed of the point P_i is ωr_i, where $OP_i = r_i$. The direction of the velocity of P_i is perpendicular to OP_i.

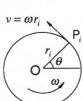

The component of force in any direction is equal to mass times acceleration in that direction. The only component of force to have any effect on the moment about the axis is that perpendicular to OP_i. The component of acceleration perpendicular to OP_i is $r_i\dot{\omega}$ and therefore

$$mr_i\dot{\omega} = \text{component of force perpendicular to } OP_i \text{ on } P_i$$

Multiplying both sides of this equation by r_i gives

$$m_i r_i^2 \dot{\omega} = \text{moment about axis of forces acting on } P_i$$

This equation is true for all particles and therefore, adding over all particles gives

$$\sum_{i=1}^{n} m_i\, r_i^2 \dot{\omega} = \begin{array}{l} \text{sum of moments about axis of all forces} \\ \text{acting on all the particles of the body} \end{array}$$

On any particle, two kinds of forces are acting: **external** ones and **internal** bonding ones. It has already been assumed that the force of P_i on P_j is equal and opposite to that of P_j on P_i. The model is further extended by assuming that the bonding force acts along the line joining the particles. If there were only two particles P_1 and P_2, then the situation would be as in the diagram opposite.

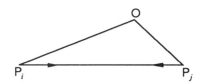

You can see from the diagram that the moment about any point O of the force of P_i on P_j is equal and opposite to that of P_j on P_i. Therefore the sum of the moments of the internal bonding forces on the two particles will be zero. This can be shown to be true for any number of particles and, hence, for a rigid body.

Therefore

$$\sum_{i=1}^{n} m_i\, r_i^2 \dot{\omega} = \begin{array}{l} \text{sum of moments about axis of all the} \\ \text{external forces acting on the body} \end{array}$$

This is the required equation relating angular acceleration to the moment of the applied force, but it is not yet in a usable form.

The quantity $\displaystyle\sum_{i=1}^{n} m_i\, r_i^2$ depends only on the distribution of

particles in the body (it is the sum of the masses times the squares of their distance from the axis) and it is a fundamental quantity in studying rigid body motion. It is called the **moment of inertia** about the axis and it will be denoted by I. The units of moment of inertia are kg m^2.

Therefore

$$I\dot{\omega} = \begin{array}{l} \text{sum of moments about axis of all the} \\ \text{external forces acting on the body} \end{array}$$

From the definition, the angular momentum about the axis of rotation of the typical particle P_i is $m_i\, r_i^2 \omega$, and therefore the total angular momentum could be defined as

$$\sum_{i=1}^{n} m_i\, r_i^2 \dot{\omega} = I\dot{\omega}$$

The basic equation can therefore be written as

rate of change of angular momentum about the axis	= moment of the external forces about the axis

This is the basic law governing motion about an axis. For rotational motion it is the angular speed that is of interest and, for such motions, Newton's law relating rate of change of linear momentum to force is replaced by the above law for the rate of change of angular momentum.

In problems involving particle motion the **principle of conservation of energy** often proves useful and it turns out to be equally useful for rigid bodies. It is therefore necessary to see how to calculate the kinetic energy for a rigid body.

Going back to the typical particle P_i, its speed is ωr_i and therefore its kinetic energy is

$$\frac{1}{2} m_i \, \omega^2 r_i^2$$

Summing over all the particles gives the total kinetic energy as

$$\sum_{i=1}^{n} \frac{1}{2} m_i \, \omega^2 r_i^2 = \frac{1}{2} I \omega^2$$

so

rotational kinetic energy $= \dfrac{1}{2} I \omega^2$

In angular motion, the angular acceleration has the same role as acceleration in linear motion, and the moment of inertia has the same role as mass in linear motion.

The basic principles to solve problems of the motion of a rigid body rotating around a fixed axis have now been established but, unfortunately, to use them you need the moment of inertia of a particular body. In most cases finding the moment of inertia uses integration and this is illustrated in the following section. You might, however, like to omit that work on a first reading and go on to solve problems. In order that you can do this, the principal results for moments of inertia are summarised below. Apart from these results, all that you may need to find moments of inertia are the following two basic theorems.

The perpendicular axes theorem

If the moment of a lamina about two perpendicular axes in its plane are known, the moment of inertia about an axis through the point of intersection of the given axes and perpendicular to the plane of the lamina is equal to the sum of the given moments of inertia about axes in the plane.

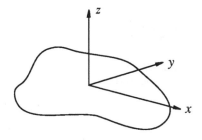

For example, for a plane lamina in the xy-plane

$$I_z = I_x + I_y$$

where I_x, I_y, I_z are the moments of inertia about the three coordinate axes.

The parallel axes theorem

This states that the moment of inertia about any axis is equal to the sum of the moment of inertia about a parallel axis through the centre of mass, and the mass times the square of the distance between the axes.

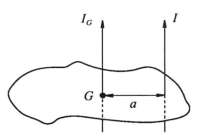

For example,

$$I = I_G + Ma^2$$

when I_G is the moment of inertia about an axis through the centre of mass, G, and I is the moment of inertia about a parallel axis, distance a away.

With these two theorems and the summary below you should be able, without looking at the calculation of moments of inertia by integration, to follow all the examples in the following section and work through all questions in Exercise 7D, except for question 4.

There are two other things that are worth remembering in working out moments of inertia.

1. The moment of inertia of a single particle of mass M at a perpendicular distance r from an axis is Mr^2.

2. The moment of inertia of a compound body is the sum of the moments of inertia of the separate parts.

Summary

All the bodies are assumed uniform.

Body	Axis	Moment of inertia
circular hoop, mass m, radius a	perpendicular through centre	ma^2
circular disc, mass m, radius a	perpendicular through centre	$\dfrac{ma^2}{2}$
rod, mass m, length $2a$	perpendicular through centre	$\dfrac{ma^2}{3}$
rod, mass m, length $2a$	perpendicular through end	$\dfrac{4ma^2}{3}$
rectangle , mass m, sides $2a$, $2b$	through centre parallel side $2a$	$\dfrac{mb^2}{3}$
rectangle , mass m, sides $2a$, $2b$	through centre parallel side $2b$	$\dfrac{ma^2}{3}$
rectangle , mass m, sides $2a$, $2b$	perpendicular through centre	$\dfrac{ma^2}{3}+\dfrac{mb^2}{3}$
solid sphere radius a, mass m	diameter	$\dfrac{2ma^2}{5}$
hollow sphere radius a, mass m	diameter	$\dfrac{2ma^2}{3}$

Another related quantity which is sometimes used is the **radius of gyration,** k. For a body with moment of inertia about an axis of I and mass m, k is such that

$$I = mk^2$$

7.7 The calculation of moments of inertia

Moments of inertia are most often calculated by integration in a similar fashion to determining centres of mass. In some simple cases integration is not necessary and symmetry can be used.

Circular hoop

The simplest moment of inertia to calculate is that of an (ideal) hoop of uniform thin wire, in the form of a circle, about an axis through its centre perpendicular to its plane. All the particles are

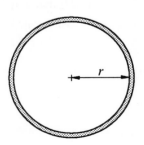

at the same distance r from the axis. The moment of inertia of an individual particle is $m_i r_i^2$ and adding over all the particles gives

$$\text{moment of inertia} = \sum_{i=1}^{n} m_i r_i^2 = Mr^2$$

where M is the total mass.

Uniform thin rod

An origin is chosen at the midpoint O of the rod as shown in the diagram. Axes Ox and Oy are chosen along and perpendicular to the rod and the moment of inertia about Oy is to be found. The rod is divided into small elements, a typical element being that lying between x and $x + \delta x$. The moment of inertia about Oy of the element is $kx^2 \delta x$, correct to the first order in δx, where k is the mass per unit length.

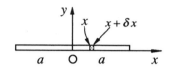

For a uniform thin rod of mass M and length $2a$,

$$k = \frac{M}{2a}$$

Adding up over all the elements is equivalent to integrating from $x = -a$ to a, so that

$$\text{moment of inertia} = \frac{M}{2a} \int_{-a}^{a} x^2 dx$$

$$= \frac{M}{2a} \left[\frac{x^3}{3a} \right]_{-a}^{a}$$

$$= \frac{Ma^2}{3}$$

Uniform rectangular lamina of sides $2a$ and $2b$

The lamina can be split up, as shown in the diagram, into thin strips parallel to the side of length $2a$. The mass of a typical strip can be denoted by δm_i. By the above result for the rod, the moment of inertia of the typical strip about an axis through its centre of mass and parallel to the sides of length $2b$ is $\dfrac{\delta m_i a^2}{3}$. Adding up over all the strips gives

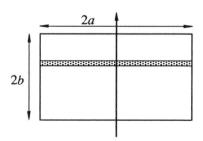

moment of inertia about axis through centre of mass and parallel to sides of length $2b$ $= \dfrac{Ma^3}{3}$

What is the moment of inertia about an axis through the centre of mass and parallel to sides of length $2a$?

The rectangle could equally well have been divided into strips parallel to the other pair of sides, and therefore

moment of inertia about axis through centre of mass and parallel to sides of length $2a$ $= \dfrac{Mb^3}{3}$

Uniform lamina in the form of a circular disc

The most convenient method of subdividing a disc is into circular hoops, as shown in the diagram. The typical hoop is bounded by circles of radius r and $r + \delta r$; its mass is $2\pi r k\, \delta r$, where k is the mass per unit area. Its moment of inertia about an axis through the centre of the disc and perpendicular to the disc is, therefore, $2\pi r k\, \delta r\, r^2$, correct to the first order in δr.

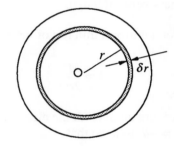

For a uniform disc of mass M and radius a,

$$k = \frac{M}{\pi a^2}$$

Adding over all the hoops is equivalent to integrating with respect to r from 0 to a, and therefore

moment of inertia $= \dfrac{M}{\pi a^2} \displaystyle\int_0^a 2\pi r^3 dr$

$$= \frac{M}{\pi a^2}\left[\frac{2\pi r^4}{4}\right]_0^a$$

$$= \frac{Ma^2}{2}$$

Uniform solid sphere

A sphere can be split up into thin discs parallel to any diametral plane; this is shown in the diagram. If the diametral plane is the plane $x = 0$, then a typical element will be that between the planes at perpendicular distances x and $x + \delta x$ from the plane $x = 0$. If the sphere is of radius a, then the radius of the disc is

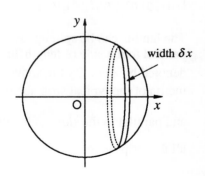

$$\sqrt{a^2 - x^2}$$

and its mass therefore, correct to the first order in δx, is

$$k\pi\left(a^2 - x^2\right)\delta x$$

where k is the mass per unit volume of the sphere. The result for the circular disc gives the moment of inertia of the disc about the x-axis as

$$\frac{1}{2}\left(k\pi\left(a^2 - x^2\right)\delta x\right)\left(a^2 - x^2\right) = \frac{1}{2}k\pi\left(a^2 - x^2\right)^2\delta x$$

For a uniform sphere of mass M and radius a,

$$k = \frac{M}{\text{volume}}$$

$$= \frac{M}{\frac{4}{3}\pi a^3}$$

$$= \frac{3M}{4\pi a^3}$$

Adding over all the discs is equivalent to integrating with respect to x from $-a$ to a, so

$$\text{moment of inertia} = \frac{3M}{4\pi a^3}\int_{-a}^{a}\frac{\pi\left(a^2 - x^2\right)^2}{2}dx$$

Activity 5

Evaluate the integration above to show that

$$\text{moment of inertia} = \frac{2Ma^2}{5}$$

Uniform circular cylinder

A uniform circular cylinder can be split up into discs perpendicular to the axis as in the diagram. If the radius of the cylinder is a and the mass of a disc is δm_i, then the moment of inertia of the disc

about the axis is $\dfrac{\delta m_i a^2}{2}$, and adding up over the elements gives, for a cylinder of mass M,

$$\text{moment of inertia} = \frac{Ma^2}{2}$$

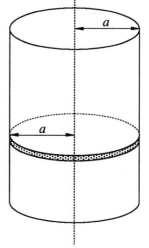

Spherical shell

The same kind of subdivision into rings can be used as on page 224 to calculate the position of the centre of mass of a hemispherical shell. The ring in that instance was found to be of radius $r \cos \theta$ and mass $2\pi k r \cos \theta r \delta \theta$, where k is the mass per unit area.

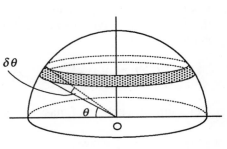

The moment of inertia of the hemispherical shell about an axis through its centre and perpendicular to its plane is therefore $(2\pi k r \cos \theta r \delta \theta)\left(r^2 \cos^2 \theta \right)$. The total moment of inertia of a hemispherical shell is found by integrating with respect to θ from 0 to $\dfrac{\pi}{2}$. Also, $k = \dfrac{M}{2\pi r^2}$, where M is the mass of the shell and r is its radius.

Therefore the moment of inertia becomes the integral

$$\frac{M}{2\pi r^2} \int_0^{\frac{\pi}{2}} 2\pi r^4 \cos^3 \theta \, d\theta$$

Activity 6

By integrating, show that the moment of inertia is given by

$$\frac{2Mr^2}{3}$$

A hollow shell is formed by joining two hemispherical shells base to base, so the moment of inertia will be the sum of the moments of inertia, i.e. $\dfrac{4Mr^2}{3}$. The shell will then be of mass $2M$, so for a spherical shell of mass M,

$$\text{moment of inertia of shell about diameter} = \frac{2Mr^2}{3}$$

This particular result could also have been obtained by symmetry.

The moments of inertia about the axes are, by definition,

$$\sum_{i=1}^{n} m_i \left(y_i^2 + z_i^2 \right), \quad \sum_{i=1}^{n} m_i \left(x_i^2 + z_i^2 \right), \quad \sum_{i=1}^{n} m_i \left(y_i^2 + x_i^2 \right)$$

By symmetry these are all equal and their value is denoted by I.

Adding these three quantities gives

$$2\sum_{i=1}^{n} m_i \left(y_i^2 + x_i^2 + z_i^2 \right) = 3I$$

On the shell $y_i^2 + x_i^2 + z_i^2 = r^2$ and therefore $3I = 2Mr^2$, giving the same result for I.

As mentioned in the last section, there are two important theorems which simplify the work involved in calculating moments of inertia and, for convenience, they will be restated.

The perpendicular axis or lamina theorem

If the moments of inertia of a lamina about two perpendicular axes in its plane are known, the moment of inertia about an axis through the point of intersection of the given axes and perpendicular to the plane of the lamina, is equal to the sum of the given moments of inertia about axes in the plane.

*Proof

Let Ox and Oy be the given axes and I_x and I_y be the moments of inertia about these axes. A typical particle of the lamina is at the point P_i with coordinates (x_i, y_j). The perpendicular distance of P_i from Ox is y_i and therefore the contribution of the particle to I_x is $m_i y_i^2$; similarly its contribution to I_y is $m_i x_i^2$.

Summing over all the particles gives

$$I_x = \sum_{i=1}^{n} m_i y_i^2$$

and
$$I_y = \sum_{i=1}^{n} m_i x_i^2$$

The square of the perpendicular distance of P_i from Oz is $x_i^2 + y_i^2$. Hence I_z, the moment of inertia about Oz, is given by

$$I_z = \sum_{i=1}^{n} m_i \left(x_i^2 + y_i^2 \right)$$

which is obviously $I_x + I_y$.

Thus

$$\boxed{I_z = I_x + I_y}$$

The parallel axis theorem

The moment of inertia of a rigid body about an axis not through
the centre of mass, is equal to the sum of the moment of inertia
about a parallel axis through the centre of mass and the product of
the mass of the body and the square of the distance between the
axes.

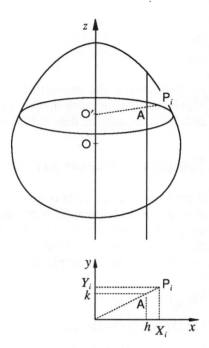

*Proof

To simplify the proof, axes Ox, Oy and Oz are chosen so that Oz is
the axis through the centre of mass. The diagram shows a particle
P_i in a plane perpendicular to Oz. O' is the point of intersection of
Oz with the plane, and A is the point where a line parallel to Oz
intersects the plane. The coordinates of P_i are (X_i, Y_i, Z_i). Since
Ox passes through the centre of mass, the coordinates X_i and Y_i are
coordinates relative to the centre of mass, so that

$$\sum_{i=1}^{n} m_i X_i = \sum_{i=1}^{n} m_i Y_i, = 0$$

The coordinates of P_i relative to A in the plane, are
$(X_i - h, Y_i - k)$, where (h, k) are the coordinates of A relative
to O'.

Hence

$$AP_i^2 = (X_i - h)^2 + (Y_i - k)^2$$

$$= X_i^2 + Y_i^2 + h^2 + k^2 - 2hX_i - 2kY_i$$

Summing over all particles gives the moment of inertia about the
axis through A parallel to Oz as

$$\sum_{i=1}^{n} m_i \left(X_i^2 + Y_i^2 + h^2 + k^2 - 2hX_i - 2kY_i \right)$$

The terms in h and k vanish since

$$\sum_{i=1}^{n} m_i X_i = \sum_{i=1}^{n} m_i Y_i = 0$$

The required moment of inertia is therefore

$$\sum_{i=1}^{n} m_i \left(X_i^2 + Y_i^2 + h^2 + k^2 \right) = \sum_{i=1}^{n} m_i \left(X_i^2 + Y_i^2 \right) + \sum_{i=1}^{n} m_i \left(h^2 + k^2 \right)$$

The first term is the moment of inertia about Oz and the second term is the total mass multiplied by the square of the distance between the axes, thus proving the theorem.

This theorem means that, once the moment of inertia has been found for an axis through the centre of mass, then it is very easy to find it about any parallel axis.

The theorems can now be used to obtain further results about the moments of inertia of simple bodies. It should also be remembered that the moment of inertia of any kind of composite body about an axis is the sum of the moments of inertia of the constituent parts about the same axis.

Example

Find the moment of inertia of a uniform rod of length $2a$ about a perpendicular axis through an end.

Solution

The moment of inertia can be found from the parallel axes theorem, which gives it as

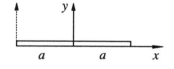

$$I = Ma^2 + \frac{Ma^2}{3} = \frac{4Ma^2}{3}$$

Example

Find the moment of inertia of a uniform rectangle with sides of lengths $2a$ and $2b$ about an axis through its centre of mass and perpendicular to its plane.

Solution

The moments of inertia about two perpendicular axes in the plane of the rectangle are known and therefore the parallel axes theorem can be used. It gives the moment of inertia as

$$\frac{Ma^2}{3} + \frac{Mb^2}{3} = \frac{M\left(a^2 + b^2\right)}{3}$$

Example

Find the moment of inertia of a uniform disc about a diameter.

Solution

By symmetry, the moment of inertia about all diameters is the same. By the parallel axes theorem, the sum of the moments of inertia about two perpendicular diameters is $\dfrac{Ma^2}{2}$ and therefore the moment of inertia about any diameter is $\dfrac{Ma^2}{4}$.

Example

A central hole of radius b is removed from a uniform circular disc of radius a, the mass of the remaining part being M. Find the moment of inertia of the remainder about an axis through the centre and perpendicular to its plane.

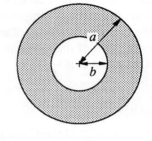

Solution

The moment of inertia of the remainder is

moment of inertia   moment of inertia
of whole disc $-$ of part removed

If k denotes the mass per unit area of the material of the disc, then the mass of the whole disc is $k\pi a^2$. Its moment of inertia about

the required axis is $\dfrac{k\pi a^4}{2}$ and the corresponding moment of

inertia for the part removed is $\dfrac{k\pi b^4}{2}$. The required moment of

inertia is therefore

$$\frac{k\pi a^4}{2} - \frac{k\pi b^4}{2} = \frac{k\pi}{2}\left(a^4 - b^4\right)$$

$$= \frac{k\pi\left(a^2 - b^2\right)\left(a^2 + b^2\right)}{2}$$

The mass M of the remainder is $k\pi a^2 - k\pi b^2$ and the required

moment of inertia is therefore $\dfrac{M\left(a^2 + b^2\right)}{2}$.

Exercise 7D

1. Two uniform rods of mass m and length $2a$ are joined at right angles. Find the moment of inertia of the system of two rods about an axis through the free end of one of the rods and perpendicular to the plane of the rods.

2. Four uniform rods of mass m and length $2a$ are joined together to form a square frame. Find the moment of inertia of the frame about

    (i) an axis through one of the corners and perpendicular to the frame,

    (ii) one of the rods.

3. Three uniform rods of mass m and length $2a$ are joined together to form a frame in the shape of an equilateral triangle. Find the moment of inertia of the frame about an axis through one of the vertices and perpendicular to the frame.

4. Show, by integration, that the moment of inertia about its axis of a uniform cone of mass m and

    base radius a is $\dfrac{3ma^2}{10}$.

5. Find the the moment of inertia of a uniform cone of mass m, base radius a and height h about a line through its vertex and perpendicular to its axis.

6. The line AOB is a diameter of a uniform disc of centre O, radius $4a$ and mass $4m$. A circular hole of radius $2a$ is made in the disc, the centre of the circle being on AB at a distance $5a$ from B. Find the moment of inertia of the remainder about an axis through b and perpendicular to the plane of the disc.

7.

```
A _____●___ B
|                            |   |
|                            | a |
|            6a              |---|
|                            |   |
|_____|___|
```

The diagram shows a uniform rod AB with a uniform circular disc attached to it, with a diameter of the disc being along AB and its centre being at a distance $5a$ from A. The rod is of mass m and length $6a$, the disc is of mass $2m$ and radius a. Find the moment of inertia of the system about an axis through A and perpendicular to the plane of the disc.

8.

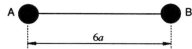

In the diagram two uniform spheres of radius a are attached to a uniform rod of length $6a$. The ends of the rod are at the centres of the spheres. Given that the spheres are of mass $5m$ and the rod of mass m, find the moment of inertia of the system about an axis through the centre of the rod and perpendicular to the rod.

9. The diagram shows a wheel and four spokes. The material of the wheel and spokes is uniform and the inner and outer radii of the wheel are $6a$ and $7a$ respectively. The spokes are of mass m and length $6a$. Given that the wheel is of mass $2m$ find the total moment of inertia about an axis through the centre and perpendicular to the plane of the wheel.

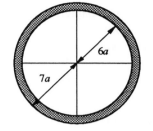

7.8 Problems of rigid body motion about a fixed axis

You now have enough information to be able to solve problems involving the motion of a rigid body about a fixed axis but, before looking at problems, it is worth summarising again the main results.

The governing principle is that the rate of change of angular momentum about an axis is equal to the moment of the external forces about that axis.

Since there may be couples acting they have to be included and therefore the first basic result is

1. rate of change of angular momentum about an axis equals the sum of moments of all external couples and the moments of the external forces about that axis, i.e.

$$I\dot{\omega} = C$$

where ω is the angular velocity, I is the moment of inertia about the axis and C is the sum of all the external moments and couples.

The second basic result is

2. the motion of the centre of mass is the same as that of a particle of mass equal to the total mass of the body, situated at the centre of mass and acted on by a force equal to the vector sum of all the external forces, i.e.

$$M\ddot{\mathbf{r}} = \mathbf{F}$$

where M is the total mass, $\bar{\mathbf{r}}$ is the position vector of the centre of mass and $\mathbf{F}$ is the vector sum of all the external forces acting.

In many problems, the axis will pass through the centre of mass and therefore there is no need to worry about its motion! In practically all cases, the angular momentum equation can be used to give the angular acceleration and the centre of mass equation will then give the forces acting.

These results are sufficient to solve any problem but it is sometimes useful in avoiding calculation to use the work–energy principle or the principle of conservation of energy.

It was shown in Chapter 6 of *Mechanics* that, for a single particle, the change in kinetic energy is equal to the work done by the forces acting on the particle. This will still be true for any number of particles provided the interactive forces are taken into account. It is possible to show that the assumptions about the bonding forces for a rigid body, i.e.

(i)   the force exerted by P_j on P_i is equal and opposite to that exerted by P_i on P_j,

(ii) the bonding force acts along the lines joining the particles,

(iii) the distance between constituent particles remains unchanged,

are sufficient to show that the work done by the bonding forces is zero.

Therefore the work–energy principle applies to rigid body motion.

You also saw in Chapter 6 of *Mechanics* that the work done by gravity is equal to negative potential energy, so that the work energy principle becomes

change in sum of potential and kinetic energies	=	work done by non-gravitational forces

Very often there are no non-gravitational forces so that energy is conserved.

Example

A flywheel can rotate about a smooth horizontal axis passing through its centre of mass, and its moment of inertia about this axis is 25 kg m^2. The flywheel is rotating with a constant angular speed of 3 rad s^{-1} when a constant couple of magnitude 5 N m is applied to it so that it comes to rest. Find the time taken to stop and the total angle the flywheel turns through in that time.

Solution

The equation of angular motion is

$$25\dot{\omega} = -5$$

where the angular speed is ω rad s^{-1}. This gives

$$\omega = -\frac{t}{5} + k$$

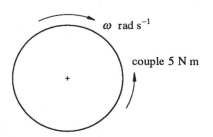

where k is a constant. This is found by using $\omega = 3$ when $t = 0$, so that

$$\omega = -\frac{t}{5} + 3$$

The flywheel therefore stops after 15 seconds, and the angle turned through can be found by integrating ω (which is $\dot\theta$), so that

$$\theta = \frac{t^2}{10} + 3t \quad (\text{since } \theta = 0 \text{ at } t = 0)$$

Substituting $t = 3$ gives $\theta = 22.5$ rad.

An alternative method of finding θ is to use the result

$$\dot\omega = \omega \frac{d\omega}{d\theta}$$

which you have already seen earlier in Chapter 6 on Circular Motion.

The equation of motion then becomes

$$25\omega \frac{d\omega}{d\theta} = -5$$

and, integrating,

$$\omega^2 = -\frac{2\theta}{5} + k$$

where k is a constant. Using the condition that $\theta = 0$ when $\omega = 3$ gives $k = 9$. This gives, as before, $\theta = 22.5$ when $\omega = 0$, i.e. the flywheel stops after turning through 22.5 radians.

Example

A solid cylinder of radius 0.25 m can rotate about a smooth horizontal axis passing through its centre of mass, and its moment of inertia about this axis is 5 kg m². A light inextensible string is wound round the cylinder and is pulled off horizontally with a constant force of 50 N as shown in the diagram. Find the angular speed when the cylinder has turned through one revolution.

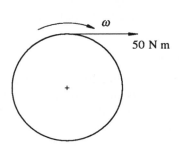

Solution

The external moment is 12.5 N m, so the equation of angular motion is

$$5\dot{\omega} = 12.5$$

One method would be to integrate this equation twice to find ω and θ. From the equation for θ you would get the time for one revolution, and this could then be substituted in the equation for ω. This is rather complicated – it is easier to use

$$\dot{\omega} = \omega \frac{d\omega}{d\theta}$$

so that $\qquad \omega \dfrac{d\omega}{d\theta} = 2.5$

Integrating, and since $\omega = 0$ when $\theta = 0$,

$$\omega^2 = 5\theta$$

Substituting $\theta = 2\pi$ gives the angular speed as 5.6 rad s^{-1}.

Activity 7

Tackle the problem above by integrating

$$5\dot{\omega} = 12.5$$

to find ω and then to find θ. Hence solve the problem.

Example

Particles of mass m and $5m$ are attached one to each end of an inextensible string. The string passes over a small pulley, free to turn about a smooth horizontal axis. The pulley is to be modelled as a uniform circular disc of radius a and mass $4m$ and the axis passes through its centre of mass. Given that the string does not slide relative to the pulley, find the acceleration of the particles.

Solution

Since the string does not slide, the pulley will have an angular speed ω as shown in the diagram. Therefore there will be a moment about the axis of the pulley and it is not possible to assume that the tensions in the string on both sides will be the same. They are denoted by T_1 and T_2 in the diagram and the magnitude of the acceleration of the particles is denoted by f.

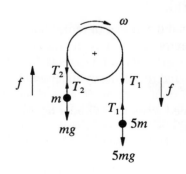

The equations of motion of the particles are

$$5m \quad : \quad 5mg - T_1 = 5mf$$
$$m \quad : \quad T_2 - mg = mf$$

The equation of angular motion of the pulley is

$$2ma^2\dot{\omega} = (T_1 - T_2)a$$

So far there are not enough equations to solve for all the unknowns and the condition that the string does not slip has to be used.

The downward acceleration of the point of the pulley where the string just comes off it is $a\dot{\omega}$, and the acceleration of the string at this point is f. The no slip condition is therefore

$$a\dot{\omega} = f$$

These equations can now be solved to give $f = \dfrac{1}{2}g$.

Activity 8

Show that the four equations result in $f = \dfrac{1}{2}g$.

There are some examples where the total moment is zero and the angular momentum is conserved. These normally occur when a system consists of two interacting parts, and are illustrated in the following examples.

Example

A small animal of mass m can move on a large uniform circular disc of radius a and mass $20m$. The disc can turn about a smooth vertical axis through its centre and initially has an angular speed ω. Initially the animal is at rest relative to the disc at a point on the rim of the disc and then it starts to walk directly towards the centre of the disc.

Find the angular speed of the disc when the animal reaches the centre.

Solution

None of the forces acting have any moment about the vertical axis and therefore angular momentum is conserved about that axis. The initial moment of inertia about the axis of animal plus disc is

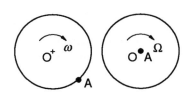

$$10ma^2 + ma^2 = 11ma^2$$

and therefore the initial angular momentum is $11ma^2\omega$. The final moment of inertia about the axis of animal plus disc is $10\ ma^2$ and therefore the final angular momentum is $10ma^2\Omega$, where Ω is the final angular speed. Therefore the final angular speed is 1.1ω.

Example

This question looks at a very idealised model of a skater rotating about a vertical axis. The body of the skater is represented by a cylinder of radius R whose moment of inertia about its axis is $60I$. The arms of the skater are represented by thin rods of mass m, which, when fully extended horizontally, each have a moment of inertia I about the axis of the cylinder. A skater is rotating with angular speed ω about a vertical axis when she extends her arms horizontally. Find her angular speed in this new position.

Solution

The forces acting have no moment about the vertical axis so that angular momentum is conserved about that axis. Since the arms are represented by thin rods, the initial moment of inertia about the axis is $60I + 2mr^2$ and the final moment of inertia is $62I$. Denoting the final angular speed by Ω, the conservation of angular momentum gives

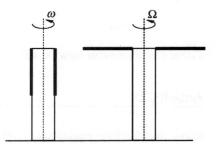

$$\left(60I + 2mr^2\right)\omega = 62\,I\,\Omega$$

The new angular speed is therefore

$$\frac{\left(60I + 2mr^2\right)\omega}{62I}$$

Exercise 7E

1. A flywheel, whose moment of inertia about its axis of symmetry is 2.5 kg m² is rotating about this axis at 240 revs/min. The motor driving the flywheel is switched off, and the flywheel slows down and comes to rest under the action of a frictional couple in 2.5 min. Find the magnitude of the frictional couple.

2. A rope passing over a pulley of radius 0.2 m and with moment of inertia 1 kg m² about its axis, has masses of 5 kg and 10 kg respectively attached one to each end. The masses are released from rest with the rope taut and the masses hanging freely at rest. Find the angular acceleration of the pulley.

3. The moment of inertia of a uniform flywheel about its axis is I and it is set in motion from rest by a couple of constant moment C. Find the time taken for the angular speed of the flywheel to reach a value ω from rest, and find the angle through which it has turned in this time.

4. A constant couple of 80 N m increases the angular speed of a flywheel from zero to 60 revolutions per minute in 20 seconds. Find, assuming that there is no frictional couple acting, the moment of inertia of the flywheel about its axis.

5. A rectangular door can turn smoothly about its hinges and its moment of inertia about the line of hinges is I. The door is opened by pulling on a handle at a perpendicular distance a from the line of hinges. A constant force of magnitude F is applied to the handle, the force always being perpendicular to the door. Find the speed of the handle when the door has been opened through an angle of $90°$.

6. One end of a string is attached to a point on the rim of a pulley of radius 0.2 m and which is free to turn about a smooth axis. The string is wound round the pulley several times and it carries at its other end a particle of mass 1 kg, which hangs freely. Given that the moment of inertia of the pulley about its axis is 0.2 kg m² and that there is no resistance to motion, find the angular acceleration of the pulley when the system is released with the string taut and the part supporting the particle vertical.

7. A flywheel can turn about a horizontal axis but is subject to a frictional couple which is directly proportional to its angular speed. It is set in motion with an angular speed of 20 rad s⁻¹ and its angular speed has been reduced to 10 rad s⁻¹ in 40 seconds. Find

   (a) its angular speed after a further 20 seconds

   (b) the time taken for its angular speed to become 12 rad s⁻¹.

8. A lamina can rotate in a horizontal plane about a vertical axis through its centre of mass G. An insect stands on the lamina at a point A a distance a from G. The insect has mass m and the moment of inertia of the lamina about the axis is $15\,ma^2$. The insect walks on the lamina, its path relative to the lamina being the straight line through A perpendicular to GA. The insect walks at a constant speed V relative to the lamina. Find the angle turned through by the lamina by the time that the insect has travelled a distance $4a$ relative to the lamina.

7.9 Motion of a compound pendulum

The problems so far have had the common property that the axis of rotation passed through the centre of mass; a more general class will now be considered, where this is not the case. These problems are referred to as **compound pendulum** problems, as the pendulums of old fashioned clocks were effectively compound rigid bodies with a heavy bob.

The typical compound pendulum is a rigid body free to rotate about a horizontal axis through a point O of itself. The body is of mass M, its moment of inertia about the axis is denoted by I and the distance of the centre of mass from O is denoted by h. The pendulum will be in equilibrium with the centre of mass G directly below O as shown in the diagram opposite. It is set in motion so that at any time t the inclination of OG to the vertical is θ.

The moment of the weight about O is $Mgh\sin\theta$ clockwise and the equation of angular motion gives

$$I\ddot{\theta} = -Mgh\sin\theta$$

Multiplying this equation by $\dot{\theta}$ and integrating with respect to t gives

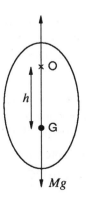

$$\frac{1}{2}I\dot{\theta} = Mgh\cos\theta + \text{constant}$$

An equivalent method of getting this equation would have been to use

$$\dot{\omega} = \omega\frac{d\omega}{d\theta}$$

The equation can be written in a slightly different form

$$\frac{1}{2}I\dot{\theta} - Mgh\cos\theta = \text{constant}$$

The first term is the kinetic energy of the body and the second is the potential energy, and this is therefore the equation of conservation of energy. It could have been written down immediately and it is probably more efficient in compound pendulum problems to write down the equation of conservation of energy and differentiate it to get the angular equation of motion.

It would now be possible, if the initial conditions were known, to find θ in terms of t but the integrations involved are rather complicated.

For small θ the equation of angular motion becomes

$$\boxed{I\ddot{\theta} = -Mgh\theta}$$

This is the equation of S.H.M. and therefore the period T of small oscillations is given by

$$\boxed{T = 2\pi\sqrt{\frac{I}{Mgh}}}$$

For the **compound pendulum**, this is the analogue of the simple pendulum formula.

Sometimes it is useful to know the reactions at O and to do this it is necessary to use the property that the centre of mass moves like a point of total mass M under the action of the total force on the body.

The centre of mass moves in a circle of radius h about O, and therefore it is convenient to take the components of the reaction at O along and perpendicular to OG as shown. The acceleration of G has, from Chapter 6, a component $h\dot{\theta}^2$ along GO, and one perpendicular to OG, $h\ddot{\theta}$, in the sense shown in the diagram opposite.

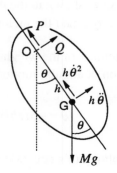

Therefore the motion of the centre of mass gives

$$Mh\dot{\theta}^2 = P - Mg\cos\theta$$

$$Mh\ddot{\theta} = Q - Mg\sin\theta$$

Here P and Q are the reactions at O along and perpendicular to OG as shown in the previous diagram. In any problem you can substitute for $\dot{\theta}^2$ and $\ddot{\theta}$ in terms of θ and hence get the reactions.

The main problem in a compound pendulum problem is finding the moment of inertia, I. It is not really necessary to find the centre of mass separately if there is a complicated body. The potential energy will be the sum of the individual potential energies, and you know from the theoretical results on the centre of mass that

mass × acceleration of centre of mass	=	sum of individual masses × acceleration of their centres of mass

Example

A uniform rod of mass $6m$ and length $2a$ can rotate freely about a horizontal axis through one end and carries a particle of mass $2m$ at the other end. The rod is released from rest when horizontal. Find its angular speed when it makes an angle θ with the vertical and find the components along and perpendicular to the rod, of the reaction at the axis.

Solution

The total moment of inertia about the axis of the particle and the rod is

$$8ma^2 + 2m(2a)^2 = 16ma^2$$

The potential energy of the rod is $-6mga\cos\theta$ and that of the particle is $-4mga\cos\theta$, so the equation of conservation of energy is given by

$$16ma^2\dot{\theta}^2 - 10mga\cos\theta = \text{constant}$$

The rod is at rest when $\theta = \dfrac{\pi}{2}$, so the constant is 0.

Therefore $\qquad \dot{\theta} = \sqrt{\dfrac{5g}{8a}\cos\theta}$

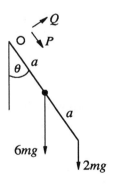

The acceleration of the particle towards the axis is $2a\dot{\theta}^2$ and that of the centre of mass of the rod is $a\dot{\theta}^2$. So the equation of motion of the centre of mass, along the rod, is

$$4ma\dot\theta^2 + 3ma\dot\theta^2 = -P - 3mg\cos\theta - 2mg\cos\theta$$

Activity 9

Show that the centre of mass is at a distance $\dfrac{7a}{5}$ from the end of the rod. Using the acceleration of the centre of mass, verify that the same result is obtained as above.

Substituting for $\dot\theta^2$

$$P = -5mg\cos\theta - 7ma\dot\theta^2$$

$$= -5mg\cos\theta - 7ma\left(\frac{5g\cos\theta}{8a}\right)$$

$$= -\frac{75}{8}mg\cos\theta$$

The acceleration of the particle perpendicular to the rod is $2a\ddot\theta$ and that of the centre of mass of the rod is $a\ddot\theta$, therefore the equation of motion of the centre of mass, perpendicular to the rod, is

$$4ma\ddot\theta + 3ma\ddot\theta = Q - 5mg\sin\theta$$

Differentiating the equation of energy gives

$$16a\ddot\theta = -5mga\sin\theta$$

and substituting this in the equation of motion gives

$$Q = \frac{45}{16}mg\sin\theta$$

Example

Find the angular speed for the previous example when the particle is replaced by a uniform circular disc of mass $2m$ and radius a with the centre of the disc placed at the end of the rod.

Solution

The main difference is the calculation of the moment of inertia. By the parallel axes theorem the moment of inertia of the disc about the axis of rotation is

$$2m(2a)^2 + ma^2 = 9ma^2$$

The potential energies will be unchanged so the equation of conservation of energy is

$$17ma^2\dot\theta^2 - 10mga\cos\theta = \text{constant}$$

The constant is again zero, so the angular speed is now

$$\sqrt{\frac{10g}{17a}\cos\theta}$$

Exercise 7F

1. A bicycle wheel has moment of inertia of 0.75 kg m² about its axis of rotation. A particle P of mass 0.04 kg is fixed to the spoke of the bicycle wheel at a distance of 0.3 m from the axle. The moment of inertia of the wheel about the axle is 0.75 kg m² and the axle passes through the centre of mass of the wheel. The wheel is released from rest when the spoke through P is horizontal. Find the angular speed of the wheel when P reaches its lowest position.

2. A uniform rod AB, of mass 0.6 kg and length 1.0 m, can rotate freely about a smooth horizontal axis through A. The rod is released when AB makes an angle of 60° with the upward vertical. Find the maximum angular speed in the subsequent motion.

3. A particle of mass 0.05 kg is rigidly attached to a point on the circumference of a uniform circular disc of radius 0.2 m and mass 0.5 kg. The disc is free to rotate about a horizontal axis through its centre and perpendicular to its plane.

   Given that the system is released when the radius to the particle is horizontal, find the maximum angular speed of the system in the subsequent motion.

4. A compound pendulum body consists of a uniform solid sphere, of mass m and radius r, rigidly attached at a point on its surface to one end B of a light thin rod AB, of length $3r$, so that the line of the rod, when produced, would pass through the centre of the sphere. The pendulum is free to rotate in a vertical plane about a smooth horizontal axis through the end A of the rod and perpendicular to the rod. Show that the moment of inertia of the rod about this axis is equal to $16.4mr^2$. The body is released from rest when AB is horizontal. Find the angular speed in the subsequent motion when the rod makes an angle θ with the downward vertical.

5. A uniform circular disc of radius a and mass $2m$ can turn freely about a horizontal axis through its centre.

   A particle of mass m is fixed at a point on the circumference. The system is made to describe small oscillations about the position where the particle is directly below the centre of the disc. Find the period of these oscillations.

6. A compound pendulum is formed of a uniform rod AB of length $2a$ and mass m with a particle of mass $6m$ fixed at a point a distance x from A. Find x so that the period of small oscillations of the pendulum is a minimum.

7. A uniform rod of mass m and length $2a$ is free to rotate about one end. The rod is released from rest when it is horizontal. Find the reaction perpendicular to the rod when the latter has turned through an angle θ.

8. A uniform circular lamina of mass m is free to turn about a horizontal axis through a point O of its circumference. It is released from rest when the radius through O makes an angle of 60° with the vertical. Find the magnitude of the reaction on the axis at O when the radius through O is vertical.

9. A uniform rectangular lamina ABCD is of mass m and AB=$2a$ and BC=$4a$. The lamina can rotate freely about a horizontal axis through the midpoint of AB. Find the moment of inertia of the lamina about the axis of rotation.

   A particle of mass $2m$ is attached to B and the system released from rest in the position where AB is horizontal and above BC.

   Find, for the position where AB is vertical, the vertical and horizontal components of the reaction at O.

7.10 Miscellaneous Exercises

1. Show by integration that the centre of mass of a uniform, solid hemisphere of base radius a is at a distance $\frac{3a}{8}$ from the centre of its plane face.

   A uniform composite body consists of a solid circular cylinder of radius a and height a and a solid hemisphere of radius a such that the plane face of the hemisphere coincides with the base of the cylinder. Determine the distance of the centre of mass of the composite body from the plane face of the hemisphere. (AEB)

2. Five circular discs of radii 5 cm, 4 cm, 3 cm, 2 cm and 1 cm are cut from a uniform slab of material of thickness 1 cm. The discs are placed on top of each other on a horizontal table in order of decreasing size. Given that the centres of the discs all lie on the same vertical line, find the height of the centre of mass of the five discs above the table. (AEB)

3. The base of a uniform solid hemisphere has radius $2a$ and its centre is at O. A uniform solid S is formed by removing, from the hemisphere, the solid hemisphere of radius a and centre O. Determine the position of the centre of mass of S. (The relevant result for a solid hemisphere may be assumed without proof.) (AEB)

4. A composite body B is formed by joining, at the rims of their circular bases, a uniform solid right circular cylinder of radius a and height $2a$ and a uniform right circular cone of radius a and height $2a$. Given that the cylinder and the cone have masses M and λM respectively, find

   (a) the distance of the centre of mass of B from the common plane face when $\lambda = 1$,

   (b) the value of λ such that the centre of mass of B lies in the common plane face. (AEB)

5. A uniform solid right circular cylinder of radius a and height $3a$ is fixed with its axis vertical, and has a uniform solid sphere of radius r attached to its upper face. The sphere and the cylinder have the same density and the centre of the sphere is vertically above the centre of the cylinder. Given that the centre of mass of the resulting composite body is at the point of contact of the sphere with the cylinder, find r in terms of a. (AEB)

6. The figure shows a solid uniform right circular cone of height h, base radius r and vertex V from which has been removed a solid coaxial cone of height $\frac{1}{2}h$, base radius r.

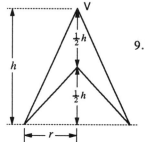

   Find the distance from V of the centre of mass of the resulting solid. (AEB)

7. Show, by integration, that the centre of mass of a uniform right circular cone of height h is at a distance of $\frac{3h}{4}$ from the vertex.

   A composite body B is formed by joining, at the rims of their circular bases, a uniform solid hemisphere of base radius a and a uniform right circular cone of base radius a and height a. The mass of the hemisphere is m. Given that the centre of mass of B lies within the cone and at a perpendicular distance $\frac{a}{8}$ from its base, find the mass of the cone in terms of m.

   The body B, when suspended from a point on the rim of the base of the cone, is in equilibrium with the axis of the cone inclined at an angle α to the vertical. Find $\tan \alpha$.

   Find also the least mass that has to be attached to the surface of the hemisphere so that when B is suspended from a point on the rim of the base of the cone, the axis of the cone is horizontal. (AEB)

8. [In this question you should assume g is $9.8\,\mathrm{m\,s^{-2}}$.]

   A flywheel is mounted on a smooth horizontal axle of diameter a. A light inextensible string is wrapped around the axle, one end being fixed to the axle. The other end of the string hangs vertically and carries a mass m which is released from rest with the hanging portion of the string taut. Given that the moment of inertia of the flywheel and axle about the axis of rotation is I, show that the mass descends with constant acceleration f, where

   $$f = \frac{mga^2}{ma^2 + 4I}$$

   The mass is observed to move, from rest, through a distance of 10 m in 5 seconds. Given that $a = 0.1$ m, calculate the angular speed acquired by the flywheel in this time.

   Given also that $m = 16$ kg, calculate I.

   Given that the 16 kg mass falls off the string at the end of the 5 second period, find the constant braking couple that will bring the flywheel to rest in a further 6 seconds. (AEB)

9. A uniform circular disc of radius a and mass m is free to rotate about a smooth horizontal axis passing through its centre O and perpendicular to its plane. A particle P of mass $8m$ is attached to the disc at a distance x from O.

The disc is then released from rest from the position where OP is inclined at a small angle α to the downward vertical, where α is sufficiently small for squares and higher powers to be neglected. Show that the motion is simple harmonic, find its period and show that the period will never be less than

$$\pi \sqrt{\frac{2a}{g}}$$

Given that when the disc is at rest in the equilibrium position with P below O it is given an angular speed Ω, find by using the energy equation, or otherwise, the angular speed of the disc when OP is inclined at an angle θ to the downward vertical.

Find the condition to be satisfied by Ω in order that the disc makes complete revolutions.

Given that this condition is satisfied, find the component along OP of the reaction at O when P is level with O. (AEB)

10. Show, by integration, that the moment of inertia of a uniform rod AB, of mass m and length $2a$ about an axis through one end of the rod and perpendicular to the rod, is $\dfrac{4ma^2}{3}$.

    The rod is free to rotate in a vertical plane about a smooth horizontal axis through A. The rod is released from rest in the horizontal position and at time t after being released, it makes an angle θ with the horizontal. Show that

    $$2a\dot{\theta}^2 = 3g\sin\theta$$

    Find, in the form of a definite integral, the time T taken for the rod first to become vertical.

    Determine also the magnitude of the vertical component of the reaction of the axis on the rod when the rod, is

    (a) horizontal,

    (b) vertical. (AEB)

11. Prove, by integration, that the moment of inertia of a uniform circular lamina, of mass m and radius a, about an axis through its centre and perpendicular to its plane, is $\frac{1}{2}Ma^2$.

    A uniform circular lamina, of mass M and radius a, is free to rotate in a vertical plane about a horizontal axis, which is perpendicular to the plane of the lamina and which passes through a point A on its circumference. Prove that the period of small oscillations, T_1, about its position of stable equilibrium is $2\pi\sqrt{\dfrac{3a}{2g}}$.

A particle of mass $\dfrac{15}{2}M$ is now attached to the lamina at a point distant x from A along the radius OA, where O is the centre of the lamina. It is found that the period, T_2, of small oscillations about the stable equilibrium position is such that

$$\frac{T_1}{T_2} = \frac{3}{2}$$

Find x. (AEB)

12. Prove, by integration, that the moment of inertia of a uniform rod, of mass m and length $2a$, about an axis through its centre and perpendicular to its length is $\frac{1}{3}ma^2$.

    Four uniform rods, each of mass m, are rigidly joined together to form a rectangle ABCD where AB $= 4a$ and BC $= 3a$. Show that the moment of inertia of the rectangle about an axis through A, perpendicular to its plane, is $\dfrac{125ma^2}{3}$.

    The rectangle is suspended from A and is free to rotate about a horizontal axis through A which is perpendicular to its plane. Find the period of small oscillations of the rectangle about its equilibrium position. (AEB)

13. A uniform thin rod OA, of mass m and length $6a$, can rotate freely in a fixed vertical plane about a fixed horizontal axis through O. A uniform circular disc, of mass $12m$ and radius a, is clamped to the rod so that its centre C lies on the rod and its plane coincides with the plane in which the rod can rotate. When OC $= x$, find, in terms of m, a and x, the moment of inertia of the system about the horizontal axis through O and the distance of the centre of mass from O.

    Show that the period T of small oscillations of the system about its position of stable equilibrium is given by

    $$T^2 g(a+4x) = 8\pi^2\left(3a^2 + 2x^2\right)$$

    and hence show that the minimum value of T occurs when $x = a$. (AEB)

14. The uniform equilateral triangular lamina ABC is of height h and mass m. Show by integration, but assuming any relevant results for a rod, that the moment of inertia about an axis through A and perpendicular to ABC is $\dfrac{5}{9}mh^2$.

    The lamina is free to turn smoothly about a horizontal axis through A and perpendicular to the plane of ABC. It is in equilibrium with BC below A when a horizontal impulse of magnitude $5m(gh)^{\frac{1}{2}}$ is applied at B in the direction BC.

Show that when the lamina has turned through an angle θ, the square of the angular speed is equal to

$$\left(\frac{g}{5h}\right)[393 + 12\cos\theta]$$

Find also the horizontal component of the reaction at A when the lamina has turned through a right angle.   (AEB)

15. A uniform rod OA, of mass $6m$ and length $2a$, has a particle of mass m attached at A. The system is free to rotate in a vertical plane about a smooth horizontal axis through O. The rod is held in a horizontal position and is then given an initial angular velocity of $\sqrt{\dfrac{2g}{a}}$.

Show that when the rod makes an angle θ below its initial horizontal position, its angular velocity, $\dot\theta$, satisfies the equation

$$3a\dot\theta^2 = 2g(3 + 2\sin\theta)$$

Hence deduce that the rod performs complete revolutions about O.

Find the radial and transverse components of the reaction exerted by the rod on the axis of rotation at O. Show that the radial component vanishes when the rod is approximately $64.9°$ above the horizontal.   (AEB)

ANSWERS

The answers to the questions set in the Exercises are given below.

1 VECTOR METHODS

Exercise 1A

1. $5\mathbf{b}-10\mathbf{a}$, $4\mathbf{a}-2\mathbf{b}$

2. (a) $\overrightarrow{AC}$　(b) $\overrightarrow{BD}$　(c) $\overrightarrow{AD}$

3. $\overrightarrow{DC} = \overrightarrow{EH} = \overrightarrow{FG} = \mathbf{a}$
   $\overrightarrow{BC} = \overrightarrow{GA} = \overrightarrow{FE} = \mathbf{b}$
   $\overrightarrow{DE} = \overrightarrow{CH} = \overrightarrow{BG} = \mathbf{c}$

4. $\mathbf{c}-\mathbf{a}$, $\mathbf{b}-\mathbf{a}$, $\mathbf{b}-\mathbf{c}$

5. $-\mathbf{a}$, $\mathbf{b}-\mathbf{a}$, $2\mathbf{b}$, $2\mathbf{b}-\mathbf{a}$

Exercise 1B

1. (a) $\mathbf{i}+\mathbf{j}+\mathbf{k}$
   (b) $2\mathbf{i}+\mathbf{j}-\mathbf{k}$
   (c) $\mathbf{i}-\mathbf{j}$

2. (a) $(3,-4,1)$　(b) $(1,2,-1)$　(c) $(0,0,-4)$

3. (a) 7　(b) 3　(c) $\sqrt{66}$　(d) $\sqrt{50}$
   $\hat{\mathbf{a}} = \frac{6}{7}\mathbf{i}+\frac{2}{7}\mathbf{j}+\frac{3}{7}\mathbf{k}$
   $\hat{\mathbf{b}} = \frac{2}{3}\mathbf{i}-\frac{1}{3}\mathbf{j}-\frac{2}{3}\mathbf{k}$

4. (a) $3\mathbf{i}+6\mathbf{j}+\mathbf{k}$　(b) $\mathbf{i}+9\mathbf{j}$
   (c) $\mathbf{i}+9\mathbf{j}$　(d) $-25\mathbf{i}+33\mathbf{j}-22\mathbf{k}$

Exercise 1C

1. (a) -14　(b) $21°$　(c) $4\mathbf{i}-2\mathbf{j}+3\mathbf{k}$

2. $4\mathbf{i}-2\mathbf{j}+3\mathbf{k}$, $21°$

3. $1:6$

4. 12

5. (a) -3　(b) $\frac{4}{3}$　(c) 10 or $-\frac{2}{3}$

6. $\pm\sqrt{2}$

7. (a) 5　(b) $2\mathbf{i}-5\mathbf{j}-4\mathbf{k}$

8. -1, -1, -1; $\dfrac{4}{3\sqrt{2}}$

9. 10

Exercise 1D

1. $\mathbf{r} = -2\mathbf{i}+\mathbf{j}+4\mathbf{k}+\lambda(3\mathbf{i}+6\mathbf{j}+2\mathbf{k})$
   $\dfrac{x+2}{3} = \dfrac{y-1}{6} = \dfrac{z-4}{2}$

2. (a) $\mathbf{r} = \mathbf{i}-2\mathbf{j}+\mathbf{k}+\lambda(-2\mathbf{i}+2\mathbf{j}-4\mathbf{k})$
   (b) $\mathbf{r} = 8\mathbf{i}+\mathbf{j}+4\mathbf{k}+\lambda(4\mathbf{i}+\mathbf{j}+\mathbf{k})$
   (c) $\mathbf{r} = 3\mathbf{i}+\mathbf{j}-2\mathbf{k}+\lambda(-2\mathbf{i}+2\mathbf{j}-4\mathbf{k})$

3. (a) $\mathbf{i}+\mathbf{j}+\mathbf{k}$　(c) No

Exercise 1E

1. $\mathbf{r} = (2,-1,0) + \lambda(-3,4,4) + \mu(1,1,2)$

2. $4x+10y-72 = -2$

3. Equivalent equations

4. $\mathbf{r}\cdot(\mathbf{i}+2\mathbf{j}-3\mathbf{k}) = 0$

7. $\mathbf{r} = 4\mathbf{i}+2\mathbf{j}+3\mathbf{k}$

8. $y+3z = 14$

Miscellaneous Exercises

1. $6\mathbf{i}+6\mathbf{j}+0\mathbf{k}$

2. 7

3. $a=-1$, $b=2$

4. $\frac{4}{3}$

5. $\frac{2}{3}\mathbf{i}-\frac{1}{3}\mathbf{j}+\frac{2}{3}\mathbf{k}$

6. $\frac{18}{7}\mathbf{i}-\frac{9}{7}\mathbf{j}+\frac{6}{7}\mathbf{k}$

9. $6\mathbf{i}+2\mathbf{j}, 0\mathbf{i}+6\mathbf{j}$

10. (a) $0,-4$　(b) $72.5°$

11. (a) $50°$　(b) $\frac{4}{3}\mathbf{i}+\frac{7}{3}\mathbf{j}+\frac{14}{3}\mathbf{k}$

12. (a) $\mathbf{i}+2\mathbf{j}+3\mathbf{k}$　(b) $40°$

13. (a) $20, \dfrac{20}{21}$

13. (b) $r = 6i + 3j + 2k + t(-4i - j - k)$

$$-\frac{14}{11}i + \frac{13}{11}j + \frac{2}{11}k$$

2 VECTOR APPLICATIONS

Exercise 2A

1. $5i + 4j; -8k$

2. $25\,g, \; 65\,g, \; 45\,g$

3. $2.75\,m$ from A; $20.5\,kg, \; 39.5\,kg$

4. (a) $10\,N$ (b) $\tan^{-1}\left(\dfrac{1}{3\sqrt{3}}\right)$

    (c) $10\sqrt{7}\,N$; $90\,Nm$ clockwise

5. $\dfrac{3W}{4}, \dfrac{7a}{3}$ from A; $\dfrac{W}{2}, \dfrac{W}{4}$

Exercise 2B

1. $X = 1, Y = 2, b$

2. $3\,N, \; 1\,N, \; 12\,Nm$

3. $5\,N$ at angle $\tan^{-1}\left(\dfrac{4}{3}\right)$ to AB, $14\,Nm$

4. (a) $2\sqrt{10}\,N$

    (b) $71.6°$

    (c) $a = \dfrac{26}{3}m, \; y = 3x - 26$

5. $48\,Nm$ in sense ABCD

6. $\sqrt{65}\,N$ at $\tan^{-1}(8)$ to OA; $y = 8x + 3$;
   $3\,N$ in direction BA

7. k

8. (a) 5 (b) $r = i + 2j + k + \lambda(7i + 6j + 6k)$

    (c) $6i + j - 8k$

9. (a) $\dfrac{4\sqrt{3}}{3}$ (b) $R = (3i + 3k)N, \; G = -(i + 2j + 3k)$

    (c) $3yi + 3zj - 3yk$

Exercise 2C

1. $-250i - 550j + 10k, \; 250i + 550j - 10k$

2. $18i + 10j$

3. (a) $i - 4j$ (b) $t = 2$

4. (a) $11i + 3j$ (b) $32.5°$

---

5. $\sqrt{58}\,km$; $6i + 8j$

6. $(v + 3)i + (7v - 29)j$;
   $[-56 + (v + 3)t]i + [8 + (7v - 29)t]j$; 4; 4

Miscellaneous Exercises

1. (a) 5 (b) $r = 2i + j + 3k + \lambda(11i + 4j + 5k)$

    (c) $-7i + 23j - 3k$

2. $10i$; $r = -2i - 2j + 10\lambda i$;

    $F_4 = -4i + 5j, \; G = 21\,Nm$ clockwise

3. (a) $R = 11i + (p - 1)j + 5k$,

      $G = (13 - 4p)i + 23j + (8p - 43)k$

4. $n = \cos\theta\sin\phi\,i + \cos\theta\cos\phi\,j + \sin\theta\,k$; $\dfrac{4}{5}$

5. $F = 3Pi - 12Pj + 6Pk, \; G = 3aP(16i - 9j - 8k)$,

    $R = 5P, \; S = 10P$

6. (a) $4j, \; j + 4k, \; 4i + 3j$

    (b) $X_D = 25\,N, \; Z_D = 75\,N$

    (c) $X_A = 75\,N, \; Z_A = 25\,N$

7. (a) $P = 8i + 6j, \; Q = 2j$

    (b) $8\sqrt{2}\,N$

    (c) $8\,Nm$ clockwise

8. $42; \; -16.8i - 12.6j; \; 38.8i + 36.6j$,
   60 in positive sense

9. (a) $Q = -2P\cos\theta$

    (b) 2θ

    (c) $Q = \dfrac{3P}{2}$

    (d) $139°$

    (e) $83°$

10. (a) $(i - 2j)\,km\,h^{-1}$

    (b) $(2t + 17)i + (-3t - 6)j, \; (3t + 5)i + (13 - 5t)j$

    (c) $t = 10$

11. $\frac{1}{2}$ hour, 24 mins; $(9i - 7.2j)\,ms^{-1}$;

    (a) $7.2\,m$ (b) $1.00\,pm$

12. (a) $nut(3i + 5j), \; (3n + 4)ui + (5n - 3)uj$

    (b) 4

    (c) $-\dfrac{12u^2}{g}$ and $\dfrac{9u^2}{2g}$

3 MODELLING WITH DIFFERENTIAL EQUATIONS

Exercise 3A

1. (a) $209e^{0.01t}$ million, 233.3 million, 2028

   (b)
Year	Value
1935	1.601×10^6
1945	1.954×10^6
1953	2.785×10^6
1977	3.688×10^6

   Actual numbers increasing, but not in line with this model.

2. 10.52%, almost 7 years

3. $\dfrac{dw}{dt} = -kw$, $k = 0.00498$; just over 65 days

Exercise 3B

1. (a) $R = \dfrac{kS}{(1 + \alpha S)}$

   (b) $(1 - \beta)R^{1-\alpha} = c(1 - \alpha)^{1-\beta}$ $(\alpha, \beta \neq 1)$

2. Graph of $h^{1-\alpha}$ against t should be straight line

3. $N\left\{1 - \left(\dfrac{N_0}{N_0}\right)^{\alpha-1}\right\}^{\frac{1}{\alpha-1}} = e^{\gamma t}\left\{\left(1 - \dfrac{N}{N_\infty}\right)^{\alpha-1}\right\}^{\frac{1}{\alpha-1}}$

4. $x(t) = k\,e^{\frac{1}{\omega}\sin \omega t}$

5. $x(t) = \dfrac{n(n+1)}{\left(e^{-(n+1)t} + n\right)}$, $t = 0$

Exercise 3C

1. (a) $y = \dfrac{3}{5}x + A$

   (b) $\ln(1 + y^2) = A - \dfrac{4}{3}\sqrt{1 + x^3}$

   (c) $y = \left[\dfrac{1}{2}\left(3x^{\frac{1}{2}} + A\right)^2\right]^{\frac{1}{3}}$

   (d) $y - \ln(1 + y) = \dfrac{x^3}{3} + k$

2. (a) $y = \dfrac{1}{3}x^2 + \dfrac{A}{x}$

   (b) $y = (x+1)^2 + \dfrac{A}{(x+1)^2}$

   (c) $y = 3\sin x \cos x + A\cos^2 x$

   (d) $y = x - \dfrac{x}{\ln x} + \dfrac{A}{\ln x}$

   (e) $y = 2x\cos x - \sin x + K\cos x$

3. All forgeries except *Lace Maker*

Exercise 3D

2. (a) $y = (A + Bx)e^x$

   (b) $y = Ae^{-4x} + Be^{-3x} + 1$

   (c) $y = A\cos x + B\sin x$

   (d) $y = Ae^x + Be^{-x} - 4x$

Exercise 3E

1. $k = 0.125 \text{ m}^{-1}$

2. $\left(\dfrac{2\ln 2}{\ln(16/13)} - 2\right)$ km

3. $\dfrac{dy}{dt} + 7y = 14 - 9.8t$

4. $v = 3t + 5e^{-t} - 4$

5. $\ln\left(\dfrac{3}{2}\right)$ s; $(100\ln 10 - 90)$ m, 100 m s^{-1}

Miscellaneous Exercises

1. $k = \ln 2$; $n(t) = n_0 2^t$

2. $\left(\dfrac{2w}{g}\right)\ln 2$

3. (a) Using 1960, 1966 values, $P = 1091e^{0.0732t}$ giving

Year	Production
1968	1960
1970	2268
1972	2626

   Reasonable agreement

   (b) Using 1946, 1960 values, $P = 2015e^{0.0513t}$ giving

Year	Consumption
1965	5340
1970	6920

   Better model needed

4. (a) (i) $x(t) = \dfrac{ab\left(e^{(b-a)rt} - 1\right)}{\left(be^{(b-a)rt} - a\right)}$ (ii) 10

   (b) (i) $x(t) = \dfrac{cx(0)}{\left(c - x(0)\right)e^{-crt} + x(0)}$

5. (b) $x(t) = \left(\dfrac{ct}{3} + x(0)^{\frac{1}{3}}\right)^3$

   (c) $t = 2^{\frac{1}{3}} - 1$

7. (a) $\dfrac{dp}{dt} = kp(1 - p)$

   (d) $p(t) = \dfrac{1}{1 + e^{-2t}}$; $p \to 1$ as $t \to \infty$

8. $\dfrac{1}{u\sqrt{ab}} \tan^{-1} \sqrt{\dfrac{b}{a}}$; $\dfrac{3}{2bu^2}$

9. (a) 9.09 ms^{-1} (b) 5 ms^{-1} (c) 0.011 s
   (d) 0.0445 m

4   HARMONIC MOTION

Exercise 4A

1. (a) π ms^{-1} (b) $\dfrac{\pi^2}{4}$ ms^{-2} (c) $\dfrac{1}{2}\pi\sqrt{3}$ ms^{-1}

2. $\omega = \dfrac{\pi}{8}$

3. (a) (i) $\sqrt{10}$ m   (ii) π s   (iii) $2\sqrt{10}$ ms^{-1}

   (iv) $\dfrac{\pi}{4}$ s

   (b) (i) 8 ms^{-2} (ii) 64 N

   (c) $\sqrt{10}\sin 2t$, $\dfrac{1}{2}\arcsin\left(\dfrac{1}{\sqrt{10}}\right)$

   $\dfrac{1}{2}\arcsin\left(\dfrac{2}{\sqrt{10}}\right) - \dfrac{1}{2}\arcsin\left(\dfrac{1}{\sqrt{10}}\right)$

4. (a) $(u + 6 - 6\cos 2t)$ ms^{-1}
   (b) $(ut + 6t - 3\sin 2t)$ m
   (c) -6 ; 20π m

5. (a) $\dfrac{\pi}{5}$ s   (b) $\dfrac{\pi}{30}$ s   (c) $\dfrac{\sqrt{3}}{200}$ ms^{-1}

6. 5; $\dfrac{1}{2}$, $\dfrac{4}{3}$; $\dfrac{1}{2}$, $\dfrac{5}{2}$ ms^{-1}

Exercise 4B

1. (a) $x = e^{\left(-\sqrt{5} + 1\right)\frac{t}{2}} - e^{-\left(\sqrt{5} + 1\right)\frac{t}{2}}$

   (b) $x = te^{-t}$

   (c) $x = 2e^{-\frac{\sqrt{3}t}{2}} \sin\left(\dfrac{1}{2}t\right)$

2. $x = ae^{-nt}(\cos 3nt - 3\sin 3nt)$

3. $x = \dfrac{u}{n}e^{-nt} \sin nt$; $e^{-\pi}$

Exercise 4C

1. (a) $x = Ae^{-3t} + Be^{-t} + \dfrac{c}{3}$; $x \to \dfrac{c}{3}$

   (b) $x = Ae^{-3t} + Be^{-t} + \dfrac{1}{8}e^t$; $x \to \infty$

   (c) $x = Ae^{-3t} + Be^{-t} + \dfrac{1}{2}te^{-t}$; $x \to 0$

2. (a) $x = A\sin 2t + B\cos 2t + \dfrac{1}{3}\sin t$

   (b) $x = A\sin 2t + B\cos 2t - \dfrac{1}{4}t\cos 2t$

3. $x = \dfrac{a}{3}\cos nt - \dfrac{a}{3}\cos 2nt$

4. $\dfrac{\mu g}{n^2}$; $x = ut - \left(\dfrac{u}{n}\right)\sin nt$; $2u$

Miscellaneous Exercises

1. $\ddot{x} + 4\omega\dot{x} + 5\omega^2 x = 0$

2. $x = \dfrac{1}{2}a\left(7e^{-2nt} - 5e^{-3nt}\right)$, $y = \dfrac{1}{2}a\sqrt{3}\left(e^{-2nt} - e^{-3nt}\right)$

3. $\ddot{x} + 4\omega\dot{x} + 5\omega^2 x = 0$; $C = 5a$, $\sec\phi = \dfrac{5}{3}$

4. (a) (i) $x = A\sin\omega t + B\cos\omega t$

      (ii) $x = A\sin\omega t + B\cos\omega t - \dfrac{at}{2\omega}\cos\omega t$

   (b) (i) $x = \dfrac{a}{2\omega^2}\sin\omega t - \dfrac{at}{2\omega}\cos\omega t$

5. $\dfrac{3mg}{2}$; $\sqrt{2ga}$; $A = \dfrac{4}{3}a$, $\phi = \dfrac{4\pi}{3}$, $\dfrac{2\pi}{3}\sqrt{\dfrac{2a}{3g}}$

6. $x = ae^{-3nt}(1 - \cos 3nt)$

7. $\ddot{x} + 2\omega\dot{x} + 2\omega^2 x = 0$;

   $C = 2a$, $\alpha = -\dfrac{\pi}{3}$; $t = \left(\dfrac{2\pi}{3} + n\pi\right)\dfrac{1}{\omega}$

8. $x = -\dfrac{1}{75}(2\sin 10t - \sin 20t)$

9. $a = 13$, $\omega = \dfrac{\pi}{8}$, $\phi = \tan^{-1}\left(\dfrac{12}{5}\right)$; $\dot{x} = -\dfrac{3}{2}\pi$, $\ddot{x} = \dfrac{5}{64}$; 5.99 s

10. $x = \sin \omega t + 2a\cos \omega t - \dfrac{1}{2}ae^{-\omega t}\sin 2\omega t$

5 IMPULSIVE MOTION

Exercise 5A

1. $4\,\text{ms}^{-1}$
2. $8400\,\text{Ns}$
3. $3\,\text{ms}^{-1}$, $13.5\,\text{m}$
4. $1.26\,\text{Ns}$
5. (a) $21\,\text{N}$ (b) $700t\,\text{N}$
6. $6\,\text{Ns}$
7. $288000t(0.05 - t)\,\text{N}$
8. $46\,\text{Ns}$

Exercise 5B

1. $1.2\,\text{ms}^{-1}$
2. $9.6\,\text{ms}^{-1}$
3. $v = 3.73\,\text{ms}^{-1}$
4. $3.\dot{1}7\,\text{km h}^{-1}$
5. $2.98\,\text{ms}^{-1}$
6. (a) $2.13\,\text{ms}^{-1}$ (b) $2.64\,\text{ms}^{-1}$ (c) $2.35\,\text{ms}^{-1}$
7. 0.024
8. $0.5\,\text{ms}^{-1}$
9. $0.25\,\text{ms}^{-1}$, $0.29\,\text{ms}^{-1}$
10. (a) $2.5\,\text{km h}^{-1}$ (b) $2\,\text{km h}^{-1}$

Exercise 5C

1. $(0.6\mathbf{i} - 0.8\mathbf{j})\,\text{Ns}$
2. $(13\mathbf{i} + 25\mathbf{j})\,\text{ms}^{-1}$
3. $5.41\,\text{Ns}$ at an angle of $56°$ to the line of wickets
4. $7.89\,\text{Ns}$ at an angle of $12.5°$ to original line
5. $11.38\,\text{Ns}$, $5.36\,\text{Ns}$
6. $2.57\,\text{Ns}$ and $0.20\,\text{Ns}$

Exercise 5D

1. $(2.6\mathbf{i} + 0.2\mathbf{j})\,\text{ms}^{-1}$
2. $0.056\,\text{ms}^{-1}$
3. $0.8\,\text{ms}^{-1}$
4. No
5. $27.7\,\text{mph}$, $43.1\,\text{mph}$
6. $(4.9\mathbf{i} + 16.7\mathbf{j})\,\text{ms}^{-1}$
7. $\dfrac{7J}{27m}$

Exercise 5E

1. $0.16\,\text{m}$
2. 0.5
3. $1.25\,\text{m}$
4. $1.43\,\text{Ns}$
5. $6.98\,\text{ms}^{-1}$
6. $8.54\,\text{ms}^{-1}$ at $35.8°$ to the horizontal
7. 0.93, $0.52\,\text{m}$, $0.37\,\text{m}$
8. 0.75, $0.11\,\text{m}$
9. $37.8°$
10. $0.75h$

Exercise 5F

1. $4.25\,\text{ms}^{-1}$, $6.25\,\text{ms}^{-1}$
2. 0.25, $4\,\text{ms}^{-1}$
3. 0.43, $4.3\,\text{kg}$
4. $1.8\,\text{ms}^{-1}$, $3.8\,\text{ms}^{-1}$
5. $0.47\,\text{kg}$, $3.6\,\text{ms}^{-1}$
6. 0.17, $9\,\text{kg}$
7. $e > 0.6$
8. 0.65
9. 0.75, $1.2\,\text{kg}$
10. $0.223\,\text{ms}^{-1}$, $0.246\,\text{ms}^{-1}$, $1.53\,\text{ms}^{-1}$

Exercise 5G

1. $(3\mathbf{i} + 5\mathbf{j})\,\text{ms}^{-1}$ and $(4\mathbf{i} + 7\mathbf{j})\,\text{ms}^{-1}$
3. $14.7°$
4. $45°$, $\dfrac{v(1+e)}{4}$
5. $30°$
6. $19.5°$
7. $25.6°$

8. 75.4°

9. 20.2 ms^{-1}, 45.9°

10. 4.6 ms^{-1}

Miscellaneous Exercises

1. 0.4 Ns, $\dfrac{19}{3}$ ms^{-1}, $\dfrac{19}{33}$, $\dfrac{14}{15}$ J

2. $\mathbf{J} = 0.6\mathbf{i} - 2\mathbf{j}$, 7.3 J

3. $\dfrac{18u}{5}$

4. $(2\mathbf{i} + \mathbf{j})$ Ns

5. $(3\mathbf{i} + 4\mathbf{j})$ Ns, $\dfrac{4}{5}\mathbf{i} - \dfrac{3}{5}\mathbf{j}$, 10 ms^{-1}

6. $\dfrac{6u}{5}$, $3mu$

8. (a) $e = 1$ (b) $\dfrac{\pi}{2}$

9. $\left(\dfrac{p-e}{p+e}\right)v\cos\theta$, $\left(\dfrac{1+e}{p+1}\right)pv\cos\theta$;

  (a) $p = 1 + 2e$

  (b) $p = e$; $\dfrac{1}{2}mV^2 e\cos^2\theta(1-e)$

10. $2u$, $\dfrac{2}{3}$; u; $\dfrac{a}{2}$

11. (a) $V = -u$, (b) 0.8 (c) $3mn^2$; u, $\dfrac{4u}{3}$, $\dfrac{1}{9}$

12. $T = \dfrac{2Mmg}{(M+m)}$, $\dfrac{1}{\sqrt{2}}$

13. About 27°

14. $\dfrac{1}{5}g$, $8mg$ (a) $\dfrac{1}{3}d$ (b) $\dfrac{2}{3}d\sqrt{\dfrac{10d}{g}}$

  (c) $\sqrt{\dfrac{gd}{10}}$

15. $\dfrac{J}{7m}$, $\dfrac{5J}{17m}$, $\dfrac{12J}{17}$

16. (b) $4mu$ (c) $8mu^2$

17. $T = 2.5$ s, 3.5 s; $V_A = 4.9 - 9.8t$,

  $V_B = 29.4 - 9.8(t - 25)$; 3 s

18. $\dfrac{\pi}{3}$

19. $\dfrac{u(1+e)}{5}$, $e > \dfrac{1}{4}$; $e' > \dfrac{1+e}{(4e-1)}$; $e = \dfrac{3}{4}$, $e' = 1$;

  $\dfrac{13}{40}mu^2$

20. $e = \dfrac{1}{2}$

21. $\tan\alpha = \left(\dfrac{1+e}{1-e}\right)\sqrt{e}$

22. $\gamma = \tan^{-1}\left(\dfrac{1+e+e^2}{2e^2}\right)$

23. (b) $6mu$ (c) mu^2 (d) $\dfrac{5mu^2}{3}$

24. $\dfrac{(1+e)\tan\alpha}{2-e+3\tan^2\alpha}$; $\dfrac{1}{5}$, $\dfrac{\sqrt{15}}{5}$, $\dfrac{1}{\sqrt{3}}$

25. (a) $2\mathbf{i} + 5\mathbf{j}$, $\dfrac{1}{4}$ (b) $\sqrt{\dfrac{3}{8}}u$

26. (a) $\dfrac{3u}{10}$ (b) $\dfrac{1}{4}m(1-e^2)w^2$

27. eu^2, $e^2 v$; $e' = \dfrac{1}{2}$

28. (a) 1 (b) $\dfrac{u}{5}(2-3e)$, $\sqrt{\dfrac{1}{6}}$

29. $\dfrac{3u}{25}$

30. $\dfrac{7mg}{3}$, $\dfrac{2g}{3}$; (a) $\dfrac{4h}{3}$ (b) $\dfrac{4}{9}\sqrt{\dfrac{gh}{3}}$

31. $-\dfrac{11u}{4}$, $\dfrac{1}{24}$; $u\left(2 - \dfrac{1}{\sqrt{2}}\right)$

32. (a) $2a\sqrt{\dfrac{e}{1+e}}$ (b) $1-e$

34. (a) (i) $\dfrac{1}{2}u$ (ii) $\dfrac{1}{3}$ (iii) $\dfrac{5mu^2}{6}$

  (b) (i) $\dfrac{3v}{8}$ (ii) $\dfrac{15mv}{8}$ (iii) $\dfrac{15mv^2}{16}$

35. $\dfrac{1}{4}u(1+e)$; $\dfrac{5mu^2}{144}$

36. (a) 15 ms^{-1}, 15 ms^{-1}

  (b) 0.32 Ns (c) 35 ms^{-1} (d) 3 s (e) 50 m

37. $\dfrac{1}{4}u$, $\dfrac{u(1-9e)}{16}$, $\dfrac{3u(1-e)}{16}$

6 PLANAR MOTION

Exercise 6A

1. 2.55 ms^{-2}

2. 2.46 ms^{-2}, 1.86 ms^{-2}

3. 2.27 ms^{-2}

4. 18.97 ms^{-1}

5. 110.2 m

Exercise 6B

1. $12.5a$

2. Ve^{-kt}

3. $\dfrac{a}{\mu} \ln(1 + \mu \Omega t)$

4. $\dfrac{u}{\mu g}$

5. 8.67 ms^{-2}

6. $\dfrac{a}{2\mu} \text{arcsinh}\left(\dfrac{v^2}{ag}\right)$

7. 54.15 m

8. $\dfrac{1}{\sqrt{\alpha}} \left(\dfrac{\mu^2 g^2}{a^2 \alpha^2 - 1}\right)^{\frac{1}{4}}$

Exercise 6C

1. $\sqrt{68ga}$

2. 626 ms^{-1}

3. 3234 N, 1666 N

4. 2.21 ms^{-1}

5. 1677 N, 810.6 N, 290 J, 178 J

6. 1486 N, 56 N

7. 4.81 rad s^{-1}

8. $3mg \cos\theta$

9. $\dfrac{a}{3}$

10. $\sqrt{2ga(1 + \pi)}$

11. $\sqrt{r\left(\dfrac{\pi F}{m} + 2g\right)}$, $F\pi + 3mg$

Exercise 6D

1. $2a\omega$, $4a\omega^2$

2. (a) $-4\pi a$, $4\pi a$ (b) $-8\pi^2 a$, $-16\pi^2 a$

3. 202.1 ms^{-1}

4. 0.89 ms^{-1}, 1.57 ms^{-1}, -0.81 ms^{-2}, 1.79 ms^{-2}

5. 14.87 ms^{-1}, 121.75 ms^{-2}

6. 31.41 ms^{-1}, 197.39 ms^{-2}

7. $\omega\sqrt{r^2\omega^2 + 4u^2}$

9. $\dfrac{ah^2}{r^2}$ directed towards the centre

Exercise 6E

1. (i) $r = \dfrac{100(1 - \sin\theta)}{(1 + \sin\theta)^2}$

   (ii) $r = \dfrac{100}{(1 + \sin\theta)}$

   (iii) $r\cos\theta = 100(\sec\theta + \tan\theta)^{-\frac{3}{4}}$

2. $r\cos\theta = 200(\sec\theta + \tan\theta)^{-15}$

3. $\dfrac{V}{\omega} \sinh\omega t$

4. $\dfrac{75ga}{4}$

6. $\sqrt{2ga}$

8. $\dfrac{mg}{2}\left(1 + \dfrac{a^3}{3r^3}\right)$

11. $\dfrac{g}{2\omega^2}(\sinh\omega t - \sin\omega t)$

Exercise 6F

1. 2.86

2. $\dfrac{4}{3}$, 9

3. $\dfrac{4}{3}$

4. -24

5. 1.42, 0.87

6. $1.892 \times 10^{27} \text{ kg}$

7. $23\,842 \text{ km h}^{-1}$

8. 7562 ms^{-1}

9. 50212 km

10. 2274 ms^{-1}, 1452 ms^{-1}

11. $\dfrac{a}{7}$

12. $-0.21\sqrt{\dfrac{GM}{a}}$, $-0.21\sqrt{\dfrac{GM}{a}}$

Exercise 6G

1. (i) $\dfrac{a}{16r} = 1 - \dfrac{15}{16}\cos\theta$

    (ii) $\dfrac{4a}{r} = 1 + 3\cos\theta$

2. $\dfrac{c}{r} = 4 - 3\cos\theta$

3. $\dfrac{4a}{r} = 1 + \sqrt{13}\,\cos(\theta + \alpha)$, $\alpha = \arctan\left(\dfrac{2}{3}\right)$

4. $\dfrac{a\sin^2\beta}{r} = 1 - \cos\beta\,\cos(\theta + \beta)$

5. $\dfrac{a}{r} = 1 - \dfrac{1}{\sqrt{3}}\sin\theta$

Miscellaneous Exercises

1. (b) $131.8°$

2. $\sqrt{ag\cos\alpha}$

3. $\sqrt{2g\ell} < u < \sqrt{5g\ell}$; $g\ell\cos\alpha$

4. $m\left(\dfrac{g}{2a}\right)^{\frac{1}{2}}$, $T = \dfrac{1}{2}mg(1 + 4\cos\theta)$, $99.6°$, $\left(\dfrac{ga}{6}\right)^{\frac{1}{2}}$

5. $\dfrac{25}{2}\lambda a$; $2a \le r \le 6a$

6. $\dfrac{6mg}{5}(1 + \cos\theta)$, $\dfrac{6mg}{5}(3\sin\theta - 2\theta)$

7. $h = \sqrt{\dfrac{k}{2}}$, $\dfrac{3a^2}{\sqrt{2k}}$

8. (a) $u < \sqrt{2ga}$

    (b) $u > \sqrt{\dfrac{7ga}{2}}$

    (c) $\sqrt{\dfrac{7ga}{2}} < u < \sqrt{5ga}$

10. $T = mg(2 + 3\cos\theta)$

11. $v^2 = u^2 - 2ga(1 - \cos\theta)$,

    $R = \dfrac{mu^2}{2} - mg(2 + 3\cos\theta)$, $60°$

12. $-2u\sin\theta$, $r = \dfrac{a\sin\theta}{(1 + \cos\theta)^2}$

14. $\dfrac{320\,a^4\lambda^2}{r^5}$

15. $\dfrac{a}{4}$, $4\left(\dfrac{k}{a}\right)^{\frac{1}{2}}$

16. $\dfrac{d^2\theta}{dt^2} + \left(\dfrac{d\theta}{dt}\right)^2 = 0$, $\dfrac{v}{a\sqrt{10}}$

17. $8V^2\left(\dfrac{1}{9} - \dfrac{a^2}{r^2}\right)$

18. $\sqrt{45 + 36\cos\theta}$, -27 ; 9 , 3

19. 1.5×10^8 km

7   RIGID BODY MOTION

Exercise 7A

1. (a) $-\mathbf{i} + 1.4\mathbf{j} + 2.9\mathbf{k}$

    (b) $-3.6\mathbf{i} + 3.9\mathbf{j} - 2.8\mathbf{k}$

    (c) $-1.7\mathbf{i} + 1.5\mathbf{j} + 0.7\mathbf{k}$

2. $\dfrac{9}{7}\mathbf{i} - \dfrac{57}{7}\mathbf{j} + \dfrac{69}{7}\mathbf{k}$

3. $2 : 3 : 5$

4. $\bar{\mathbf{r}} = 3\mathbf{i} + 2\mathbf{j} + 2\mathbf{k}$

5. $t = \dfrac{\pi}{\omega_2 - \omega_1}$, $R\mathbf{j}$

Exercise 7B

1. $\left(\dfrac{5a}{3}, 0\right)$

2. $(4a, 0)$

3. $(0, 9.6a)$

4. $(3.6a, 0)$

5. $(5.4a, 0)$

6. $(3.6a, 0)$

7. $\left(\dfrac{25a}{7}, 0\right)$

Exercise 7C

1. $3r$

2. $\dfrac{93h}{40a}$

3. $\dfrac{2a}{3}$

4. $3.21a$

5. $\dfrac{117r}{63}$

Exercise 7D

1. $\dfrac{20ma^2}{3}$

2. (i) $\dfrac{40ma^2}{3}$ (ii) $\dfrac{20ma^2}{3}$

3. $6ma^2$

5. $\dfrac{3m\left(a^2+4h^2\right)}{20}$

6. $69ma^2$

7. $63ma^2$

8. $95ma^2$

9. $133ma^2$

Exercise 7E

1. $0.42\,\text{N m}$
2. 6.25 rad s^{-2}

3. $\dfrac{I\omega}{C}$, $\dfrac{I\omega^2}{2C}$

4. 2.55 kg m^2

5. $\sqrt{\dfrac{\pi a^3 F}{I}}$

6. $\dfrac{25}{3}\text{ rad s}^{-2}$

7. (a) 5 rad s^{-1} (b) 8.3 s

8. $\dfrac{\pi}{64}$

Exercise 7F

1. 0.57 rad s^{-1}
2. 6.7 rad s^{-1}
3. 4.08 rad s^{-1}

4. $\sqrt{\dfrac{g\cos\theta}{2.05r}}$

5. $2\pi\sqrt{\dfrac{2a}{g}}$

6. $\dfrac{a}{3}$

7. $\dfrac{mg\cos\theta}{4}$

8. $\dfrac{5mg}{3}$

9. $\dfrac{17ma^2}{3}$; $\dfrac{57mg}{23}$, $\dfrac{12mg}{23}$

Miscellaneous Exercises

1. $\dfrac{3a}{20}$

2. $\dfrac{31}{22}\text{ cm}$

3. $\dfrac{45}{56}a$ from O

4. (a) $0.25a$ (b) $\lambda = 2$

5. $\dfrac{(54)^{\frac{1}{4}}a}{2}$

6. $\dfrac{5h}{8}$

7. $4m$; $\tan\alpha = 8$; $\dfrac{5m}{8}$

8. $\Omega = 80$; $I = 0.45$; $G = 6$

9. $\dot\theta^2 = \dfrac{32gx(\cos\theta - \cos\alpha)}{\left(a^2 + 16x^2\right)}$, $\Omega^2 > \dfrac{64gx}{\left(a^2 + 16x^2\right)}$,

   $8mx\left\{\dfrac{32gx}{\left(a^2 + 16x^2\right)} - \Omega^2\right\}$

10. $T = \sqrt{\dfrac{2a}{3g}}\displaystyle\int_0^{\frac{\pi}{2}}\dfrac{d\theta}{\sqrt{\sin\theta}}$ (a) $\dfrac{1}{4}mg$ (b) $\dfrac{5}{2}mg$

11. $x = \dfrac{1}{3}a$

12. $2\pi\sqrt{\dfrac{25a}{6g}}$

13. $\bar{x} = \dfrac{1}{13}(3a + 12x)$; $I = 18ma^2 + 12mx^2$

14. $\dfrac{262mg}{5}$

15. $R = -\dfrac{5mg\cos\theta}{3}$, $S = \dfrac{mg}{3}(48 + 53\sin\theta)$

INDEX